# MUSHROOMS AND
# TOADSTOOLS

*of Britain and Northern Europe*

Geoffrey Kibby

**Bounty**
Books

This edition first published in 2006 by Philip's,
a division of Octopus Publishing Group Ltd

This edition published in 2013 by Bounty Books,
a division of Octopus Publishing Group Ltd
Endeavour House, 189 Shaftesbury Avenue, London WC2H 8JY
www.octopusbooks.co.uk

An Hachette UK Company
www.hachette.co.uk

ISBN: 978-0-753725-30-6

Printed in China

# CONTENTS

# PREFACE

As a boy of thirteen I remember walking through the woods and finding a small, bright violet mushroom almost glowing against the deep green moss from out of which it grew. It seemed almost magical to me then – as it still does today some forty years later – and it spurred me on to buy my first book on fungi, the first of a great many books and the beginning of a lifetime's fascination with these strange and little-known organisms.

Now I write my own books and this one is the fruit of that lifetime's study. It incorporates a wide selection of both common and rare species and makes use of the latest research and the most up-to-date names for each species. Fungi can be found everywhere, in every country and in almost every habitat, giving scope for limitless study or just the simple pleasure of seeing them in their natural surroundings. I hope this book will help you to discover the wonder and fascination of the often beautiful and always intriguing world of fungi.

**Geoffrey Kibby**

$F$ungi are a very distinct group of organisms. They are now considered to be a separate kingdom of the living world, being as different from the other "plant" kingdoms – the bacteria, algae and green plants – as they are from the animal kingdom. Some 100,000 species of fungi have been described, while probably the same number await discovery. The vast majority of fungi are minute: many only visible to the naked eye as mats of cotton-like threads, such as the blue mould of *Penicillium* often found on stale bread. It is impossible to identify these fungi without the aid of a microscope. For most of us, however, the word "fungus" conjures up an image of the mushrooms and toadstools that are found growing in our woods and fields. It is these "larger fungi" with which this book is concerned and which are illustrated in the plates.

Together with the bacteria, the fungi are the "decomposers" of our environment and they are just as important as the green plants which are the "producers". Fungi lack the green pigment, chlorophyll, found in the green plants and some algae. It is this pigment that is essential in converting the energy of sunlight directly into a form that is available for use by these higher plants, because fungi do not have this pigment they must obtain the energy required for their life-giving processes indirectly from other sources. Fungi basically utilize the organic materials produced by other plants and animals in three ways:

▼ *Russula sardonia is typical of the brightly coloured members of the genus* Russula. *These brittle fungi come in a wide range of colours and are often very hot to the taste.*

- they may feed on dead or decaying organisms or their products, whether this be the dead trunk of a tree, the decomposed remains of a plant in the soil, a dead insect, or man-made products derived from plants and animals, such as foodstuffs and clothes. This form of obtaining nutrients is known as saprophytism and the fungi are therefore known as saprophytes.

- or they may take the role of parasite. Whereas saprophytism is a highly beneficial side to the life of fungi in that nutrients are cycled within the environment without harm to other life, parasitism represents the darker side of fungal ecology – at least from Man's point of view. These fungi prey on living plants and animals, obtaining all the nutrients they require from the living host. In many cases the result will be the death of the host. Some fungi will first feed parasitically on a host but, having killed it, will then feed saprophytically on the remains. It is with this side of fungal nutrition that Man most often comes into contention. Fungi are some of the most serious pests of his crops and garden plants, the attack of a microscopic fungus can kill a mammoth 100-year-old tree in a matter of a year or two.

- many fungi live in close harmony with the roots of living plants, without either partner suffering from the association and both normally benefiting. These symbiotic associations are known as mycorrhizae (fungus roots) and it is now known that these associations with fungi occur in most families of flowering plants. Without the fungus the vigour of the "host" plant suffers and growth is retarded; in some instances (including many orchids) the fungus association is essential if any growth is to occur at all. Many of these mycorrhizal fungi are mushrooms or toadstools and few people realize that without the fungus, which is only visible to the eye for a short time each year as a large fruitbody, many of our woods and forests would not exist in the form they do today.

## Classification

There are different degrees of relatedness in living organisms. For example, Labradors, Poodles and wolves are all related (all being "dogs" in the broader sense) but Labradors are more closely related to Poodles than they are to wolves. Examples of other members of the "dog" group are the dingo, coyote, jackal, and the fox. Similarly there are unifying qualities that puts creatures as varied as bees, butterflies, cockroaches and beetles into one large group called the insects. Finally, "dogs" and insects are part of a very large group – the animals. The varying degrees of relatedness lead to the concept of a hierarchy of different levels of classification and there are particular terms to denote the different levels in the hierarchy. Individuals that are very closely related are grouped into the one **species**. Related species are grouped into a **genus** (plural: genera), man for example is in the genus *Homo* and forms the species *Homo sapiens*. Related genera are grouped into a **family** and going to still higher levels of classification there are **Orders, Classes, Phyla** (with Phylum the singular) and finally **Kingdoms**.

The whole fungal Kingdom – **Kingdom Fungi** – can be divided into five or more Phyla (singular – Phylum), but only those belonging to the **Phyla Ascomycota** and **Basidiomycota** commonly grow to sufficient size to be recognized as larger fungi. It must be noted however that not all ascomycetes and basidiomycetes are larger fungi; many are microscopic and are hence not included here. Good examples of microscopic basidiomycete fungi are the rusts and smuts, serious pests of our crops. But, whatever the size, the reproductive structures for members of one of these subdivisions is basically the same. It must be stressed that there is no definitive classification scheme, different authors have organized the fungi in different ways, the scheme presented here is just one of several modern schemes.

## Phylum Basidiomycota

In the Phylum Basidiomycota there are four Classes: Basidiomycetes, Urediniomycetes, Ustilaginomycetes and Incertae sedis. The species within the Phylum Basidiomycota described in this book are all basidiomycetes. This group includes such varied fungi as the mushrooms, toadstools, puffballs, stinkhorns, and earthstars. The unifying feature of the members of this group is the nature of the spore-producing cells. (It must be noted that although the fungi dealt with here are "larger" fungi, the spore-producing apparatus is microscopic and cannot be seen with the naked eye.) The spores are produced by a club-shaped cell called the basidium on which the spores develop externally and hence the spores are called basidiospores.

Within the basidiomycetes the position of these spore-producing cells varies and tradition-

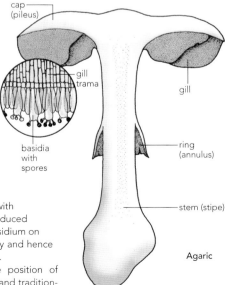

▼ *Structure in the larger basidiomycetes (Basidiomycota). The typical agaric has external basidia lining the gills. In other basidiomycetes the basidia may line tubes (brackets and boletes), spines (spine, tooth or hedgehog fungi), wrinkles, "veins" or flat surfaces.*

cap (pileus)

gill trama

gill

basidia with spores

ring (annulus)

stem (stipe)

Agaric

**Basidiomycetes**

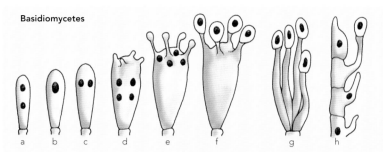

Formation of the microscopic spore-producing basidia and asci which distinguish basidiomycetes and ascomycetes. In the simple holobasidium characteristic of most basidiomycetes *(above left)* the two nuclei in the young basidium (a) fuse and exchange genetic material (b), then divide into four (c, d) which pass up the stalked sterigmata (e) to form spores externally on the mature basidium (f) Jelly fungi *(above right)* have divided basidia. The two shown are (g) *Tremella* and (h) *Auricularia*.

▼ *Puffballs, earthball, stinkhorns and bird's nest fungi, although often unrelated, all form their spore-carrying basidia inside the fruitbody and are often conveniently grouped together under the name Gasteromycetes.*

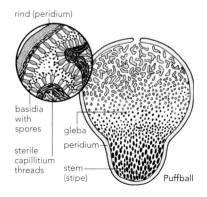

rind (peridium)

basidia with spores

gleba

sterile capillitium threads

peridium

stem (stipe)

Puffball

ally a further division of these fungi into two very artificial groups was based on this variation: the "Hymenomycetes" and "Gasteromycetes". In the "Hymenomycetes" the fertile layer or hymenium, which contains the basidia, lines the surface of, for example, the gills of a gill fungus and the pores of a bracket fungus. When mature the hymenium is in contact with the outside air and mature spores are dispersed from the hymenium directly into the atmosphere. The "Hymenomycetes" contains most of what we typically think of as mushrooms and toadstools, now dispersed among several different Orders. In the "Gasteromycetes" (for example the puffballs and earthstars) the basidia are formed in the internal tissues of the fruitbody and when mature are released within the "skin" of that body. Before the spores can be released to the atmosphere, and become dispersed, the outer wall must be broken, for example simply by disintegration or by the force of raindrops falling on the outer surface, which projects the spores into the atmosphere. One group of "Gasteromycetes", the stinkhorns (Order Phallales), relies upon insects and other invertebrates to disperse its spores, the foul-smell-

### Ascomycetes

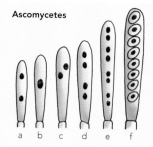

a b c d e f

In ascomycetes the spores develop entirely within the ascus. The two nuclei within the young ascus fuse (a, b) and split into usually eight (c, d, e) before maturing (f).

ing spore-mass is quickly eaten by flies, which pass the spores unharmed through their digestive tracts to later germinate. Another group of "Gasteromycetes" has become subterranean. These are the false truffles (Order Hymenogastrales), which rely on small mammals to dig them up and so disperse the spores. However, recent studies into the DNA of fungi shows that many of the "Gasteromycetes" are actually unrelated and have probably evolved from very diverse ancestors within the Basidiomycetes, they have simply adopted a similar spore-producing method. They remain grouped together here – as in most books – purely for convenience.

## Phylum Ascomycota

In the Phylum Ascomycota which consists of some nine Classes the major group that concerns us here is the Class Ascomycetes. The vast majority of species in this group are very small and are not described in this book. But some are quite large and more easily identified. They include the cup fungi, morels, earthtongues and truffles and some of what are commonly called the flask fungi. In the ascomycetes the specialized spore-producing cell is called an ascus and is characteristically club-shaped. Each ascus produces its spores inside the cell (note that spores are not produced outside the cell on stalks as in the basidiomycetes), usually numbering eight spores although this varies, which are then shot out through the tip of the ascus. The overall form of the fruitbody that produces the asci varies and is characteristic of the different groups. In the simpler members of the

### Typical cup fungus

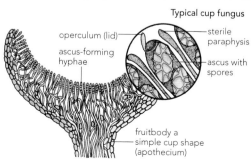

operculum (lid)

ascus-forming hyphae

sterile paraphysis

ascus with spores

fruitbody a simple cup shape (apothecium)

▶ In a typical cup fungus (Order Pezizales) the fertile layer is exposed; not all cup fungi form simple cups – the morels for instance form complex sponge-like caps on stalks.

Order Pezizales (the cup fungi) the asci are produced in a hymenium that lines the inner surface of a simple flattened or cup-shaped disc (apothecium). In the more complex morels the cup is folded and convoluted like a sponge, with the hymenium lining the pockets, while in the truffles the cup is so convoluted and infolded that the hymenium has become totally enclosed and is subterranean. In the flask fungi (principally in the Order Xylariales) the asci are produced in minute, hollow, pear-shaped structures (perithecia) which open by a

| The principal groups of the Kingdom Fungi illustrated in this book are: | | |
|---|---|---|
| **Phylum – Ascomycota :** Fungi with sexual spores contained inside special cells called asci; usually forming fruitbodies. Includes most of the fungal partners in lichens. The principal groups illustrated in this book include: | **Class – Ascomycetes** | **Sub-class: Pezizomycetidae** |
| | | **Sub-class: Leotiomycetidae** |
| | | **Sub-class: Sordariomycetidae** |
| **Phylum – Basidiomycota :** Fungi with sexual spores produced externally on cells called basidia; usually forming fruitbodies. Principal groups illustrated in this book include: | **Class – Basidiomycetes** | **Sub-class – Agaricomycetidae** |
| | | **Sub-class – Tremellomycetidae** 7 Orders including: |

small pore (ostiole) to the outside. Many perithecia may be gathered together to form a stroma, usually a hard woody mass with the pores of the perithecia opening at the surface.

Spore dispersal in the Ascomycetes takes place when the spores have reached maximum size, and fluid pressure within the ascus is high. Suddenly the tip of the ascus will either just split (inoperculate) or a special lid-like area (operculum) will flip up and the spores shoot out like bullets from a gun, travelling several centimetres. This can be seen with the

| | |
|---|---|
| **Order – Pezizales:** | **16 Families** including the following Families shown in this book<br>**Family – Pezizaceae:** cup fungi (part)<br>**Family – Tuberaceae:** truffles<br>**Family – Morchellaceae:** morels,<br>**Family – Helvellaceae:** helvellas<br>**Family – Discinaceae:** false morels<br>**Family – Sarcoscyphaceae :** cup fungi (part) |
| **Order – Helotiales:** | **16 Families** earthtongues (shown in this book) and many plant parasites |
| **Order – Xylariales** (flask fungi, part) | **9 Families including:**<br>**Family – Xylariaceae:** cramp balls, dead-men's fingers etc. |
| **Order – Hypocreales** (flask fungi, part) | **7 Families including:**<br>**Family – Nectriaceae:** coral spot |
| **Order – Agaricales:** mushrooms (also some puffballs and false truffles included for convenience in the "Gasteromycete" section)) | **28 Families** |
| **Order – Boletales:** Boletes (also earth-balls and some gilled fungi) | **19 Families** |
| **Order – Cantharellales:** Chanterelles, some club fungi | **6 Families** |
| **Order – Hymenochaetale:** some bracket fungi | **4 Families** |
| **Order – Phallales:** stinkhorns, earthstars and some club and coral fungi | **6 Families** |
| **Order – Polyporales:** bracket fungi | **24 Families** |
| **Order – Russulales:** Brittle Caps and Milk Caps | **11 Families** |
| **Order – Thelephorales:** tooth-fungi, earth-fans etc | **3 Families** |
| **Order – Auriculariales:** tree ears | |
| **Order – Tremellales:** jelly fungi | |

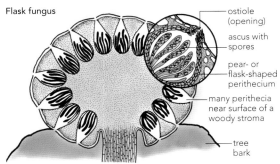

Flask fungus

ostiole (opening)

ascus with spores

pear- or flask-shaped perithecium

many perithecia near surface of a woody stroma

tree bark

◀ *In the flask fungi (Order Xylariales) the asci are grouped into "flasks" (perithecia); in larger species like the one illustrated many perithecia together form a stroma, which is usually hard and woody and often black.*

naked eye and also heard! If a mature fruitbody of a larger cup fungus is disturbed all the asci which are at maximum tension will fire off together and release a cloud of thousands of spores which will be seen as a puff of "smoke" and heard as very quiet rustling. However, in the truffles of the Order Tuberales (as also in the false truffles of the Basidiomycota), dispersal is usually by animals, although some species still retain the forcible dispersal mechanism.

Both basidia and asci may be interspersed with other, sterile cells. These are generally rather long, narrow, sometimes hooked cells acting probably as "packing" to support and separate the spore-producing cells. In the Basidiomycotina some very specialized and often very large cells (cystidia) can be found scattered over the hymenium and other parts of the fruitbody. Often many times larger than the basidia and of different shapes, cystidia can be of great importance in identification of difficult species; their function is not certain but they are often rich in oily substances.

Truffle

▶ *In the truffles (Order Tuberales) the asci are completely enclosed in the underground fruitbodies. Another group of Discomycetes is the earthtongues and their allies (Order Helotiales), these form simple, club-shaped fruitbodies.*

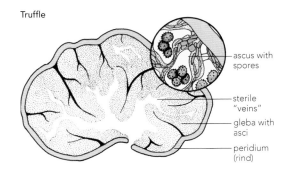

ascus with spores

sterile "veins"

gleba with asci

peridium (rind)

The previous table (see pages 10–11) and the classification used elsewhere in the book are broadly based on Ainsworth and Bisby's Dictionary of the Fungi, 9th edition (2001).

The Latin binomial (= double name) name of a fungus, e.g. *Agaricus campestris*, consists of parts denoting the genus (*Agaricus*) and the species within it (*campestris*). In the text opposite the illustrations the better known of any previously used names (synonyms) are given in parentheses following the sign =. Within the Kingdom Mycota the subsequent levels of classification (taxa) are, in ascending order of size: family (names ending in -aceae), order (-ales), class ( -mycetes), sub-division (-mycotina) and division ( -mycota). In the Guide section of the book, genus and family and sometimes order are indicated in the subheadings.

## The Structure of Larger Fungi

In the larger fungi the basic unit of construction is formed of microscopic cotton-like threads called **hyphae**. The term **mycelium** is used to describe the complete web of hyphae that makes up each individual fungus. The mycelium forms the basic vegetative structure, each hypha penetrating and branching throughout the growing medium (such as humus, wood, and so on), absorbing the required nutrients over its entire surface area. Individual hyphae or parts of the mycelium become highly modified in the fruitbodies, but even in the most complex "toadstool" the basic hyphal structure can still be easily recognized when viewed through a microscope.

Many people believe that when they observe a mass of toadstools in autumn these are the only parts of the fungus that ever form. In fact all year round masses of hyphae are to be found growing in the surface layers of the soil and only at the time of reproduction do the fruitbodies we all recognize develop and become visible.

The function of the fruitbodies is to produce spores, which are dispersed and will germinate to produce new mycelial colonies. The form of the fruitbody is the traditional basis for classifying fungi, and in the larger fungi described in this book the fruitbody characters are used to identify fungi right down to the species level.

Of the more than 8,000 fungus species in Britain alone some 3,500–4,000 may be described as "larger fungi" – those which are easily visible or can be handled. Many of these have very distinctive shapes and have over the years acquired such common names as puffballs, fairy clubs and earthstars (see the Index); many of these names are to be found in almost worldwide usage, with but little variation.

Some confusion arises because there is no clear difference between "mushrooms" and "toadstools" – both are words of convenience meaning different things to different people. In Britain "mushroom" may refer popularly only to the single cultivated species of the genus *Agaricus* sold in shops, or it may, as in this book, extend to representatives (not all edible) of half a dozen genera, including all species of *Agaricus* ("true" mushrooms). In other parts of Europe one term (e.g. "champignon") often covers all fungi, both microscopic and the large numbers of fungi that are eaten and enjoyed, and in North America most edible fungi are referred to, by mycologists at least, as mushrooms. "Toadstool" generally implies inedibility or the fear of poisonous qualities; in this sense it is sometimes used to describe any larger fungus with an umbrella-shaped cap on a central stem, other than *Agaricus bisporus*, the Cultivated Mushroom.

## The Typical Agaric

Most of the fungi illustrated in this book are members of the Agaricales (mushrooms and toadstools), commonly referred to as Agarics. A closer look at the life and structure of a typi-

**Veils**

The veils of tissue that frequently cover either the entire fungus or just the developing hymenium are of great use in identifying and classifying fungi. Whether these veils are tough and fleshy, thin and fragile or even cobweb-like can all help to determine genus or species. One must examine the cap, stem apex and stem base to see if any veils are present.

cap

scales (remains of universal veil)

gills

rings (remains of partial veil)

universal veil

stem

partial veil

volva (remains of universal veil)

base or bulb

mycelium

▶ The structure of the **partial veil or ring** usually falls into one of these categories:
a) pendent
b) with a cortina or cobweb-like, often leaving a faint ring or ring zone
c) sheathing or stocking-like
d) thick, fleshy, turned-back

▶ In the genus Amanita, the **volva** is of paramount importance for correct identification:
a) 2-4 hoop-like ridges (A. pantherina)
b) irregular bands or ridges (A. muscaria)
c) gutter-like or marginate bulb (A. citrina; A. porphyria with bag-like margin)
d) bag-like with thin, irregularly torn margin (A. phalloides, A. caesarea, A. vaginata and allied species)

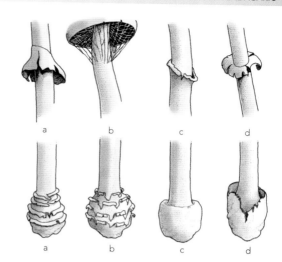

cal agaric will help to reveal those characters used in identification, how and in what form they arise in the fruitbody. An example of a highly evolved and complex toadstool is the Fly Agaric, *Amanita muscaria*, and this will serve as a model. All fruitbodies begin as a tiny knob of tissue arising from the underground mycelium; at first little structure can be distinguished but soon the tissues begin to differentiate and form the separate structures of the cap (technically called the pileus) and the stem (stipe). If you cut a very small button mushroom in half you can see the features appearing.

In the Fly Agaric at the young stage there is a surrounding "veil" of protective tissue which remains intact until the expansion of the fruitbody. This is usually referred to as the universal veil. When the fungus has expanded, the veil, forced to tear under the strain, is usually found clinging to the cap as white, woolly fragments or warts and at the base of the stem as rough gutter-like bands. Before expansion takes place however the gills (lamellae) of the toadstool will have developed. These are the radiating, very thin, plate-like structures found below the cap of most agarics and easily seen on the cultivated mushroom of the shops (A. bisporus). These gills grow downwards from the undersurface of the young cap. In the Fly Agaric they are protected by a second veil which stretches from the edge of the cap inwards to the stem and is called the partial veil. When the cap expands this will be forced to tear away from the cap margin and is left hanging from the stem as a ring (or annulus). Not all

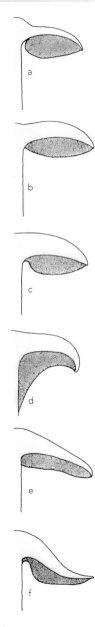

toadstools have these veils of tissue. In some only the partial veil is present and instead of being a sheet of thick tissue as in the Fly Agaric it is merely a fine, cobweb-like film called the cortina. The nature of the different veils and the way they tear and are left attached to the fungus are often of great importance in the identification of species. This is best displayed in the members of the genus *Amanita*. In the Fly Agaric the universal veil is left as simple bands around the stem-base but if we look at *Amanita phalloides*, the Death Cap, it is seen to form a large, thick bag (volva) enclosing the stem. Other species of *Amanita* have slightly different volvas and ridges at the stem-base which are usually constant for each species and therefore help in identification.

The gills of toadstools can vary enormously from genus to genus and between species in the same genus. Again these differences are of value in identification. The spacing of the gills, from crowded to widely spaced is usually constant for each species. The way the gills approach the stem and join on to it (the gill attachment) can be broadly classified as follows:

• Free to remote: not connected to the stem, sometimes separated by a distinct gap or collar.
• Adnexed to adnate: joining the stem for part (adnexed) or all (adnate) the depth of the gill.
• Decurrent: joining the stem and "running down" it to a greater or lesser extent.
• Sinuate or emarginate: the gill is notched just before joining the stem.

Combinations of these terms are often used to describe intermediate forms (e.g. adnate-decurrent, meaning the gill is broadly attached and tends to become slightly decurrent).

Not all larger fungi have gills; some have spines or wrinkles, in the boletes their place is taken by closely packed tubes, but the description of pore-attachment to the stem remains the same.

◄ *The way the gill approaches and joins onto the stem is often specific for certain genera and most species. Gill attachments will be of one of the following types (or a combination of two types, such as sinuate-decurrent)*
*a) free*
*b) adnexed (just reaching stem)*

*c) sinuate (with sudden notch or upward curve by stem = emarginate)*
*d) decurrent (running down the stem to a greater or lesser extent)*
*e) adnate (joined to stem by full depth of gill, but not running down the stem)*
*f) sinuate, with decurrent "tooth" running down stem*

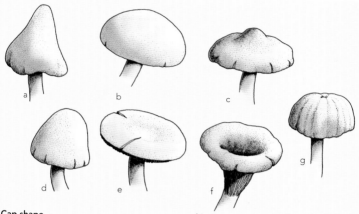

**Cap shape**

Cap shape is often important in identification, as it is usually constant within a species. The commonest shapes are shown here:
a) conical

b) convex to convex-expanded
c) umbonate (with "humped" centre)
d) campanulate (bell-like)
e) expanded and flattened
f) funnel-like, infundibuliform
g) depressed at centre, umbilicate

## Fruitbody expansion

The rapid expansion of the fruitbody (often a matter of a few hours) is exactly that, expansion as opposed to growth; most of the growth has already taken place in the previous days, underground in the unexpanded "button". When conditions are right the button will start to absorb moisture and air, cells will expand, and under pressure the tissues will force upwards and outwards, tearing any veils that are present. During the expansion and often brief life of a fruitbody various mechanisms are employed to ensure the successful use of the gills and subsequent spore discharge. If the gills or tubes are not aligned exactly vertically in relation to gravity, then the spores, which are formed on the gills or tubes, will not be released into the air correctly and will hit and stick to adjoining gills or tubes instead of having a free, unhindered fall between them.

If, therefore, the cap is for any reason misaligned the gills can correct this fault to some extent by repositioning, tilting to the vertical. The whole cap can also be realigned by the bending of the stem. This is easily demonstrated by placing an agaric on its side, preferably a young specimen just expanding: within a matter of an hour or two the stem will bend near the top at the apex so as to bring the cap hori-

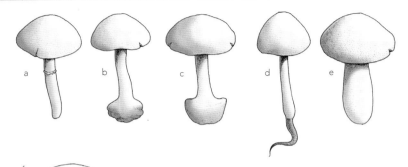

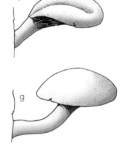

▲ **Stem shape** is often
very distinctive in
agarics and various
terms describe the
commoner types:
a) simple, cylindrical,
equal (parallel-sided)
b) bulbous (rather
abruptly so in the
example shown)
c) marginately bulbous
(with distinct ridge to
upper edge of bulb)
d) rooting, radicant
e) clavate (evenly
swelling, club-shaped)
f) lateral (from one
edge of cap)
g) eccentric (below cap
but set to one side)

zontal; this, combined with minute gill movements, ensures
successful spore discharge. The importance of this is obvious:
stemmed fruit bodies growing out from a vertical bank (a common occurrence) can still disperse their spores successfully.

Gill colour varies considerably and is further altered by the
colour of the spores when mature (the gill colour and spore
colour are not necessarily the same). The main colour groups
of spores are white to cream; shades of ochre to medium rust
or deep brown; pinkish; dark cocoa- or purple-brown to black.
Other more unusual colours also occur such as red or blue-
green, but they are exceptional. These various colours form
another useful adjunct to identification (see the Key), although
it must be stressed it is an artificial one, as fungi with different
spore colours are often closely related, and vice versa.

The textures of the fruitbody differ greatly so that there
can be smooth, rough, velvety, hairy or sticky-capped (viscid)
species and a great many other less easily defined textures.
These are all of importance in identification and are frequently mentioned in the species descriptions and key later in the
book. Consistency of the flesh may also help in identification,
as for example with the *Russula* and *Lactarius* species.

Although most agarics follow the basic shape of a cap
surmounting a stem, these two features naturally vary in size,
thickness, shape, etc. and several well-defined types are
referred to. The cap can therefore be subglobose, expanding and then flattening; acutely pointed, which is usually
referred to as conical; it can be umbonate, which means with
a distinct bump or hump at the centre; dish-shaped caps
are described as depressed, while if they are deeply funnel-
shaped they are infundibuliform; the edge of the cap may
be thinly grooved like the milled edge of a coin (striate) or
more deeply furrowed (sulcate). The stem may be equal (i.e.
parallel-sided); clavate, which means club-shaped, broadening toward the base; bulbous means with a more abruptly

swollen base; a marginate bulb refers to an abruptly defined bulb with a flattened upper edge. Other terms are explained in detail in the Glossary.

## Useful and Harmful Fungi

All organisms, whether plant, animal or fungi, bring about changes in their environment simply by the normal processes of life: feeding for example, or excretion and respiration, and the results as far as man is concerned can often be highly beneficial or disastrous. Fungi are certainly one of the largest causes of trouble to mankind the world over. They attack his food crops, timbers, stored goods, clothing, buildings, his animals and even his own body. Even seemingly non-edible products such as optical glass, paint, kerosene and plastics can be damaged by fungi.

Perhaps the most readily observed fungal attacks are those of the moulds and mildews. The thick blackish-speckled mass on damp bread is a familiar sight; the fungus involved is *Rhizopus stolonifer*, the common bread mould, a member of a large group of fungi called the Mucorales or pin-moulds because of the pinlike heads which contain the spores. This same fungus can also be a serious cause of rotting in stored fruit, particularly apples, causing a soft brown circular patch which soon spreads until the whole apple is a soft, rotten mass. But the same species is used to man's advantage in commerce in the production of various chemicals such as cortisone. Many related species are also used to produce such important products as citric and oxalic acids and alcohol. This double character of being both a pest and a useful agent is very common among fungi. The familiar green and blue circular moulds caused by *Penicillium* species and their allies, although pests of stored foodstuffs such as citrus fruits, jams and jellies, apples, leather and fabrics, are also of course famous for their part in the historic development of antibiotics, including penicillin and its many derivatives. Other species of the genus produce the distinctive tastes in many of our foods: *P. roqueforti* flavours Roquefort cheese and *P. camemberti* does the same for Camembert. *Penicillium* moulds are also used in the production of Danish blue and Gorgonzola cheeses. Like the pin moulds they are also effective producers of various organic acids in commerce. The related genus *Aspergillus*, which includes some of the common black moulds, contains some of the most successful of all fungi: aspergilli can attack almost any damp substance, while some are serious causes of disease in livestock and occasionally in man, usually affecting the respiratory organs to cause aspergillosis. As with *Penicillium* they are also used in industry as fermenting agents and to produce acids.

The yeasts, simple, mainly unicellular fungi are a part of the subdivision Ascomycotina. They are distant relatives of the cup fungi illustrated in this book which produce spores in cells called asci. However in the yeasts this method of reproduction appears to be less frequent than asexual reproduction by budding or transverse division. It would be fair to say that the yeasts have had the greatest impact of any fungus on man and that life would be truly different without them; the key to their usefulness lies in their ability to ferment sugars. The alcohol industry, bakeries, and also some vitamin production depends on the action of yeasts in releasing either carbon dioxide or alcohol as they break down carbohydrates. When oxygen is present carbon dioxide is the waste product while in oxygen-deficient conditions alcohol is produced. Yeasts also impart special flavours to their byproducts and often contain high quantities of various complex substances such as the vitamin B-complex. Other yeasts are cultivated for direct consumption as food, being a rich source of protein and amino acids.

▼ *Baker's or brewer's yeast,* Saccharomyces cerevisiae, *is used to help bread to rise during baking and to convert sugar into alcohol during brewing.*

However as with other fungi, yeasts can also be pests, some causing troubles in the brewing industry and others in some foods by producing unpleasant flavours. Man can also suffer from the serious disease cryptococcosis caused by a yeast which affects either the respiratory system or more usually the nervous system when it is known as Cryptococcus meningitis.

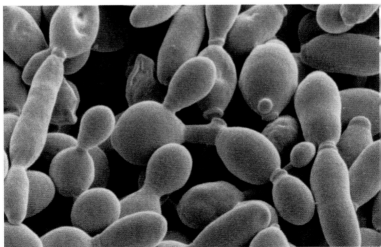

Turning to our crops in the field, such as wheat, barley and other grasses, together with all the many other vegetables and fruits grown, are all prey to a host of plant pathogens of fungal origin.

## Rusts and smuts

The rusts and smuts are major pathogens and both are placed by many in the Class Basidiomycotina. The rusts (Order Uredinales) comprise parasitic fungi which cause enormous damage and which often have very complex life-histories involving different host plants, and various resting or overwintering states. Typical of the rusts is *Puccinia graminis* the Black or Stem Rust of wheat. This overwinters on wheat stubble and straw in the form of special spores called teleutospores, which germinate in spring. The resulting mycelium gives rise to normal basidiospores which when dispersed infect a secondary host, the barberry. A further type of spore, the aecidiospore, is then produced which is dispersed in great numbers, whereupon it infects fresh wheat plants which then produce the familiar speckled or "rust" symptom.

At this stage yet another type of spore, the uredospore, is produced which is not violently discharged but is easily dispersed by wind to infect other wheat plants, but not the barberry host. Uredospores and the resultant infections occur throughout the summer months, but as autumn approaches teleutospores are again produced, and so the cycle starts again. This cycle of *Puccinia graminis* is typical of many other rust species which also have two hosts. Some species, however, have only one host, such as the blackberry rust, *Phragmidium violaceum*.

Rusts cause serious damage in such various crops as coffee, conifers, asparagus, beans and carnations. All cost us money and time and a continual battle is being waged between man and fungus, with the production of new fungicides and the breeding of disease-resistant strains of food-plants.

The smuts (Order Ustilaginales) are also important pathogens of plants but do not have such complex life-cycles as the rusts and never alternate from one plant to another. Again various cereals and grasses are affected as well as many other flowering plants and the infection is typically a dry, dusty, "smutty" coating. The spores are often produced in the reproductive organs of the host plant so that, for example, in the smut of false oats caused by *Ustilago avenae* the grain is replaced by smut spores.

The well-known ergot, *Claviceps purpurea*, which infects various cereal crops, is an ascomycete that has produced violent and extensive outbreaks of disease since historic times.

► *Ergot fruiting bodies. Coloured scanning electron micrograph (SEM) of the fruiting bodies of the fungus ergot* (Claviceps purpurea). *Fruiting bodies are the sexual reproductive structure of fungi. This fungus infects cereal crops and grasses, causing a reduced yield. During infection ergot induces the plants' cells to divide and enlarge, resulting in a large mass (black), called the sclerotium, which allows the fungus to survive adverse conditions. Ingestion of ergot causes poisoning (ergotism) in animals and humans, which can be fatal. Symptoms can include vomiting, gangrene and hallucinations. A number of medical drugs, as well as LSD, are derived from ergot.*

It produces a black, pointed body that protrudes from the seed heads of grasses and cereals and is formed of matted hyphae bound together to form a mass called a sclerotium. This "ergot" contains several very dangerous and potent alkaloids which severely affect both animals and man, with varied symptoms that lead in many cases to death. Bread made from infected grain has in past ages wiped out very large numbers of people; thankfully, with modern harvesting and cleaning techniques as well as the use of fungicides, ergotism as it is called is now a rare occurrence.

Many other fungi cause diseases in man such as athlete's foot and ringworm, both of which are common and troublesome the world over, while others are much rarer and more restricted, although frequently very serious. These include blastomycosis and related forms which cause deeper, often chronic, infections of body tissue. Even toadstools are not above infecting man – *Schizophyllum commune*, a worldwide agaric species found on timber has, albeit very rarely, been found causing fungal infections in human beings.

The larger fungi are however much more familiarly known as destroyers of human property, especially in the notorious Dry Rot, *Serpula lacrymans*. This basidiomycete is a relative of the familiar bracket fungi of our woodlands, which is almost exclusively found in houses, forming spreading, highly invasive sheets of tissue which soon decay and soften wood, plaster etc. until the whole structure collapses, an all too common and expensive occurrence. Other toadstools are, of course, of use to man as food and conversely some poison him when mistaken for edible species, but these are discussed in detail in the following pages.

# Fungi as Food

If you are a collector of fungi, sooner or later you may be tempted to eat some. Then the question of fungi as food will arise – just how safe are they, are they good to eat and do they contain any useful vitamins or protein? These are some of the questions being asked more than ever today when collecting and eating of wild foods is all the trend and so many books are encouraging you to try new and exotic foods. Firstly it must be made quite plain that there are poisonous fungi and that they can be, and sadly often are, fatal, particularly in Europe and occasionally in America, although very rarely in Britain where eating of wild fungi is still less common than in other parts of the world. Having said this it is only fair to state that by far the majority of the larger fungi are not poisonous and many are both edible and delicious. This being so one must find some guidelines for distinguishing the two and it is here that so many people go astray.

None of the old folk traditions regarding wild fungi and how to "test" them for safety hold true – repeat NONE! Cooking fungi with a silver sixpence or spoon, to see if it turns black, peeling the cap, boiling in salt water, only using fungi in fields, only using white toadstools – are a few of the traditional (and very much alive even today) tests for safety. These tests simply will not work against all poisonous fungi. The Death Cap, *Amanita phalloides*, will pass all these tests (even the last two on occasions) and still possibly kill you. The only safe and sure method is to be able to recognize the edible and poisonous species concerned by sight and never to eat anything which is in the least doubtful. Never take notice of helpful and well-meaning friends with a smattering of country lore, try instead to obtain identification from an expert until you are proficient yourself. Attend organized fungus forays in your area; most natural history societies run them or know of a local expert who can help.

The recognition of edible species is by no means a difficult task if certain very well known and highly valued species are chosen. There are half a dozen or more delicious species easily identified even by complete beginners and which are entirely safe and eaten the world over. None of these is a true mushroom of the genus *Agaricus* to which the shop mushroom belongs – the wild mushrooms can be surprisingly difficult for a beginner to identify and this has led to accidents in the past. The following species are all quite distinct from the ordinary mushroom and the dangerous toadstools in both shape and colour.

23

▲ There are a number of species of fungi that are delicious to eat, and most are described in this book; however always consult an expert if you're uncertain as to whether or not a species is edible.

## Kings of edible fungi

First and the undoubted king in the fungus world is *Boletu edulis* known as the Cep in France, Steinpilz in Germany, Po cini in Italy, Penny Bun in some parts of England plus othe names around the world. This is considered by many th most delicious and useful of the edible fungi. It is a bolete which means is has tubes underneath the cap instead of gills This immediately rules out nearly all the dangerous toad stools which are almost entirely gilled species.

Second come the Morels – the various species of *Morche la*. These occur in the spring and look like a sponge on a stalk Again very easy to recognize, they are considered by many especially in the USA, as equal and possibly superior to th previous species. Next is the Chanterelle, *Cantherellus ciba ius*, a beautiful egg-yellow to apricot toadstool with a top shaped cap and blunt, ridgelike "gills", again a widely value species sold all over Europe in the markets. The Shaggy Ink cap *Coprinus comatus* is another unmistakable species wit a very tall, cylindrical, shaggy-white cap soon turning to blac inky liquid; picked when still young and solid it makes a del cately flavoured and tender delicacy stewed or baked. Th Giant Puffball (*Calvatia gigantea*) is exactly what its name sug gests – a huge white ball-like fungus which when mature pro duces a powdery white spore-mass but when still young, ca be cut into steaks and fried with very good results; it reaches 10–40 cm across or more. The Blewits, *Lepista nuda* and *L. saeva* are a personal favourite and well liked by a great many mycophagists (as fungus eaters are known). (For a first tasting of Blewits a small quantity is recommended: a few people have an allergic reaction to these species.) Their lilac-violet colouring and very late (autumn to early winter) appearance make them again easy to recognize.

These six species would make a good selection to start with and are impossible to confuse with such things as the Death Cap. Many other edible fungi can also be recommended among which the best are the Parasols, *Macrolepiota procera* and *M. rhacodes*; the Black Trumpets, or Horn of Plenty, *Craterellus cornucopioides*, Oyster mushroom, *Pleurotus ostreatus*, St George's Mushroom, *Calocybe gambosum*, many of the *Boletus* species, and finally the Beafsteak or Ox-tongue fungus, *Fistulina hepatica*. All these species are illustrated in this book and are worth trying if the opportunity arises.

Always eat a very small quantity of a new fungus at first – some people are allergic to many foods including fungi, others just find them indigestible. Do not leave picked fungi for long before preparing them for food or for preserves or placing in the freezer. Fungi inadvisably placed in a polythene bag will decompose fast. Only use fresh, young material for cooking although not so young as to be unrecognizable. To prepare fungi for cooking is very easy. Simply wipe the cap with a damp cloth; avoid soaking or too much washing – this makes them soggy. Do not bother to peel the caps, as this is entirely unnecessary and a waste of effort. Gills and pores may also be left on unless they are very soft or are damaged. The stem is usually removed if tough; otherwise chop or slice it along with the cap. Fungi may be oven-dried for storage and later use or even pickled as ketchup.

Any method of cooking used for green vegetables may be used for fungi – stewing, steaming, baking etc.– and fungi may also be treated as a meat dish by frying, grilling etc. Many species are delicious when stuffed with a spicy filling or used in omelettes. Use your imagination, and fungi can become a valuable addition to any meal. In addition, many cookery books give recipes for fungi and some volumes concentrate exclusively on such cooking.

## Poisonous Fungi

Hopefully you will never experience the effects of eating a poisonous fungus, but it is still important (and interesting) to know what they are and how the poisons work. The number of really dangerous species of fungi is relatively small and restricted on the whole to one or two particular genera. However there are a number of other poisonous species which although perhaps not deadly differ widely in their effects on the human body and in the chemicals involved in the poisoning. Because of these differences it is possible broadly to classify those fungi by their poisons into a few basic groups.

### Amatoxins and phallotoxins – the deadly *Amanitas*

Foremost amongst poisonous fungi must come the various species of the genus *Amanita*, in particular the infamous Death Cap, *Amanita phalloides* and the less well known but equally deadly Destroying Angel, *A. virosa*. No other fungi have such numerous or complex toxins and this fact has made treatment in the past extremely difficult and uncertain. The poisons in *Amanita* fall into two main groups, the phallotoxins and the amatoxins, the two groups differing in their effects on the body and the time involved in their actions. In the Death Cap there are believed to be six related phallotoxins and five or more amatoxins. The symptoms produced by these toxins are many and variable. After eating a meal of Death Cap (which incidentally tastes quite good) the first effects are often not felt for some 5–30 hours, thus making stomach-pumps of little use, as the toxins have been well distributed by the blood-stream. First the victim will suffer from abdominal pains, diarrhoea and vomiting. This will increase until the victim is in a state of shock from fluid losses, exhaustion, etc., and if treatment is not carried out death soon ensues. If treatment is available these symptoms are usually soon combated and the patient may seem to revive for a day or two, but then quite suddenly will suffer a relapse where the pulse is weak, blood pressure drops drastically and there may be hallucinations. Finally death occurs and an autopsy shows major liver and kidney damage and muscle damage around the heart. This was until quite recently the classic picture of Death Cap poisoning with over 90% of fungus-induced deaths being caused by this species. Now with new techniques of blood filtration by carbon-column haemodialysis units, and the use in America of the drug thioctic acid, effective treatment is possible if the poisoning is diagnosed in time.

As mentioned previously *Amanita virosa* also has the same sort of toxins present and is just as deadly. There are a few other species which must be regarded as deadly such as *A. verna, A. bisporigera* and *A. tenuifolia*. Only *A. verna* occurs in Europe (but not in Britain), the others being of North American origin. All are basically white species much like the Death Cap in shape. The distinguishing features of this group should be noted carefully: the basal bag-like volva and the ring on the stem, the white, free gills and the cap colour from olive-green through brown to pure white. In Europe the Death Cap is by far the commonest of these *Amanita* species and varies considerably in cap colour even within one woodland. In America the white species are more frequent, although the Death Cap does also occur there.

Other genera recently discovered to contain some of these toxins include *Galerina*, *Lepiota* and *Conocybe*. Not all the species in these genera are poisonous but *Galerina marginata* and *Lepiota brunneoincarnata* have certainly been implicated in poisonings.

▲ *The Destroying Angel* (Amanita virosa) *is less well known than the notorious Death Cap,* (A. phalloides) *but can, however, be just as deadly if eaten.*

### The muscarine poisons

A large number of species, including some other *Amanita* species, produce rapid, serious, but not usually fatal poisonings. Their toxins all affect the central nervous system to cause vomiting, profuse sweating, blurred vision, reduced heart beat and blood pressure and even convulsions with sometimes hallucinations as well! The best example of this type of mushroom must be the famous Fly Agaric, *Amanita muscaria*, used for centuries for its hallucinogenic properties and as a natural fly-killer. The toxins contained are muscarine – thought not to be the active principal involved in the poisonings – plus muscimol and ibotenic acid. The toxic effect of this fungus varies enormously from region to region and with season, some forms being apparently harmless. However, the recent interest in hallucinogens should not encourage people to experiment, as the other side effects can be both unpleasant and dangerous.

The Panther Cap, *Amanita pantherina*, contains similar toxins. Muscarine itself, although not present in large quantities in the amanitas is common in two other genera of gill-fungi, *Clitocybe* and *Inocybe*. The poisonous species of these genera cause very serious poisonings, even death in some cases; *Clitocybe* includes a number of small, white, grassland species which contain this toxin (*C. rivulosa* is one illustrated), while *Inocybe* is almost entirely composed of

▲ Inocybe rimosa, *like most of the genus, can be dangerously toxic and should never be eaten.*

poisonous species, mainly small brownish toadstools with fibrillose caps and brown gills.

For muscarine poisoning the specific antidote is atropine with other treatments for the various symptoms as they occur, while for muscimol and ibotenic acid symptomatic treatment is only with an anti-hallucinogen, never atropine, which can aggravate an already dangerous situation.

## Hallucinogenic toadstools

In Mexico natives still eat certain toadstools to induce hallucinations, mainly species of *Psilocybe*, *Panaeolus* and *Conocybe*. These contain the toxin psilocybin which rapidly affects the senses, causing confusion, anxiety, hallucinations and often giddiness. *Psilocybe* species are now collected world-wide for so-called recreational use, but misidentification is very easy and could lead to serious poisonings, it is also illegal in Britain to collect or consume these fungi.

## Gastrointestinal irritants

A very large number of species cause digestive upsets some of which can be quite severe. However most of these irritant substances are destroyed by thorough cooking and some quite well-known edible species are in fact mildly poisonous if eaten raw or undercooked. The genera mainly responsible are *Russula*, *Lactarius*, *Tricholoma*, *Morchella* and even some boletes. Some true mushrooms (*Agaricus*) can cause upsets, even when cooked, in sensitive persons, especially *A. xanthodermus*, which is distinguished by its bright yellow stains when bruised. The author also has personal knowledge of sickness caused by eating *A. vaporarius*, although other people who ate it at the same table were unaffected.

## Orellanine toxins

These often fatal toxins also cause kidney damage, eventually causing complete kidney failure. They are typified by a very late onset of initial symptoms (nausea, etc.), which can take many days or even weeks to appear after ingestion These toxins are most commonly found in members of the genus *Cortinarius*, of which the most infamous are *C. oral-lanus* and *C. speciosissimus*, the latter species is not uncommon in parts of England and Scotland.

## Other toxins

The False Morel, *Gyromitra esculenta*, despite its specific name and being quite widely eaten without normally any ill effects, has caused severe poisonings, even death, in Europe. It contains a compound called "Gyromitrin" which is broken down in the stomach to form monomethylhydrazine (a constituent of rocket fuel!) which is usually evaporated during cooking. However if the fungus is undercooked it seems that enough of the chemical remains to cause illness, the fumes given off during cooking can also be toxic. The toxin attacks both the liver and kidneys. It would also appear that ageing in this species sometimes causes an accumulation of the toxic principles so that old, perhaps slightly rotten, specimens are particularly dangerous.

Finally the common Ink Cap, *Coprinus atramentarius*, causes a strange poisoning only if consumed with alcoholic drinks. It contains a chemical recently named coprine which is similar in effect to the drug antabuse used in treating alcoholics. Symptoms include palpitations, rapid pulse, flushing of the extremities and face, nausea and vomiting. They soon subside only to recur when more alcohol is drunk, and this can last for several days. Similar effects have been reported after consuming the common Cloud Cap, *Clitocybe nebularis*.

All these cases sound alarming and indeed they are, but with common sense and caution, this account need not cause undue worry. Once again you must know exactly what you are eating to avoid risks. Should the worst happen (and small children particularly are liable to eat things when nobody is watching) seek medical aid immediately, and take any specimens of the offending fungus (even if only in the form of vomit) to the hospital with you for identification.

## Collecting and Studying Fungi

A little time and preparation spent beforehand can often make a subject much more rewarding, and this is very true of mycology. Knowing where, how and when to collect makes a great difference to the success or failure of a day's study or quest for food. And when you have your day's collection safely home in good condition, how you go about handling the specimens, and the techniques used to investigate them, can make all the difference between a successful identification or not.

### Where to look

All woodlands of course will produce some fungi, and some will be very rich indeed, but you should pay particular attention when out collecting to the edges of woodlands and fields: these may have a much wider range of species than the centre and often produce rarities seldom seen elsewhere. The reasons for this are not always clear: temperature, moisture and plant variety no doubt all play a part. Similarly pathways and grassy rides passing through the woodland can also be very rewarding and make the day much more leisurely – scrambling through dense woods with thick undergrowth can be both unproductive of fungi and exhausting to the mycologist!

Mixed woodlands are better on average than pure stands of trees except where the latter are very ancient, mature woods or are on particular soils; beech on chalk, for example, can be extremely rich. The conifer plantations which cover extensive areas and which are relatively young can often be surprisingly poor except at the edges and very late in the season. Bogs and marshes have their own special flora, a very fascinating one to study although not usually producing the more showy species found in drier woodlands.

▼ Collecting fungi is an enjoyable and rewarding pastime, and local societies can be found in most regions of the country; most of these will also have contacts in many European countries if you want to foray farther afield.

Studies can very usefully be made of specialized habitats such as burnt stumps, sawdust heaps, sand dunes, dung, even back gardens! All such areas have a particular range of species determined by the chemistry of the soil or other growing medium, moisture content etc. and because of this it is often possible to predict exactly what species should be found by carefully noting the terrain. Do not collect more material than you can easily examine the same day; fungi are soft, easily decaying organisms and accurate identification depends on having perfect specimens. If you collect too many you will end up with only a portion identified and the rest too dried up or collapsed to be of use. Although collecting the fruitbodies does not damage the fungus you should nevertheless show some consideration for others and not collect every specimen if a number are present; just take a representative selection of stages of growth and leave the rest for others to see.

## Containers

A large flat basket or trug is ideal for collecting the larger toadstools; tins, tubes and boxes for very small and fragile species. Never use polythene bags which rapidly turn fungi into a liquid mess; by far the best method is to wrap each toadstool individually in a twist of waxed paper of the kind found lining cereal boxes (not grease-proof paper). Have a selection of squares ready cut and wrap the fungi rather as a boiled sweet is wrapped in confectioners. This paper helps retain moisture, colour and stiffness in the fungus and also prevents the specimens from crushing each other in the basket. Always treat the fungus with great care when picking, particularly the stem which is easily damaged and is of great importance in identification. Make sure you uproot all the stem, especially the base, which can be vitally important if you intend to eat your finds: the stem is a key character in such deadly species as the Death Cap.

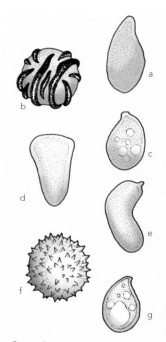

**Spore shapes**
a) fusiform, as in *Boletus* species; b) ornamented, as in *Russula* and *Lactarius* species; c) ovate; d) bullet-like, as in *Lepiota*; e) sausage-like, arcuate; f) globose, spiny; g) pip-shaped

Take a written note in the field of any noticeable but often short-lived characters such as surface texture, odour and colour changes and look to see if the fungus appears to be growing under or by a particular tree or plant.

When you begin to examine your finds, try to develop the habit of examining them in a regular order, for example note the cap shape, texture, colour, presence of marginal veil, then gill spacing, attachment to stem, colour and so on all the way down. Finally when you have notes on all visual characters check the odour (which can often identify a puzzling specimen in seconds if very distinctive).

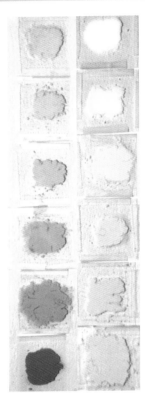

▲ *Examples of spore prints. Spore colour can often be extremely helpful when identifying species in certain genera.*

### Taking a spore print

You should now take a spore print if spore colour is not obvious (gill colour can be a good guide but is not always; for example some species have purple gills and white spores). To take a print separate or cut the cap from the stem and place it, gills or tubes down, onto a piece of glass, cover with a tin or old cup to prevent loss of moisture and wait about half an hour to an hour after which enough spores should fall so that when scraped together (let dry for five minutes first) they will show their colour when placed over a sheet of pure white paper. These same spores can be examined under a microscope, if one is available, and their size measured. Never use spores from the gill surface for this purpose, unless a spore print is not available, as they may not be fully developed and so give you a false reading unless 20 or so are measured.

Always cut your specimens down the centre, which reveals the gill and tube attachments where relevant and also shows any flesh changes.

A drawing or painting of your finds, no matter how simple, will be a valuable source of reference in the future and is a good discipline in itself for remembering and noticing important features. Fungi can make beautiful subjects for anyone with artistic talent (whether this is already known to exist or not!). Of course a good photograph is also a very valuable asset.

Chemical tests are often a useful adjunct in identification and in some instances are species-specific, i.e. only one species in a genus will react to a particular chemical in a particular way. Useful reagents to keep are: Ferrous sulphate ($FeSO_4$) or ferric sulphate ($Fe_2(SO_4)_3$), both available as crystals (one large crystal in a tube is enough); ammonia ($NH_4OH$) in a 50% solution with distilled water; phenol, 2% in distilled water; formalin, 2% solution in distilled water; potassium hydroxide (KOH), 10% in distilled water; and a solution called Melzer's iodine, which is very important but is difficult to obtain as it contains chloral hydrate, a dangerous poison. Its constituents are iodine 0.5g, potassium iodide 1g, distilled water 20 cc, mixed together, then chloral hydrate 20 g added. Some other less useful reagents are mentioned where necessary in the species descriptions. Many of these chemicals are dangerous, either poisonous or caustic or both. Handle them with great care, using a glass rod to apply, and store out of reach of children.

Finally, if you have easy access to a particular area of woodlands or fields try recording the species found in one restricted area, say a particular stand of trees or a stream-side, over a period of a number of years. You will often build up a surprisingly large list of species and only then get a true impression of the fungus flora of your area. It cannot be stressed enough that frequent and continual trips to an area are essential, if possible throughout the year, to reveal its full potential. Each season will be different and unique, revealing some new species or rarity, often in large numbers, some-times not to be seen again for a great many years. This is the essence and the excitement of mycology in the field, not knowing what will be in the next field, the next woodland or roadside verge.

## Further Reading

**Kirk, P.M.** Editor (2001), *Ainsworth and Bisby's Dictionary of the Fungi 9th Edition*, CABI Bioscience. An important reference work for up-to-date information on names, meanings of terms and classification.

**Bon, Marcel** (2005), *Mushrooms and Toadstools*, A & C Black. A standard and very comprehensive illustrated guide.

*British Fungus Flora: Agarics and Boleti*, various authors, 10 vols. Royal Botanic Gardens, Edinburgh 1969–2005 . Each vol-ume deals with different groups of basidiomycetes and includes descriptions and keys (no colour pictures). Indispensable, with descriptions and keys to British species of each group.

**Dennis, R. W. G.** (1968), *British Ascomycetes*, Cramer. A standard work on the cup fungi of Britain and N. Europe.

*Field Mycology* (1999– ). Published by Elsevier for the Brit-ish Mycological Society. A full colour magazine covering all mycological topics for fungal enthusiasts, whether beginners or more advanced students, an essential reference work.

**Legon, N., & Henrici, A.** (2005), *Checklist of the British & Irish Basidiomycota*. Royal Botanic Gardens, Kew. The most up-to-date reference to the British species, an essential work.

**Phillips, Roger** (2006), *Mushrooms*. Pan Macmillan. An essen-tial reference work with hundreds of colour photographs.

**Spooner, Brian & Roberts, P.** (2005), *Fungi*, Collins New Naturalist. The most complete and scholarly as well as thor-oughly enjoyable book on all mycological subjects (not an identification guide).

## Fungus Societies

There are two principal fungus societies in Britain with numerous local groups; these provide a wonderful way to meet other enthusiasts and to study the fungi under the guidance of experienced and helpful experts. The two principal groups are the British Mycological Society (www.britmycolsoc.org.uk) founded in 1896 and with some 2000 members worldwide. They organise meetings and fungus forays around the country as well as publishing scientific journals and the popular magazine *Field Mycology*.

The other principal society is the Association of British Fungus Groups (www.abfg.org), an "umbrella" group pulling together a number of local groups and concerned with recording fungi around Britain. They also publish a magazine, *The Forayer*.

## How to Use the Key and Guide

In any book of this sort the choice of which species to includ
is a difficult one. Based as it is on the author's opinion as t
which species are most likely to be found, and which sp
cies, although uncommon or rare, are worthy of inclusio
it must inevitably be a personal choice. Another mycologi
might easily pick different species or disagree about whic
rare species should be included. The difficulty of choic
arises because there are some 3,600 species of larger fun
in Britain alone. There will of course be a central core of sp
cies that are well known as common fungi everywhere and s
must be included, but as more and more choices are mac
the decisions as to what must be dropped becomes an ag
nizing one. In this volume a conscious decision was mac
that where uncommon or rare species were involved w
would try to show those not often illustrated in other simil
works. Some of the species have in fact not been illustrate
in a popular handbook before at all. Even some of the con
moner species shown in the following pages are rarely see
or even mentioned in popular mycological works, pure
because of the problem of limited space. It is hoped there
fore that by the aid of this book you should be able to ider
tify a very large proportion of the fungi you see and that you
chances of identifying a rare species are increased. Wher
suitable, other related species to those illustrated have bee
mentioned in the text.

Assuming you have in front of you a fungus which yo
wish to identify, what is the best way to go about finding it i
this book? Firstly it must be stressed that there is no reasc
at all why you should not just flip through the colour plate
and try to spot your find. If you have a common or frequer
species you stand a good chance of seeing it, but be sur
to confirm the identification from the description opposit
each plate.

### Common problems

Fungi are notoriously variable in appearance, and even
common species can vary remarkably. If difficulties or unce
tainty arise, try tracking the fungus down in the Key that fo
lows. The key is of the dichotomous type, with paired choice
or couplets of contrasting characters. To begin you shoul
check the pictorial key to the different types of fungal shap
and structure, and when satisfied as to which group a spec
men belongs to, go to the appropriate section of the Key
So, if you have a simple disc-shaped fungus as shown in th
pictorial key then follow on to step 7 in the written keys whic
deals with the cup fungi. For gill fungi you will need to mak

a spore print, and also for some other species. The rules for using a key successfully are very simple: always read both contrasting couplets carefully and only follow a line which agrees entirely with your fungus. For example:

38. Cap viscid to glutinous, white – 39

38. Cap dry – 40

If your toadstool was white but not viscid-glutinous then you should follow the second choice. The number shown at the end indicates the next step, where you make your next choice. Should you find your fungus doesn"t seem to come out correctly anywhere, there are various possible reasons why. Firstly, check very carefully that you haven"t followed the wrong couplet or skipped a line (easily done); second, check (if you have more than one specimen available) that you are not using the oldest most faded specimen of those you have. A fresh, reasonably young specimen is essential for a good chance of success. The third possibility is that you have a genus not included in the key. A key that includes all possibilities is both large and unwieldy and often requires detailed microscopical examination. With this key you should at least be able to discover to which genera it is close, and perhaps obtain assistance from a mycologist at a museum or botanical garden to complete the identification. This should not arise often as by far the majority of important genera are included. At no point does a couplet rely entirely on a microscopical character, although these have been included where useful. A spore print to determine colour is however often essential.

Some of the genera included in the key have not been illustrated in this book, and are indicated as "(not incl.)". In other genera species may key out at different points as "(part)". This applies particularly to the Bracket fungi. Also where appropriate some fungi have been keyed out to species where distinctive or where only one species of the genus is known. The small marginal illustrations should help in placing key characters and shapes quickly and thus aid to quick and accurate identification. The newcomer to such keys should expect to make mistakes in the beginning, and try to double-check the identification with somebody else with more experience. Within a short time you should be able to recognize the principal genera by sight alone. Practice makes perfect!

---

**Key to poisonous species**

 *Poisonous*

 *Deadly Poisonous*

---

# FIELD KEY

## Gill Fungi

Spore colour (make a spore print, see p. 32)

| | | |
|---|---|---|
| a | spores white, through shades of cream-colour, pale yellow to ochre, occasionally pinkish but never salmon-pink | Go to 1 |
| b | spores from bright tawny orange through shades of brown (dull, rust, cigar, clay, ochraceous) to rich brown | Go to 39 |
| c | spores black, sooty brown, chocolate or purplish | Go to 59 |
| d | spores salmon-pink to lilaceous pink | Go to 67 |
| e | spores red or blue-green | Go to 73 |

**a** spores white, through shades of cream-colour, pale yellow to ochre, occasionally pinkish but never salmon-pink

| Key | Description | Go to... |
|---|---|---|
| 1 | stem strongly eccentric to lateral, or absent | 34 |
| 1 | stem central or at most only slightly eccentric | 2 |
| 2 | with volva or volval remains at stem base and often on cap as warts, flakes etc.: *Amanita* P52 ▶ | |
| 2 | without a volva or volval remains | 3 |
| 3 | ring present or cobweb-like or sheathing veil on stem | 4 |
| 3 | without ring, or cobweb-like or sheathing veil on stem | 13 |
| 4 | granular veil sheathing lower stem up to slight ring-like zone (latter may be absent); gills adnate to sinuate: *Cystoderma* (part) P69 ▶<br><br>*Lepiota* (part) P65 ▶ | |
| 4 | veil, if sheathing, not granular or with ring only and gill attachment may be different | 5 |
| 5 | veil sheathing and usually slimy; gills rather thick, waxy; all species on ground: *Hygrophorus* (part) P162 ▶ | |

| | | |
|---|---|---|
| 5 | with membranous ring or cobweb-like veil | 6 |
| 6 | gills adnate to slightly decurrent; cap and stem finely squamulose to scaly; medium to large species usually tufted on wood, attached by black bootlace-like rhizomorphs which spread under wood and through soil: *Armillaria* (part) P148 ▶ | |
| 6 | gills not decurrent and/or other characters different | 7 |
| 7 | gills free | 8 |
| 7 | gills adnate-adnexed to sinuate | 10 |
| 8 | cap smooth, viscid; ring membranous; on ground: *Limacella* | (not incl.) |
| 8 | not this combination of characters; cap usually dry, mostly with scales/fibrils, especially at centre; on ground | 9 |
| 9 | delicate, tiny to very large fleshy species, with ring-zone to thick double collar-like ring: *Macrolepiota*, *Lepiota* (part), P64 ▶<br><br>*Cystoderma* (part, not incl.) P68 ▶ | |
| 9 | delicate, graceful, very fragile species; cap noticeably striate-sulcate at margin: *Leucocoprinus* | (not incl.) |
| 10 | cap viscid to glutinous, white, ivory to greyish | 11 |
| 10 | cap dry or at most moist (if gills thick, waxy, growing on soil, (see *Hygrophorus*) | 12 |
| 11 | on beech; cap white, ivory to greyish, glutinous; gills broad, widely spaced; stem slender, very tough with distinct narrow ring: *Oudemansiella mucida* P148 ▶ | |
| 11 | on ground; cap cream-colour to tan, slightly viscid; gills not widely spaced; stem with faint ring-zone and lower stem often "weeping" rust-coloured droplets, especially in damp weather: *Chamaemyces fraccida* | (not incl.) |

| 12 | stem with large marginate basal bulb; cortina leaving ring-zone; cap reddish brown; on ground; like a white Cortinarius: *Leucocortinarius bulbiger* | (not incl.) |
| 12 | stem without marginate bulb; with fine woolly ring at apex; cap grey, fibrillose; under willows: *Tricholoma cingulatum* P127 ▶ | |
| 13 | cap, stem and gills brittle, crumbly, rather granular, not fibrous; spores ornamented with spines and ridges which stain black in iodine | **14** |
| 13 | cap, stem and gills soft to touch but fleshy and fibrous, not crumbly and granular; spores different | **15** |
| 14 | broken flesh exudes white or coloured "milk"; taste often distinctive (peppery, sweet etc.): *Lactarius* P180 ▶ | |
| 14 | flesh not exuding milk when cut; cap colours widely variable - bright red, purple, yellow, green, brown, white etc.: *Russula* P172 ▶ | |
| 15 | gills thick, rather distant, pinkish, reddish brown or violet, dusted white with spores; on ground in woods, heaths etc.; small to medium species; spores minutely spiny: *Laccaria* P139 ▶ | |
| 15 | gills (if thick) of different colour, not noticeably dusted with spores, often waxy or translucent in appearance or not particularly thick and distant | **16** |
| 16 | gills rather thick with texture waxy to watery and translucent appearance: *Hygrophorus* (part), P162 ▶ *Hygrocybe* P164 ▶ | |
| 16 | gills not particularly thick and/ or not waxy and translucent | **17** |

| 17 | gills adnate to decurrent (if clustered on wood, see *Xeromphalina* (not incl.), *Armillaria tabescens*, *Mycena* species) | **18** |
| 17 | gills free, adnexed-adnate or sinuate | **22** |
| 18 | gills forking, pale to deep orange, edge blunt and rounded; cap colours similar; in heaths under birch, bracken etc.: *Hygrophoropsis aurantiaca* P138 ▶ | |
| 18 | colour different or gills not forking and blunt | **19** |
| 19 | gills usually blunt, spotted reddish; cap grey to blackish; spores blue-black in iodine: *Cantharellula umbonata* | (not incl.) |
| 19 | gills not usually forking although one or two may do so, edge sharp and well-formed | **20** |
| 20 | cap small (2-3 cm) to very large, often pale whitish to grey-brown; stem fibrous, not "polished", over 5 mm in diameter: *Clitocybe*, P136 ▶ *Leucopaxillus* P137 ▶ | |
| 20 | usually very small species, cap below 2-3 cm; stem smooth, "polished", under 5 mm diameter | **21** |
| 21 | usually in moss or on bare soil; cap often rounded with central depression to funnel-shaped; spores not blue-black in iodine; gills rather widely spaced; stem usually short: *Omphalina* P140 ▶ | |
| 21 | on pine stumps or litter in clusters; small tough species, cap convex; spores blue-black in iodine: *Xeromphalina* | (not incl.) |
| 22 | flesh tough and leathery, can dry out then revive with water without decaying; gills often interconnected with "veins"; very tiny to medium-sized species: *Marasmius* (and some related genera, all small to medium) | (not incl.) |
| 22 | flesh, although it may be tough, will not so revive | **23** |

37

| 23 | cap tiny to medium-sized, bell-shaped to umbonate, often sharply so, not fleshy; margin usually noticeably striate, not incurved when young; gill attachment variable, adnate to slightly decurrent; colours variable - browns, greys, yellow, pink, white all frequent; often tufted, but solitary species also; on wood and ground: *Mycena* P152 ▶ | |
|---|---|---|
| 23 | characters different | **24** |
| 24 | stem long, tough, fibrous, with extended "taproot" below soil; cap viscid-glutinous or velvety-hairy, with radial wrinkles; usually by stumps: *Xerula* P149 ▶ | |
| 24 | stem without "taproot" or other characters different | **25** |
| 25 | cap deep reddish brown; stem swollen, spindle-shaped, very tough, fibrous, splitting, misshapen; often in clusters at base of deciduous trees: *Collybia fusipes* P143 ▶ | |
| 25 | colour different and/or stem different from preceding | **26** |
| 26 | clustered or solitary on wood | **27** |
| 26 | on ground or other fungi | **30** |
| 27 | in dense clumps on deciduous trees; caps 4–10 cm, minutely scaly at centre; stems slender; overall colours tan to brownish: *Armillaria tabescens* P148 ▶ | |
| 27 | characters very different or on coniferous timber | **28** |
| 28 | on deciduous timber; caps rather small (2-6 cm), yellow-orange, smooth and rather viscid; stem slender, yellow above, reddish brown, velvety below, black at base; late autumn through winter: *Flammulina velutipes* P146 ▶ | |
| 28 | on deciduous or coniferous timber, also sawdust; medium to large fleshy species; other characters different | **29** |

| 29 | on conifers and sawdust; cap yellow overlaid with minute purple-red to brownish downy scales; gills golden yellow: *Tricholomopsis* P146 ▶ | |
|---|---|---|
| 29 | on deciduous timber; caps greyish brown, smooth but radially fibrillose, not scaly; gills whitish, broad, distant; stem white, tough and fibrous, often with white thick fibrous "roots" or runners: *Megacollybia platyphylla* P147 ▶ | |
| 30 | in dense clusters with stem-bases often fused; caps white to grey-brown; medium to large and fleshy, texture elastic-rubbery; gills adnate to very slightly decurrent: *Lyophyllum* (part) P128 ▶ | |
| 30 | not in such dense clusters with fused basal mass, although may occur in tufts with bases adhering or smaller, more slender species | **31** |
| 31 | growing on other, old fungi: *Asterophora* P113 ▶ | |
| 31 | not growing on other fungi | **32** |
| 32 | gills sinuate or sinuate-adnate; cap often radially fibrillose to scaly, occasionally smooth: *Tricholoma* P123 ▶   *Melanoleuca* P130 ▶   *Calocybe* P128 ▶ | |
| 32 | gills adnexed, adnate or almost free; cap usually smooth, never fibrillose or scaly | **33** |
| 33 | strong odour of new meal, flour, cucumber, or rancid; entirely greyish, grey-brown to black; rather tiny to small species: *Lyophyllum* (part) | (not incl.) |
| 33 | without these odours; colours usually white through shades to brown; medium to large species: *Collybia* (part) P140 ▶ | |

| 34 | edge of gills serrated or split lengthwise | 35 |
| 34 | edge of gills entire (not broken) | 36 |
| 35 | edge of gills serrated, notched: *Lentinus* P159 ▶ | |
|  | *Lentinellus* P207 ▶ | |
| 35 | edge of gills split lengthwise; without a stem; simple bracket-like cap: *Schizophyllum commune* | (not incl.) |
| 36 | fruitbody rather tongue-shaped with short lateral stem; spores blue-black in iodine: *Panellus* P158 ▶ | |
| 36 | fruitbody shape different or longer stem, spores not blue-black in iodine | 37 |
| 37 | gills yellowish to orange; cap orange-yellow, tomentose: *Phyllotopsis nidulans* | (not incl.) |
| 37 | not this combination of characters; caps often clustered or overlapping, sometimes fused; stem variable in length, often absent | 38 |
| 38 | very tough, woody when dry; irregularly shaped caps clustered and often fused; on deciduous stumps; brown with violet down on stem when young: *Panus torulosus* P158 ▶ | |
| 38 | never hard and woody; caps distinct, bracket-like to rounded, even funnel-shaped, with or without stem of variable length, eccentric to lateral; on living or felled trees; colours usually white through grey to brownish or blue-grey: *Pleurotus* P156 ▶ | |

**b** spores from bright tawny orange through shades of brown (dull, rust, cigar, clay, ochraceous) to rich brown

| 39 | cap bracket-like, with or without tiny lateral stem: *Crepidotus* P114 ▶ | |
|  | *Tapinella* P203 ▶ | |

| 39 | stem central to slightly eccentric, not lateral | 40 |
| 40 | with distinct membranous ring on stem | 41 |
| 40 | ring fine, cobwebby, often rapidly vanishing, or entirely absent | 45 |
| 41 | very large species 15–25 cm high; yellow-orange colours; cap texture granular; on soil: *Phaeolepiota* P115 ▶ | |
| 41 | not this combination of characters | 42 |
| 42 | stem deeply rooting; associated with animal or bird burrows in ground near tree roots; cap pale ivory to tan with irregular vague filmy scales; strong bitter-almond (marzipan) odour when fresh: *Hebeloma radicosum* P102 ▶ | |
| 42 | with different characters from preceding | 43 |
| 43 | stem not scaly; cap white to dull brown, smooth or wrinkled, not scaly or scurfy; spores dull cigar- or chocolate-brown: *Agrocybe* P160 ▶ (see also Rozites) | |
| 43 | stem often scaly; cap mostly yellowish to orange, occasionally whitish; spores tawny orange to rust- or ochre-brown | 44 |
| 44 | spores tawny orange to rust; only on wood (sometimes buried) at base of trees, never high up; gills bright yellow-orange, often spotted rust-brown; stem stout, often bulbous: *Gymnopilus junonius* P113 ▶ | |
| 44 | spores ochre- to rust-brown; usually on wood (often high up on trees), occasionally soil; gills not usually with rust-like spots; stem frequently scaly; cap dry to glutinous: *Pholiota* (part) P92 ▶ (see also Rozites; *Kuehneromyces mutabilis* may key out here, but cap is hygrophanous) | |
| 45 | distinct cobweb-like veil joining cap-margin to stem when young, often left as fine cobwebby ring or zone | 46 |

| | | |
|---|---|---|
| 45 | without cobweb-like veil or if it is present, it is very faint and soon lost, not leaving a ring zone | **49** |
| 46 | on wood, often tufted; spores tawny orange to ochre-brown; cap shades of orange, tan to orange-brown, minutely scaly and dry to smooth, sometime glutinous: ***Gymnopilus*** (part) P113 ▶ *** Pholiota*** (part) P91 ▶ | |
| 46 | not on wood; spores ochre-, rust- to dull cigar-brown | **47** |
| 47 | spores rust-brown; often with copious cobweb-like veil; cap almost any colour (any fungus with rust-brown, not ochre, spores, and bluish colours is a member); texture dry to glutinous or hygrophanous: ***Cortinarius*** P105 ▶ (some Pholiota and Rozites species may be confused) | |
| 47 | spores ochre- to dull cigar-brown | **48** |
| 48 | usually cap radially fibrillose to rough and minutely scaly, mostly dry, and stem fibrous; odour often earthy, unpleasant, to strongly fruity (e.g. of pears); spores cigar- to dull brown, strongly nodulose, or smooth and elongate to bean-shaped: ***Inocybe*** P96 ▶ | |
| 48 | cap mostly smooth, or only fibrils of veil at margin, whitish to clay or brick-red, often viscid; frequent odour of radish, or sweetly sickly; spores clay- to ochre-brown, ovate-elliptic: ***Hebeloma*** (part) P103 ▶ | |
| 49 | gills decurrent, soft, bruising brown; medium to large brown cap, margin inrolled, tomentose: ***Paxillus*** P202 ▶ | |
| 49 | gills not decurrent or if so, then cap whitish | **50** |
| 50 | gills free; very delicate, fragile species; cap bell-shaped to flat, strongly striate, egg-yellow, soon appearing to dissolve away; on dung, rich soil, grass: ***Bolbitius vitellinus*** P161 ▶ | |

| | | |
|---|---|---|
| 50 | gills not free and/or other characters different | **51** |
| 51 | cap conical to bell-shaped | **52** |
| 51 | cap more or less broadly convex to flattened | **55** |
| 52 | cap sharply pointed, conical; stem rooting: ***Phaeocollybia*** | (not incl.) |
| 52 | cap bluntly conical; stem not deeply rooted | **53** |
| 53 | odour strong of fish or cucumber; cap brownish; stem dark, slender: ***Macrocystidia cucumis*** P155 ▶ | |
| 53 | without odour of fish or cucumber | **54** |
| 54 | cap surface dull or shiny, cap rather deep, campanulate or almost cylindric (5-8 cm), very slender, straight; in grass; cap-surface cells rounded: ***Conocybe*** P161 ▶ | |
| 54 | cap more or less shiny, even viscid; stem short, slender, often curving; usually in moss; cap-surface cells filamentous: ***Galerina*** P115 ▶ | |
| 55 | cap roughened with minute pointed upright scales: ***Phaeomarasmius*** | (not incl.) |
| 55 | cap smooth or with whitish scales at margin only | **56** |
| 56 | cap whitish; gills decurrent; cap margin slightly hairy; spores clay-brown: ***Ripartites*** | (not incl.) |
| 56 | cap whitish to brown; gills not or only slightly decurrent | **57** |
| 57 | cap white to clay-brown or brick, more or less smooth, margin inrolled at first, often with fibrils from veil; gills and spores finally dull clay- or ochre-brown; often with radishy odour: ***Hebeloma*** (part) 103 ▶ | |

| 57 | not this combination of characters; cap pale to rich brown, with or without vague scurfy marginal scales | **58** |
| 58 | cap pale whitish brown to ochre with faint marginal scales; small species on bare soil; spores smooth, thin-walled; gills may be slightly decurrent: *Tubaria* | (not incl.) |
| 58 | cap ochre to brown, not scaly; under alders or willows; spores minutely warted, rough: *Naucoria* | (not incl.) |

**c   Spores black, sooty-brown, chocolate or purplish**

| 59 | gills and cap dissolve into inky liquid on maturity ( or tiny grooved caps in very large clusters); tiny to very large: *Coprinus* P78 ▶ | |
| 59 | gills not dissolving into inky liquid | **60** |
| 60 | gills thick, broadly spaced, decurrent; cap viscid to glutinous; medium to large: *Chroogomphus* P204 ▶ | |
| | *Gomphidius* P204 ▶ | |
| 60 | gills not thick, decurrent | **61** |
| 61 | gills mottled black on grey because of uneven spore ripening; stem slender, stiff, straight, easily snapping; cap more or less convex to bell-shaped: *Panaeolus* P84 ▶ | |
| 61 | not this combination of characters | **62** |
| 62 | gills free, often remote from stem; on ground, never wood; usually with membranous ring or at least a ring zone; cap white to brown, smooth to scaly; small to very large: *Agaricus* (true mushrooms) P72 ▶ | |
| 62 | gills adnate, adnexed or sinuate; on ground or wood | **63** |

| 63 | gills mostly adnate, purple-brown; stem usually with ring or veil; cap blue-green, yellowish to brown or reddish, often viscid-glutinous or dry with marginal scales; on dung, soil, woodchips or in grass: *Stropharia* P88 ▶ | |
| 63 | gills not adnate and/or other characters different | **64** |
| 64 | stem and cap-margin with abundant cobweb-like veil; gills black, edge often "weeping" black droplets in damp weather; cap ochre to orange, woolly-fibrillose; on ground: *Lacrymaria* P81 ▶ | |
| 64 | not the above combination of characters | **65** |
| 65 | cobweb-like veil when young but not a membranous ring; gills sinuate to adnate; often tufted on wood, medium-sized, fleshy or solitary and slender on ground; cap dry, more or less smooth, brightly coloured yellow or reddish to brown; spores purple-brown: *Hypholoma* P86 ▶ | |
| 65 | gills usually adnate; generally fragile species, thin-fleshed; on wood or ground | **66** |
| 66 | very fragile with delicate cap conical to convex, then flattened, usually greyish to brown, hygrophanous; gills adnate; clustered or solitary, on ground or wood; veil present or not, may form ring and/or scales on stem and cap: *Psathyrella* P82 ▶ | |
| 66 | cap convex to sharply pointed, margin incurved when young; colours yellowish to brown; gills adnate, often almost triangular; stem stiff, slender, breaking with a snap: *Psilocybe* P87 ▶ | |

**d  spores pale to deep salmon-pink**

| 67 | stem to one side of bracket-like cap: *Claudopus* (angular spores) and *Rhodotus* (pink to apricot wrinkled cap; spores warted) | (neither incl.) |
| 67 | stem central to only slightly eccentric | **68** |

41

| | | | |
|---|---|---|---|
| 68 | stem with volva (thin, easily lost when picked): *Volvariella* P61 ▶ | | |
| 68 | without cup or volva | 69 | |
| 69 | gills deeply decurrent: *Entoloma* P119 ▶ | | |
| | *Clitopilus* P120 ▶ | | |
| 69 | gills free or if attached not truly decurrent | 70 | |
| 70 | gills free; cap and stem easily separable; on wood or soil: *Pluteus* P62 ▶ | | |
| 70 | gills attached to stem for part or all of their depth | 71 | |
| 71 | gills sinuate to adnate; medium to large fleshy species; cap convex-flattened, not pointed; usually late autumn-early winter; spores ovate, prickly: *Lepista* P132 ▶ | | |
| 71 | usually small to medium, fibrous and rather fragile, generally not thick fleshy species; all with angular many-sided spores; gills mostly adnate-adnexed, or sinuate ... | 72 | |
| 72 | gills more or less sinuate; cap medium-sized, usually pointed, or with rather raised centre, fibrillose: *Entoloma* P117 ▶ | | |
| 72 | small, fragile caps, rounded or bell-shaped to pointed; gills adnexed-adnate: *Entoloma* (part, smooth caps, not incl.), *Entoloma* (part, scaly cap and/or bluish colours) P119 ▶ | | |

**e spores red or blue-green**

| | | |
|---|---|---|
| 73 | spores and gills blue-green; delicate, small, with granular veil: *Melanophyllum eyrei* | (not incl.) |
| 73 | spores and gills reddish; small stocky species; stem with granular veil: *Melanophyllum echinatum* P69 ▶ | |

## Boletes

The few Boletales with gills are included in Gill Fungi, above

| | | |
|---|---|---|
| 1 | thick overlapping scales on cap; stem rough, shaggy; whole fungus grey-black; flesh reddens when cut: *Strobilomyces strobilaceus* P200 ▶ | |
| 1 | cap without scales or scales not grey-black | 2 |
| 2 | cap with pointed umbo, covered with fine pointed scales (scabrosities), yellow-ochre to rust-brown; pores large, honeycomb-like, yellow; stem with ring at top; under larches: *Suillus cavipes* | (not incl.) |
| 2 | not this combination of characters | 3 |
| 3 | stem covered with small woolly tufts which are usually white, then reddish brown to black: *Leccinum* P194 ▶ | |
| 3 | stem smooth or sticky, with fine network, sometimes ring at top | 4 |
| 4 | cap usually sticky to glutinous; stem with or without ring; always connected to various conifers: *Suillus* P197 ▶ | |
| 4 | cap at most moist to viscid in damp weather only; never with ring; usually below deciduous trees | 5 |
| 5 | mature pores pink (not red, buff) as is spore-mass; stem with raised network; taste bitter: *Tylopilus felleus* P202 ▶ | |

5    pores not pink, usually some shade of yellow, white, greenish or orange to red; often bruising blue    **6**

6    cap and stem smooth, greyish black; spores purple-brown: *Porphyrellus porphyrosporus* P201 ►

6    not blackish; spores yellow to ochre or brown    **7**

7    pores vivid chrome to golden, not bruising blue; cap moist, clay- to strawberry-pink, 2–5 cm: *Aureoboletus cramesinus* P199 ►

7    pores duller yellow or quite different colour, often bruising blue; cap not pinkish; mostly over 5 cm across    **8**

8    stem usually hollow; flesh firm, brittle; pores white to pale yellowish; texture of cap skin velvety or roughened; spores pale yellow: *Gyroporus* P200 ►

9    always attached to earthballs (*Scleroderma*); small, yellow-brown: *Boletus parasiticus* P193 ►

8    stem solid, never clearly hollow; other characters mostly different    **9**

9    not on *Scleroderma* or other fungi; stem smooth or reticulate; pores white to yellow or red; cap whitish, clay, brown, to reddish; flesh and pores often bruising: *Boletus* P187 ►

## Chanterelles and trumpets

Smooth or wrinkled undersurface, no true sharp-edged gills

1    grey-black, trumpet-like; almost smooth on outer surface, hardly any wrinkles or folds: *Craterellus cornucopioides* P222 ►

1    distinct folds, wrinkles or blunt flared, irregularly shaped cap; colours various, grey to brown or yellow-orange    **2**

2    small (2–5 cm across), dark brown; grey, wrinkled lower surface: *Cantharellus cinereus*    (not incl.)

2    almost gill-like blunt wrinkles and folds; cap brown, orange or apricot, occasionally flushed violet    **3**

3    cap brown; stem yellow to orange: *Cantharellus infundibuliformis* 221 ►

3    entirely apricot-orange; thick-fleshed: *Cantharellus cibarius* P221 ►
Some less common species (not incl.) occur, differing mainly in colour (e.g. *C. amethysteus* with violet flush and scales)

## Puffballs, stinkhorns and allies

Fungi without gills or pores; spores in powdery central mass or as smelly slime or as "eggs" in tiny "nest"

1    mature fungus has slimy, foul-smelling spore-mass spread over cap or cage-like arms; if it starts as a whitish "egg", then with jelly-like layer under skin    **2**

1    mature fungus without foul odour; mature spores usually powdery or in tiny egg-like masses    **4**

2    fruitbody breaks out from "egg" (size of hen's); stem bears separate thimble-shaped cap covered at first with green-black slime: *Phallus* P228 ►

2    "egg" and fruitbody much smaller or, if bigger, fruitbody reddish, cage-like    **3**

3    starts as a small (1-3 cm) "egg", sends up spongy pointed stem without separate cap: *Mutinus caninus* P229 ►

3    arises from large (5-8 cm) "egg"; fruitbody cage-like, reddish, with smelly greenish slime on inside: *Clathrus ruber* P229 ►

43

| 4 | fruitbody like a brownish onion, splitting open to form a star shape with a rounded puffball at the centre: **Geastrum** P234 ▶ |  |

| 4 | fruitbody globose, with stem or not or like tiny "nest" with "eggs" | 5 |

| 5 | very large (10-30 cm) globose fruitbody; skin smooth, white, leathery, cracking with age; in fields and hedgerows: **Calvatia gigantea** P233 ▶ |  |

| 5 | smaller, if rounded, or different shape entirely | 6 |

| 6 | tiny (2 cm or less) "bird's nest" with one to ten "eggs" | 10 |

| 6 | rounded, 2 cm or more; with or without a base or stem | 7 |

| 7 | on soil; round; skin thick, tough, usually scaly or warty, sometimes smooth, cream to yellow-ochre or brownish; mature spore-mass inside purplish to black or olive-brown with strong but not foul odour: **Scleroderma** P236 ▶ |  |

| 7 | on soil or grass, occasionally wood; skin much thinner; tiny warts, spines or scales, if present, are easily brushed off or broken; spores puff out when mature (puffballs) | 8 |

| 8 | fruitbody round or with basal stem; usually whitish, often with fragile warts or spines; spore-dispersal through apical pore: **Lycoperdon** P233 ▶ <br><br> **Bovista** P231 ▶ |  |

| 8 | with thin tough stem buried in sandy soil or without single apical pore (skin flakes with age on upper parts) | 9 |

| 9 | puffball (1-3 cm) just projecting above sandy soil with thin buried stem below: **Tulostoma** P231 ▶ |  |

| 9 | puffball (3 cm or more) with stem or not; upper part flaking away to release spores, often just base remaining: **Handkea** P232 ▶ |  |

| 10 | tiny star-shaped cup or "nest" 1-3 mm across with one tiny "egg": **Sphaerobolus** | (not incl.) |

| 10 | "nest" rounded, larger (1–2 cm), with some 5–10 "eggs" | 11 |

| 11 | "nest" deep brown to grey, funnel-shaped, flaring: **Cyathus** P230 ▶ |  |

| 11 | "nest" straw-yellow to ochre, cup-shaped: **Crucibulum** P230 ▶ |  |

## Toothed fungi

Pendent teeth or spines on lower surface

| 1 | on trees, logs etc | 2 |

| 1 | on ground or pine cones | 3 |

| 2 | large, irregularly branched; pure white to ivory with long to very long pendent spines; on usually dead deciduous and coniferous trunks: **Hericium** P206 ▶ and other rarer genera | |

| 2 | tongue-shaped, soft, jelly-like; whitish grey with short soft teeth; on pine stumps: **Pseudohydnum gelatinosum** P227 ▶ | |

| 3 | on soil in leaf-litter or pine needles; medium to large; stem thick | 4 |

| 3 | on pine cones; very small, spoon-shaped; stem slender, lateral: **Auriscalpium vulgare** P208 ▶ | |

| 4 | cap large with thick coarse scales, deep grey-brown: **Sarcodon imbricatum** P208 ▶ | |

| 4 | cap small to medium, reddish brown to pinkish, smooth or at most cracked, never distinctly scaly: **Hydnum** and related genera P220 ▶ | |

Many rarer genera of terrestrial toothed fungi are to be found

## Club-, Coral-, Cauliflower- or Fan-like or irregularly lobed fungi

| | | |
|---|---|---|
| 1 | simple unbranched club, sometimes clustered | 2 |
| 1 | branched clubs or cauliflower-, coral- or fan-shaped | 6 |
| 2 | on deciduous wood | 4 |
| 3 | club tall (10-25 cm), swollen, sometimes flattened above; usually in beech litter: *Clavariadelphus* P222 ► | |
| 3 | club shorter, more slender, blunt and club-like to sharply pointed *Clavaria*, *Clavulina* (part, not incl.), *Cordyceps* (not incl.), *Clavulinopsis* (part) P223 ► | |
| 4 | tiny bright yellow-orange pointed clubs: *Calocera cornea* | (not incl.) |
| 4 | colour different | 5 |
| 5 | small (1-5 cm high) pointed and flattened clubs (sometimes branching, antler-like), white, base blackened, tips like burnt candle wick: *Xylaria hypoxylon* P251 ► | |
| 5 | larger (3-8 cm) clubs, clustered; hard, black, swollen, often finger-like: *Xylaria polymorpha* P250 ► or *X. longipes* (not incl.) | |
| 6 | branched, antler-, fan- or coral-like | 7 |
| 6 | cauliflower-like or with soft irregular lobes | 9 |
| 7 | on bare soil or pine needles; dull soft brown; irregularly branched and flattened, fan-like: *Thelephora* | (not incl.) |
| 7 | on soil, coral-like or on wood, colour and shape different | 8 |
| 8 | on soil (or on wood, olive-colour, never yellow-orange); coral-like, often brightly coloured: *Ramaria* (spores ornamented) P224 ► | |

| | | |
|---|---|---|
| | *Clavulina* (part) P223 ► | |
| | *Clavulinopsis* (part, not incl.) | |
| 8 | on wood; in loose or dense clusters of slender, pointed and branched clubs: *Calocera viscosa* (bright yellow-orange) P227 ► | |
| | *Xylaria hypoxylon* (white and blackish) P251 ► | |
| 9 | large, rounded, cauliflower-like, with many crisp flattened lobes, pale tan; on or by conifers, rarely other trees: *Sparassis crispa* P224 ► | |
| 9 | soft, gelatinous, much more irregularly lobed, 5-10 cm across; yellow or deep brown; on deciduous or coniferous timber: *Tremella* P226 ► | |

## Cup fungi, Morels, Helvellas, Earthtongues

| | | |
|---|---|---|
| 1 | with a stem, long or short, and a head or cap | 2 |
| 1 | without a stem; a simple cup-, disc- or top-shape | 10 |
| 2 | simple cup 2–6 cm across on definite stem either narrow or stout: *Helvella macropus* P241 ► some small *Peziza* (see 16 below) | |
| 2 | tongue-like or much more complex | 3 |
| 3 | head simple, tongue-shaped and flattened or rounded or button-shaped, gelatinous | 4 |
| 3 | cap complex, wrinkled, sponge-, saddle- or thimble-shaped | 6 |
| 4 | head tongue-shaped, flattened, not separated from stem; green to blackish: *Microglossum* P249 ► | |

45

Trichoglossum or (similar with rounded head on insect larva) P248 ▶

Cordyceps (not incl.)

4 head a soft irregular gelatinous "button" or tongue-like but clearly divided from stem 5

5 cap rounded, button-like, margin inrolled, olive-green; yellowish central stem... Leotia (in deciduous woods) or the same but yellow with grey stem and in coniferous woods... Cudonia (not incl.)

5 bright yellow flattened or tongue-shaped head with paler stem pushing up into one edge; in conifer woods... Spathularia or the same but orange head, by ponds, swamps... Mitrula P249 ▶

6 cap wrinkled, brain-like or convoluted, saddle-shaped 7

6 cap like a sponge with pits and ridges or smooth, thimble-shaped 8

7 cap wrinkled, brain-like: Gyromitra P239 ▶

7 cap convoluted, often saddle-shaped: Helvella (part) P240 ▶

8 cap smooth, thimble-shaped: Verpa P239 ▶

8 cap like a sponge with pits and ridges 9

9 cap base fused with stem: Morchella (part) P237 ▶

9 cap base not fused with stem: Morchella (part) P238 ▶

10 lop-sided, rabbit's ear-like cup: Otidea P244 ▶

10 rounded or irregular cup, or disc- to top-shaped, but not like a rabbit's ear 11

11 tiny scarlet disc 0.5 cm across with fringe of black lashes or hairs at edge: Scutellinia P244 ▶

11 not with the above combination of characters 12

12 very irregular gelatinous mass forming small clusters of top-shaped fruit-bodies 0.5-1 cm across, deep violet; shapeless when immature; on wood: Ascocoryne sarcoides P247 ▶

12 cup or disc, often irregular; on soil or wood 13

13 a velvety brown to purplish "ear" on wood; elastic and rubbery: Auricularia auricula-judae P225 ▶

13 shape and texture (fragile, brittle) different... 14

14 tiny (0.5 cm) bright green cups; usually on oak, staining wood green: Chlorociboria aeruginascens P246 ▶

14 not with the above combination of characters 15

15 deep brownish black, disc-shaped, then edges turned downwards, cushion-shaped; very short white root-like structures below; on burnt sites under conifers: Rhizina (not incl.)

15 without this combination of characters 16

16 bright orange medium to large cups; often by pathsides: Aleuria aurantia P243 ▶

16 small to large cups and discs, coloured cream, tan, brown, orange-red, violet etc.; on soil or wood and other rotting matter: Peziza P242 ▶, Sarcoscypha P245 ▶ and other genera of smaller cup fungi

## Polypores (includes brackets and Resupinate (crust-like) fungi

On wood or soil; tough, fleshy or woody; with pores, or just wrinkled surfaces clinging to wood

| | | |
|---|---|---|
| 1 | with a distinct stem, either central or lateral | **31** |
| 1 | without a distinct stem | **2** |
| 2 | resupinate to bracket-shaped; distinct pore layer | **9** |
| 2 | bracket-like or more often entirely resupinate or resupinate with edge protruding to form thin poorly shaped bracket; without distinct pores | **3** |
| 3 | resupinate, often forming irregular brackets; lower surface wrinkled, without shallow "pores"; firm, fleshy | **5** |
| 3 | bracket-like or (usually) resupinate with ill-formed brackets; lower spore-producing surface wrinkled and vein-like, forming shallow "pores"; soft, elastic or rubbery | **4** |
| 4 | spores white: *Phlebia* (part) 210 ▶ | |
| 4 | spores brown: *Serpula* (contains Dry Rot) | (not incl.) |
| 5 | lower surface of fruitbody (irregular brackets) contains long brown spines: *Hymenochaete* | (not incl.) |
| 5 | without spines | **6** |
| 6 | outer surface of the resupinate fruitbody usually radially veined, often bright orange: *Phlebia* (part) P210 ▶ | |
| 6 | outer surface not radially veined | **7** |
| 7 | spores brown; fruitbody resupinate, brownish and rather lumpy at centre, yellowish white at margin: *Coniophora* (contains Wet Rot or Cellar Fungus) | (not incl.) |
| 7 | spores white | **8** |
| 8 | fleshy; either resupinate or with brackets: *Stereum* P209 ▶ | |
| | *Chondrostereum* P209 ▶ and some related genera | |

| | | |
|---|---|---|
| 8 | not fleshy; without distinct brackets, often a very thin crust or even coloured "wash" on wood; various corticiaceous fungi | (not incl.) |
| 9 | tubes free from each other, easily separated; fruitbody a tongue-shaped fleshy red bracket; flesh red, often "bleeds" when cut: *Fistulina hepatica* P220 ▶ | |
| 9 | tubes fused to form a united pore layer | **10** |
| 10 | perennial brackets, building up more than one layer of tubes; mostly hard, woody | **11** |
| 10 | annual brackets (occasionally resupinate), forming one tube layer only before drying or decaying; usually fleshy | **14** |
| 11 | spores brown | **12** |
| 11 | spores white | **13** |
| 12 | large extremely hard brackets on deciduous timber; chestnut brown, margin whitish; pores white, bruise brown: *Ganoderma* (part) P221 ▶ | |
| 12 | woody brackets on conifers (usually several feet up); deeply cracked upper surface: *Cryptoderma* | (not incl.) |
| 13 | large (12-25 cm) thick, very hard woody brackets, hard upper crust: *Fomes* P213 ▶ | |
| 13 | small to medium (5-12 cm) brackets, generally fleshy to corky not woody, with upper crust or surface slightly furry: *Oxyporus*, *Fomitopsis*, *Heterobasidion* | (none incl.) |
| 14 | pores very elongate to labyrinth-like or bracket not regularly formed, mostly resupinate instead | **15** |
| 14 | pores distinct and rounded, or only slightly elongate; in regular brackets | **19** |
| 15 | pores labyrinth-like: *Daedalea* P217 ▶ | |
| | *Daedaleopsis* P215 ▶ | |
| 15 | pores very elongate, almost like thick woody gills, or fruitbody resupinate | **16** |

| 16 | elongate, gill-like pores | **18** |
| 16 | without bracket, or else very irregular caps and mainly a resupinate pore layer | **17** |
| 17 | completely resupinate; not very fleshy: *Fibuloporia* and related genera | (none incl.) |
| 17 | resupinate but with irregular caps at margin; fleshy and tough: *Datronia* (not incl.) *Gloeoporus* (not incl.), *Bjerkandera adusta* P216 ▶ | |
| 18 | bracket whitish to pale brown: *Lenzites* P215 ▶ | |
| 18 | bracket brown: *Gloeophyllum* | (not incl.) |
| 19 | pores bright red, orange or lilac to violet | **20** |
| 19 | pores white, cream, yellow, yellowish green or greyish to brown | **22** |
| 20 | pores red to orange: *Pycnoporus* | (not incl.) |
| 20 | pores violet, lilac or apricot | **21** |
| 21 | pores lilac to violet: *Hirschioporus* | (not incl.) |
| 21 | pores pale orange to apricot: *Hapalopilus* | (not incl.) |
| 22 | pores grey, yellowish, greenish to brown | **23** |
| 22 | pores white, cream or yellow | **25** |
| 23 | pores grey: *Bjerkandera* (part, incl. *B. adusta*) P216 ▶ | |
| 23 | pores yellowish to greenish, bruising/ageing darker, brown | **24** |
| 24 | large thick bracket, splits easily; flesh with silky sheen; upper surface tomentose to shaggy; deciduous trees: Inonotus | |
| 24 | bracket with broad basal stump; shaggy top surface with yellow margin; at base of conifers: *Phaeolus* P214 ▶ | |
| 25 | tube layer distinct from flesh | **26** |
| 25 | tube layer not distinct from flesh | **30** |
| 26 | pores bright yellow; upper surface yellow to orange; large, fleshy: *Laetiporus sulphureus* P213 ▶ | |
| 26 | pores white | **27** |

| 27 | only on birch; small to large, shell- to kidney-shaped, white to pale brown; flesh white, spongy: *Piptoporus betulinus* P212 ▶ | |
| 27 | on birch with different characters or at base of other deciduous trees in large fan-like or fronded brackets, rarely with multiple rounded heads | **28** |
| 28 | large to very large bracket at base of deciduous trees; fan- or frond-like to many-headed: *Grifola* P217 ▶<br><br>*Meripilus* P216 ▶ | |
| 28 | small brackets, not this combination of characters | **29** |
| 29 | bracket white to cream: *Tyromyces* | (not incl.) |
| 29 | bracket various shades of brown: *Polyporus* (part) P219 ▶ | |
| 30 | bracket thick, corky or woody; pores medium to large: *Trametes* P218 ▶ | |
| 30 | bracket thin, leathery; pores small: *Trametes* P214 ▶ | |
| 31 | pores dark greyish to brown; cap funnel-shaped, round with central stem; on burnt soil: *Coltricia perennis* | (not incl.) |
| 31 | pores whitish and/or cap not round with central stem | **32** |
| 32 | shell- or kidney-shaped with lateral stem short or long; cap "varnished", chestnut to red-purple: *Ganoderma lucidum* P212 ▶ | |
| 32 | cap rounded, brownish, not "lacquered"; stem central to eccentric with base usually black, tomentose: *Polyporus* (part) P218 ▶ | |

## Globose or Stud-like fungi on wood

| 1 | flesh very hard, woody | **2** |
| 1 | flesh like rubber | **3** |
| 2 | medium to large hard black "ball"; when cut in section shows concentric bands or zones: *Daldinia concentrica* P251 ▶ | |

| 2 | small reddish brown balls scattered in large numbers; no concentric bands: *Hypoxylon fragiforme* | (not incl.) |
| 3 | clusters of "studs" or thick "buttons" 2–5 cm across, 1–2 cm deep (globose, margin inrolled, when young), top may be depressed, cup-like; feels like soft rubber: *Bulgaria inquinans* P247 ▶ | |
| 3 | similar but with a short stem; more jelly-like: *Exidia recisa* (yellow-brown), *E. truncata* (black, not incl.) | 4 |

### Truffles

(only Tuber, true truffles, is included in this book)

| 1 | skin smooth; interior with "chambers" | 2 |
| 1 | skin smooth, spiny or warty; interior solid with coloured "veins" or convoluted veins or canals opening at surface | 6 |
| 2 | pale whitish, or grey-brown to greenish | 3 |

| 2 | ochre to deep brown; often with root-like rhizomorphs | 5 |
| 3 | interior purplish brown; outside white to greenish; odour of cocoa; in beech woods: *Arcangeliella* | (not incl.) |
| 3 | interior greyish to olive | |
| 4 | interior olive, hard; skin flaking, peeling: *Hysterangium* | (not incl.) |
| 4 | interior pale grey with small open chambers: *Hymenogaster* | (not incl.) |
| 5 | interior with open chambers; skin ochre to brownish: *Rhizopogon* | (not incl.) |
| 5 | without distinct chambers; skin dark brown: *Melanogaster* | (not incl.) |
| 6 | interior powdery; skin minutely warty or spiny, yellowish brown: *Elaphomyces* | (not incl.) |
| 6 | interior not powdery; skin smooth or warty, not yellowish brown: Tuber and related genera | (not incl.) |

# GLOSSARY

**Adnate** (gills or tubes): attached to stem for most of their depth

**Adnexed** (gills or tubes): narrowly attached to stem for less than a quarter of their depth

**Adpressed** (scales): "pressed" or "ironed down" onto the cap, not sticking up

**Amyloid**: describes the blue-black reaction of spores or flesh to iodine solutions (see also Dextrinoid)

**Apothecium**: the cup or disc-shaped (open) fruitbody of a Discomycete

**Appendiculate** (cap edge): with fringe of veil-remnants

**Arcuate-decurrent** (gills): distinctly curved along their margins and as running down stem

**Ascus**: cell in which the spores of an ascomycete are formed

**Basidium**: usually club-shaped cell on which spores are borne in basidiomycetes

**Bulbous** (stem): abruptly swollen

**Campanulate** (cap): bell-shaped

**Capillitium**: sterile threads mixed with the spores in some Gasteromycetes

**Cartilaginous**: stiff, breaking with a snap when bent

**Clavate** (stem): club-shaped, gradually broadening

**Conical** (cap): see *Psilocybe semilanceata* (pp. 84–5)

**Convex** (cap): shape when cap-section is curved or rounded on the outside

**Cortina**: fine cobweb-like veil connecting cap margin to stem; often vanishes with age

**Crenate** (cap or gills): with blunt teeth-like form or scalloped

**Cuticle**: skin-like outer tissue of some caps and stems

**Cystidium** (pl. cystidia): specialized often large cell, not bearing spores, on gill edges and face

**Decurrent** (gills or tubes): with part attached to and running down stem

**Deliquescent** (cap and gills): turning to liquid at maturity

**Dentate** (cap or gill margin): toothed

**Denticulate** (cap or gill margin): minutely toothed

**Depressed**: with centre sunk or dented

**Dextrinoid**: describes the reddish brown reaction of spores and flesh to iodine solutions

**Distant** (gills): far apart

**Eccentric** (stem): off-centre

**Emarginate** (gills): eroded or notched at junction with stem

**Equal** (stem): parallel-sided

**Expanded** (cap): rounded then spreading outwards and flattening

**Fibrillose**: may be smooth but has distinct radiating or longitudinal fibres (fibrils) in the surface

**Fissured**: with cracks or splits in surface

**Flaring** (ring): opening outward, skirt-like

**Fleshy**: rather thick but soft to firm, never hard, easily decaying as opposed to woody

**Flexuose** (stem): wavy or bending

**Floccose**: with loose cottony or slightly woolly surface, usually in tufts (flocci)

**Form; forma**: taxonomic grouping within a species, lower in hierarchy than variety

**Free** (gills or pores): not touching or connected to the stem

**Fruitbody**: entire toadstool or spore-bearing part of fungus

**Fusiform** (spores): spindle-shaped

**Gill**: thin plate-like structures on the undersurface of an agaric cap which produce spore-bearing cells

**Gleba**: central, fertile mass of a *Gasteromycete*

**Globose** (cap or spores): rounded

**Glutinous**: with sticky mucous or jelly-like to slimy substance (gluten) on surface

**Granulose**: covered with fine granules

**Heteromerous**: cells of flesh a mixture of round and long (as in *Russula*)

**Hygrophanous**: changing colour when dry; usually darker, translucent when wet, paler, opaque, when dry

**Hymenium**: fertile layer of spore-bearing basidia or asci

**Hypha** (pl. hyphae): individual microscopic threads making up mycelium

**Incurved** (cap margin): curving down and inwards

**Inrolled** (cap margin): curving down and inwards, tending to roll up

**Involute**: curving down and inwards

**Infundibuliform** (cap): deeply funnel-shaped

**Imbricate** (scales, brackets): overlapping like roof tiles (see *Sarcodon imbricatum*)

**Lateral** (stem): joined to cap edge

**Latex**: fluid (often coloured) exuded by cap-or stem-flesh when broken (e.g. *Lactarius*)

**Lobate** (cap): with irregular lobes or bulges

**Marginate** (stem bulb): with a distinct margin or ridge of tissue

**Mealy** (surface or taste): covered with powdery granules or taste like fresh meal or flour

**Milk**: see Latex

**Mycelium**: mass of interwoven hyphae, in larger fungi usually forming cobweb-like filaments in the substrate (e.g. soil or wood)

**Mycorrhiza**: symbiotic relationship between fungus my celium and roots of a plant (e.g. many trees and orchids)

**Nodulose** (spores): with blunt knobs or lumps (e.g. *Inocybe*)

**Ochraceous**: bright yellow-brown

**Ovate** (cap or spores): more or less broadly egg-shaped

**Partial veil**: tissue protecting gills in some agarics when young; may survive as ring or cortina

**Pendent** (ring): hanging down

**Peridium**: outer skin or wall of *Gasteromycete* fruit body

**Pileus**: (commonly called the "cap") part of a fungus fruitbody bearing the spores beneath it

**Polygonal**: (spores or scales): with many flattened facets or sides

**Pruinose**: as if dusted with fine white powder, like "bloom" of grape

**Pubescent**: with short, soft, velvety hairs

**Punctate**: speckled with tiny dots (punctate)

**Resupinate**: adhering closely to ground or wood with spore surface facing outward (e.g. *Phlebia radiata*)

**Reticulate**: with raised network on surface e.g. *Boletus luridus* stem (or spore of *Strobilomyces*)

**Recurved** (scales): curved up and back on themselves

**Ring**: girdle of tissue around stem of some agarics; ring zone: faint remnant of the partial veil

**Scabrosities**: small raised "woolly" scales, as on stem of Leccinum

**Scaly**: with adhering flakes, or surface tearing into small to large blunt or pointed scales

**Scurfy**: with very fine scattered flakes or loosely attached scales

**Semiglobate**: shaped like a dome

**Serrate** (gill or cap edge): toothed like a saw

**Sinuate** (gills): curving abruptly upward near stem

**Spore**: minute reproductive unit of, for example, a fungus for spore deposit (p. 31)

**Squamulose**: with tiny scales (squamules)

**Stipe**: the "stem" which supports the cap (pileus) of many fungi

**Striate** (cap margin): marked with thin lines or fine grooves (see also Sulcate)

**Subfusiform** (spore): broadly spindle-shaped or like a short, fat cucumber

**Subglobose** (spores): almost spherical

**Sulcate**: grooved or furrowed (e.g. cap margin of *Russula foetens*)

**Tomentose**: thickly covered with soft, matted short hairs

**Trama** (of gill): loosely woven central structure

**Tubes**: spore-producing layer in many bracket fungi and some agarics (e.g. *Boletus*)

**Turbinate**: shaped like an old-fashioned spinning-top (flattened on top, diameter decreasing downward)

**Umbilicate** (cap): with a small central depression in otherwise rounded cap

**Umbonate**: cap has a central hump (umbo) bluntly rounded or sometimes pointed

**Undulate** (cap margin): irregularly wavy

**Universal veil**: protective tissue enclosing young unexpanded fruitbody of an agaric; may survive as volva and/or scales on cap

**Var., = variety**: taxonomic grouping within species, lower in hierarchy than subspecies, higher than form/ forma

**Veil**: see Universal veil; Partial veil

**Viscid**: wet and slippery (see also Glutinous)

**Volva**: basal cup or bag of some agarics (e.g. *Amanita phalloides*)

**Warted, Warty**: with small blunt warts on surface (e.g. some spores)

**Waxy** (gills): thick, rather watery, translucent like soft candlewax

# GUIDE TO SPECIES

Most mushrooms and toadstools are gill fungi or agarics (order Agaricales). These are fleshy, usually rather soft and often with a distinct stem bearing the cap, on the underside of which the spores are produced on gills, tubes or spines. On the basis of their structure, agarics are divided into families – Amanitaceae, Volvariaceae, etc. The boletes and allied fungi, in which tubes usually take the place of gills, are separated in this book into the Order Boletales.

## AMANITACEAE

This widespread and very important family contains some of the best-known poisonous and edible fungi. They are particularly abundant in warmer, southern temperate regions. Amanita species have white spores and a veil, which may form various types of volva and/or a ring as well; the cap may be covered with fragments of universal veil. *Limacella*, another and much rarer related genus, has the same characteristic microscopic gill structure but no volva, and always a more or less viscid cap.

### AMANITA

#### *Amanita pantherina* (Panther Cap) ☠

*Amanita pantherina*

Cap with striate margin

Volva forms 2–3 rings

**Key characters** ring not striate; 2–3 hoops or ridges at bulbous stem base; cap edge often striate. **Description: Cap** 6–11 cm, convex then expanded; greyish brown to dull brown with pure white warts; margin striate when mature. **Gills** white, free, broad and rather crowded. **Stem** from rather squat to quite slender; white, smooth, with a bulbous base and often with hoops of tissue at top of bulb. **Ring** thin, not striate, white, often half-way down on stem. **Spores** white, ovate, 9–12 X 7–9 µm, non-amyloid. **Chemical test:** sodium hydroxide on cap = orange-yellow. **Occurring** in mixed woodlands from summer to autumn; preferring alkaline soils, uncommon to occasional. *Dangerously toxic but not usually fatal. In many districts rather rare.* **Notes** often confused with *A. excelsa*.

Spores 9–12 × 7–9 µm non-amyloid

White, free gills

White ring near stem apex

#### *Amanita muscaria* (Fly Agaric) ☠

Volva reduced to zones of white scales

**Key characters** unmistakable red cap and white or yellow warts; white stem, bulbous ridged base. **Description: Cap** 8–25 cm, bright scarlet or occasionally orange (in the U.S.A. yellow forms are common), smooth; warts often washed off by rain. **Gills** white, free, broad, crowded. **Stem** tall, white, with bulbous base with rings or ridges of warts

Spores 9–11 × 6–8 µm non-amyloid

*Amanita muscaria*

*Please note: the spore diagrams in this guide are not to scale*

at the upper edge. **Ring** large, skirt-like, white, often with yellow warts at margin. **Spores** white, elliptic, 9–11 X 6–8 µm, non-amyloid. *Dangerously poisonous, and hallucinogenic.* **Occurring** from late autumn, usually under birch and pines, common.

*Amanita excelsa*

### Amanita excelsa (= A. spissa)

**Key characters** striate ring; bulbous, slightly scaly base; usually greyish or brown cap. **Description:** Cap 6–15 cm, convex then expanded, colour extremely variable, with pearly white, grey and dark brown forms common; smooth, with remains of veil sometimes as greyish-white warts but usually as greyish-white powdery patches. **Gills** white, crowded, free. **Stem** white to greyish, bulbous, volva almost absent but sometimes scaly at upper edge of bulb. **Ring** white, striate, skirt-like. **Spores** white, elliptic, 8–10 X 6–8 µm. **Smell** often absent, or potato-like. *Edible, but should be avoided.* **Occurring** in mixed woods, summer and autumn, often abundant.

Spores 8–10 × 6–8 µm

No volva but bulbous base has 3 or 4 zones of woolly scales

### Amanita rubescens (Blusher)

**Key characters** strongly striate ring; no volva; similar to A. excelsa but always with reddish tints. **Description:** Cap 6–15 cm, usually reddish brown to pinkish brown (very variable) with warty or flaky patches. **Gills** white, crowded, free. **Stem** bulbous, occasionally with slight scaly zones at base. **Flesh** slowly reddens where damaged, especially in stem base where insect-infested. **Spores** ovate, 8–10 X 6–7 µm, amyloid. *Edible when cooked but poisonous raw; best avoided.* **Occurring** in woods generally, summer to autumn, very common.

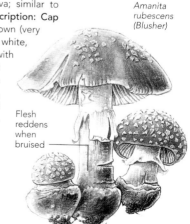

*Amanita rubescens* (Blusher)

Flesh reddens when bruised

Spores 8–10 × 6–7 µm amyloid

53

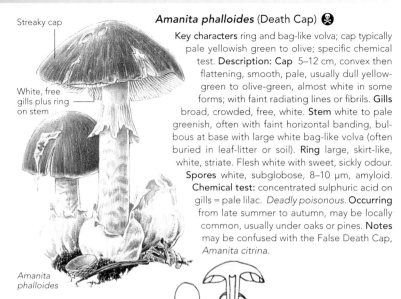

Streaky cap

White, free
gills plus ring
on stem

*Amanita
phalloides*

## *Amanita phalloides* (Death Cap) ☠

**Key characters** ring and bag-like volva; cap typically pale yellowish green to olive; specific chemical test. **Description: Cap** 5–12 cm, convex then flattening, smooth, pale, usually dull yellow-green to olive-green, almost white in some forms; with faint radiating lines or fibrils. **Gills** broad, crowded, free, white. **Stem** white to pale greenish, often with faint horizontal banding, bulbous at base with large white bag-like volva (often buried in leaf-litter or soil). **Ring** large, skirt-like, white, striate. Flesh white with sweet, sickly odour. **Spores** white, subglobose, 8–10 µm, amyloid. **Chemical test:** concentrated sulphuric acid on gills = pale lilac. *Deadly poisonous.* **Occurring** from late summer to autumn, may be locally common, usually under oaks or pines. **Notes** may be confused with the False Death Cap, *Amanita citrina*.

Spores 8–10 µm
amyloid

*Amanita
citrina*

## *Amanita citrina* (False Death Cap)

**Key characters** yellow or white cap; gutter-like volva; distinct smell of raw potato. **Description: Cap** 5–9 cm, pale lemon-yellow or pure white, smooth and without fibres; usually with large flattened patches of veil. **Gills** white, free. **Stem** white, smooth, with "gutter" around the upper edge of the bulb. **Ring** flaring, white or yellowish. **Flesh** with strong odour of earthy potato. **Spores** almost globose, 8–10 X 7–8 µm, amyloid. *Very distasteful but not poisonous.* **Occurring** in mixed woods, especially beech or pine, summer to autumn, common.

Swolen base
with volva

Spores 8–10 X 7–8 µm
amyloid

## *Amanita caesarea* (Caesar's Mushroom)

**Key characters** unmistakable combination of orange cap, yellow stem and gills, and white volva. **Description: Cap** 6–20 cm, convex then expanded, clear orange; smooth, often with white volval remnants adhering. **Gills** broad, crowded, free; egg- to chrome-yellow. **Stem** yellow, rather stout, bulbous with large sac-like white volva. **Spores** elliptic, 10–14 X 6–11 µm, non-amyloid. *Edible and delicious.* This species, once highly valued by the Romans, is not easily confused with any other **Amanita** species. **Occurring** in broadleaf woods, especially oaks, summer and autumn. **Notes** prefers warm southern regions (the American type, found on the East coast, is a distinct species, A. jacksonii and is more slender, with a slightly umbonate cap); neither is yet found in Britain.

Amanita
caesarea

Spores 10–14 × 6–11 µm
non-amyloid

## *Amanita virosa* (Destroying Angel) 💀

**Key characters** white cap conical then expanding, large volva and shaggy stem; specific chemical test. **Description: Cap** 6–12 cm, smooth, pure white and usually slightly sticky. **Gills** white, crowded, free. **Stem** tall, rather slender and often curved; usually rather rough and floccose, white, with large volva. **Ring** white, thin, often torn or missing. **Flesh** white with often a sickly, sweet odour. **Spores** white, globose 8–10 µm, amyloid. **Chemical test:** potassium hydroxide on cap = chrome yellow, distinguishing this species from other white amanitas. *Deadly poisonous species containing many different toxins to which antidotes are only now being developed.* **Occurring** in mixed woods, usually (although not always) commoner at more northerly latitudes, autumn. Occasional to frequent. **Notes** the related North American species A. bisporigera is similar, but has a smooth stem, and only two spores per basidium, instead of four.

Slender
scaly stem
supports
conical cap

Amanita
virosa

Thick sac-like
volva cups
bulbous base

Spores 8–10 µm
amyloid

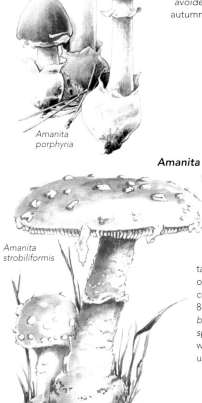

Cap margin smooth, not striate

Ring darkens with age

Amanita porphyria

### *Amanita porphyria*

**Key characters** colours greyish with distinct violaceous tints; volvate base. **Description:** Cap 4–10 cm, convex to broadly umbonate, smooth, greyish brown with a violaceous tint; often with flat patches of white veil remnants adhering. **Gills** white, crowded, free. **Stem** white, occasionally tinted lilac; bulbous with a white, bag-like volva. **Ring** pendent, flaring, striate and often torn; usually tinted strongly lilac or violaceous brown at margin. **Spores** subglobose, 7–10 X 6–8 µm, amyloid. *Not poisonous but rather distasteful, should be avoided.* **Occurring** under birches or conifers, autumn, occasional to frequent.

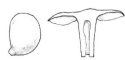

Spores 7–10 × 6–8 µm
amyloid

### *Amanita strobiliformis* (= *A. solitaria*)

*Amanita strobiliformis*

**Key characters** large white cap with thick polygonal warts; thick creamy veil remnants on cap margin and ring. **Description:** Cap 8–20 cm, soon flattened, white to greyish-white, smooth with thick, polygonal white warts. **Gills** white, crowded, free. **Stem** stout, often tall and rooting with pointed base. **Ring** often torn or incomplete, with texture of cream cheese. **Spores** elliptic, 10–12 X 8–10 µm, amyloid. *Not poisonous but may be confused with other white dangerous species.* **Occurring** in open deciduous woodlands on calcareous soils, autumn, uncommon.

Spores 10–12 × 8–10 µm
amyloid

## Amanita echinocephala

**Key characters** sharp warts on cap and stem base; slightly greenish gills and spores. **Description:** Cap 7–20 cm, convex, white, discolouring brownish; smooth with numerous sharply pointed warts adhering but easily rubbed off. **Gills** white or very slightly greenish, free. **Stem** stout, bulbous with spiny warts around base. **Ring** pendent, white, striate. **Spores** white with a very pale greenish tint, 9–11 X 6–8 µm, amyloid. *Its edibility is highly doubtful, and the species should be avoided.* **Occurring** in broadleaf woods on calcareous soils, autumn, uncommon.

Small, conical warts on cap surface

Stem base scaly but no volva

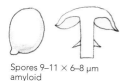

Spores 9–11 × 6–8 µm amyloid

*Amanita echinocephala*

## Amanita crocea

**Key characters** cap and stem clear orange; stem shaggy-scaly, rather robust. **Description:** Cap 5–15 cm, a beautiful clear orange with no reddish brown. **Gills** white. **Stem** pale orange with horizontal bands of felty scales. **Volva** white but pale orange inside. **Spores** white, subglobose, 9–13 X 8–11 µm, non-amyloid. *Edible but not recommended.* **Occurring** under birches, this species is frequent in Scotland and Northern Europe but rare elsewhere, autumn. **Notes** very close to the more common *A. fulva* but stouter cap and stem with brighter colours.

*Amanita crocea*

Spores 9–13 × 8–11 µm non-amyloid

*Amanita battarrae*

### Amanita battarrae

**Key characters** cap olive-yellow to brown with light and dark zones. **Description: Cap** 5–10 cm, light olive-hazel with distinct lighter and darker zones, as illustrated; edge strongly striate-sulcate. **Gills** white. **Stem** pale cream-brown, slightly scaly. **Volva** large, bag-like, white or yellowish. **Spores** white, subglobose, 11–16 X 10–13 µm, non-amyloid. *Edible but best avoided.* Occurring in broadleaf woodlands, especially birches, autumn, uncommon. **Notes** very similar in shape to *A. fulva* and *A. vaginata* but quite distinct from either, larger and more robust, with distinctive colouring.

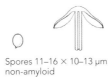

Spores 11–16 × 10–13 µm
non-amyloid

Cap surface smooth, shiny

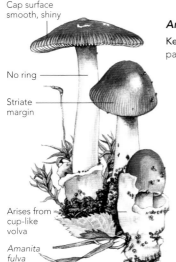

No ring

Striate margin

Arises from cup-like volva

*Amanita fulva*

### Amanita fulva and A. vaginata (Grisettes)

**Key characters** cap orange-brown or grey; stem paler, with volva but no ring; often smooth patches left on cap. **Description: Cap** 4–10 cm, ovate then soon expanded and slightly umbonate, smooth, dry and often with skin-like remnants of white veil-tissue; edge strongly striate-sulcate, orange-brown in *A. fulva*, pearly-grey in *A. vaginata*. **Gills** free, white. **Stem** tall and slender, tapering upwards, white to pale brown or grey. **Volva** tall and sac-like,

Spores 9–11 µm
non-amyloid

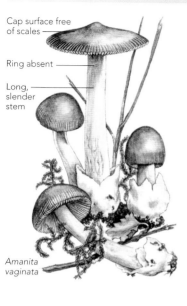

Cap surface free of scales

Ring absent

Long, slender stem

*Amanita vaginata*

white outside, grey or brown within. **Flesh** fragile, crumbly, white. **Spores** white, globose, 9–11 µm, non-amyloid. *Edible and good but best avoided, like all amanitas, to avoid confusion with poisonous species.* **Occurring** in mixed woodlands, especially birch, summer and autumn, common.

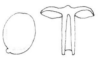

Spores 9–11 µm
non-amyloid

## *Amanita ceciliae  (= A. inaurata, = A. strangulata)*

**Key characters** large size, dark grey-brown or umber colours; stout, shaggy stem with short flaky volva.
**Description:** Cap 6–15 cm, dark grey-brown to umber-brown, smooth with greyish veil remnants angular, not smooth. **Gills** white, free. **Stem** tall, rather stout, grey-brown, rather tough with shaggy-felty horizontal bands of veil-tissue. **Volva** less bag-like than previous species, flaky with upper edge with thick angular warts readily breaking away. **Spores** white, globose, 10–13 µm, non-amyloid. *Edibility uncertain; possibly poisonous, best avoided.* **Occurring** in mixed woodlands, summer to autumn, rather uncommon. **Notes** rather similar to the common *A. fulva* or *A. vaginata*, but larger, darker and more robust.

Spores 10–13 µm
non-amyloid

Cap margin is grooved

No ring on stem

*Amanita ceciliae*

## PLUTEACEAE

This family has two principal genera, *Volvariella*, which is mainly tropical and has a volva, and *Pluteus*, without a volva, which is much more widely distributed with a very much larger number of species. They all share the common features of a pinkish spore deposit, gills free from the stem and with a unique arrangement of converging cells within the gills. A very large majority of the species in both genera occur on rotting wood or any rich organic matter such as straw. Some species of *Volvariella* are cultivated for food and can be purchased in tins sold under the name of Paddy-Straw Mushrooms.

### VOLVARIELLA

#### Volvariella gloiocephala (= speciosa)

**Key characters** cap large and very sticky, usually grey-green; small volva; in rotting grass or straw, haystacks etc. **Description: Cap** 5–10 cm, very slightly fibrous but otherwise smooth and very sticky-viscid in wet weather; pale grey to brown or almost white. **Gills** broad, pink, free. **Stem** white with short, thin white volva often almost missing or left behind in the soil when picked. **Spores** pink, elliptic, 13–18 X 8–10 µm. *Edible but not highly recommended.* **Occurring** in summer and autumn, occasional to common in wet, rotted grass, stubble fields and on mulched flower beds in gardens and parks.

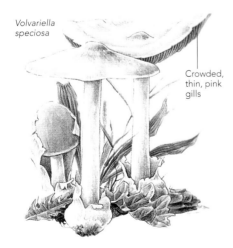

*Volvariella speciosa*

Crowded, thin, pink gills

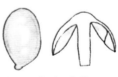

Spores 13–18 × 8–10 µm

## Volvariella murinella

**Key characters** small to tiny, cap grey with jagged margin; grey volva. **Description: Cap** 2–4 cm pale grey, smooth. **Gills** broad, pink, free. **Stem** short, white with small grey volva. **Spores** pink, ovate, 6–8 X 4–5 µm. *Edibility uncertain*, but the species is too tiny to eat even if edible. **Occurring** in short grass, in fields and gardens, summer and autumn, frequent but often overlooked.

*Volvariella murinella*

Spores 6–8 × 4–5 µm

## Volvariella bombycina

**Key characters** large, silky-hairy pale cap and large volva. **Description: Cap** 5–12 cm, with a beautiful silky, finely hairy surface; pale yellowish or almost white. **Gills** free, very broad and white, then soon deep pink. **Stem** white, bulbous with brownish sac-like volva. **Spores** pink, ovate-elliptic, 7–9 X 5–6 µm. This lovely species is *edible and delicious*. **Occurring** on dying or dead elms, more rarely on other trees, autumn, uncommon.

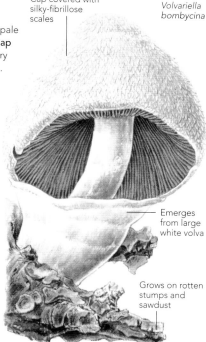

Cap covered with silky-fibrillose scales

*Volvariella bombycina*

Emerges from large white volva

Grows on rotten stumps and sawdust

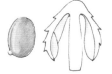

Spores 7–9 × 5–6 µm

61

*Pluteus cervinus*

Thin, pink gills are very crowded

Grows from old stumps

Spores 6–8 × 4–5 μm

## *PLUTEUS*

### *Pluteus cervinus*

**Key characters** smooth to fibrillose cap (shades of brown) and fibrous stem; no volva. **Description: Cap** convex, then soon expanded and slightly domed, often with a central depression, radially fibrillose but otherwise smooth; pale to dark brown. **Gills** broad, free, deep pink. **Stem** white with darker brown-black fibres, slightly bulbous. **Spores** pink, ovate-elliptic, 6–8 X 4–5 μm. *Edible but not highly favoured.* **Occurring** on deciduous wood, stumps, logs and sawdust, all year, very common. **Notes** on conifers the similar but rarer *P. atromarginatus*, with black gill edges, may be found.

### *Pluteus aurantiorugosus  (= P. coccineus)*

**Key characters** bright orange cap and stem; gills yellow, then pink. **Description: Cap** 2–5 cm, scarlet and globose when young, soon expanded and bright orange to yellow-orange. **Gills** yellow at first then soon pale pinkish, free. **Stem** slender and long, not bulbous, pale orange-yellow. **Spores** pink, subglobose, 5 X 4–5 μm. *Edibility uncertain;* but too small for use. **Occurring** on decayed elms or ash, autumn, rare to occasional. **Notes** one of the loveliest of all small toadstools, and not easily confused with anything else.

Spores 5 × 4–5 μm

*Pluteus aurantiorugosus*

### *Pluteus salicinus*

**Key characters** bluish-grey cap and lower half of stem. **Description: Cap** 3–8 cm, smooth but finely fibrillose and minutely scaly at centre, grey with a blue-green tint. **Gills** broad, pink. **Stem** slender, pale blue-green fading to white above. **Spores** pink, elliptic, 8 X 5–6 μm. *Edible but not rec-*

ommended. **Occurring** usually on willow trees and stumps, occasionally on beech, autumn, common. **Notes** the colouring distinguishes this graceful species.

Cap and stem have greenish tints

Spores 8 × 5–6 µm ovoid

*Pluteus salicinus*

### Pluteus umbrosus

**Key characters** dark brown, wrinkled and hairy-scaly cap, stoutish stem also brown and woolly-scaly. **Description: Cap** 3–8 cm, umber or sooty-brown; surface minutely wrinkled and roughened or reticulate with small, sparse woolly or hair-like scales; margin conspicuously fringed. **Gills** broad, crowded, pink, edge brown. **Stem** stout with dark brown squamules. **Spores** pink, elliptic, 6–7 X 4–5 µm. *Edible but not recommended.* **Occurring** on decaying deciduous trees and stumps, autumn, occasional to frequent.

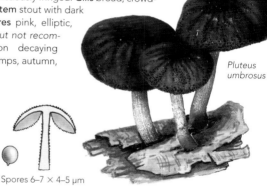

*Pluteus umbrosus*

Spores 6–7 × 4–5 µm

### Pluteus lutescens

**Key characters** dark brown cap with yellowish stem; gills pale yellow when young. **Description: Cap** 2–4 cm, sooty-brown, smooth or slightly wrinkled, slightly umbonate when expanded. **Gills** pale yellow then soon pinkish, free. **Stem** slender, not usually bulbous; yellow, especially in lower half. **Spores** pink, subglobose, 6–7 X 5–6 µm. *Edible but not worth eating.* **Occurring** on fallen twigs and rich soil, autumn, occasional. **Notes** a small but attractive species easily recognized when strongly coloured, less so in paler varieties.

*Pluteus lutescens*

Gills finally pink

Spores 6–7 × 5–6 µm

63

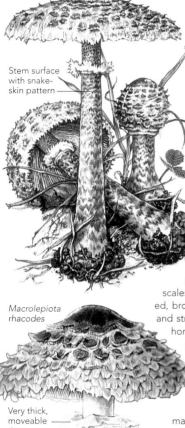

Macrolepiota
procera

Stem surface
with snake-
skin pattern

Macrolepiota
rhacodes

Very thick,
moveable
ring

Stem smooth,
not scaly

Flesh white,
turns saffron
red on
exposure

Large,
bulbous
stem base

# AGARICACEAE

This distinctive family contains several important temperate genera. There are very few *Melanophyllum* species, a few *Cystoderma* species but a great many *Lepiota* and *Agaricus*, including the best-known and most valuable fungus in the world – the common cultivated mushroom *A. bisporus*. Most members of the Agaricaceae have free gills and some form of external veil Many species also have a well developed partial veil. Spore colour varies from white to dark brown.

## MACROLEPIOTA

### *Macrolepiota (= Lepiota) procera* (Parasol Mushroom)

**Key characters** very large, with distinctive shape; darker bands on stem. **Description: Cap** 10–25 cm, globular, soon flattening, with prominent umbo; pale biscuit-brown to hazel with thick flakes or scales, the remains of the universal veil. **Gills** crowded, broad, free, white to pale cream. **Stem** very tall and straight, bulbous, pale brown with darker wavy horizontal zones. **Ring** large, thick, rather complex, high on stem. **Spores** white, ovate, 13–17 X 8–11 µm, dextrinoid. *Edible and delicious, with a unique flavour.* **Occurring** in fields and hedgerows, woodland margins, summer and autumn, widespread and common.

Spores 13–17 × 8–11 µm
dextrinoid

### *Macrolepiota (= Lepiota) rhacodes* (Shaggy or Woodland Parasol)

**Key characters** stout, no dark bands on stem; shaggy-scaly appearance. **Description: Cap** 8–15 cm, soon flattening, not as prominently umbonate as *M. procera*; dull greyish brown to dark brown with large, coarse brown flakes or scales on white background. **Gills** broad, free, white to cream, staining red. **Stem**

rather short, stout, smooth, without dark bands, strongly bulbous. **Ring** thick, double. **Spores** white, ovate, 8–11 X 5–7 µm, dextrinoid. *Edible and delicious.* **Occurring** in shade of woodlands, gardens on compost heaps, mulch beds, etc., autumn, frequent. **Notes** the very similar *M. olivieri* differs in its duller, more grey-brown cap with scales of same colour as background, usually more slender and common under conifers.

Spores 8–11 × 5–7 µm
dextrinoid

### *Macrolepiota (= Lepiota) mastoidea*

**Key characters** slender, delicate; cap strongly umbonate; pale colours and almost no scales. **Description: Cap** 5–10 cm, very pale biscuit-brown to almost white; finely roughened, granular, breaking up into tiny flakes. **Gills** white, free. **Stem** tall, very slender, colour as cap, smooth. **Ring** high up, double. **Spores** white, 14–18 X 8–11 µm, dextrinoid. *Edible and delicious.* **Occurring** in woodland clearings and margins, autumn, uncommon.

*Macrolepiota mastoidea*

Spores 14–18 × 8–11 µm
dextrinoid

Small, pointed scales
easily break off

Forking
gills

## *LEPIOTA*

### *Lepiota aspera (= L. friesii)*

**Key characters** warty cap and stem base; forked gills; repulsive odour and taste. **Description: Cap** 6–10 cm, conical then umbonate; pale yellow-brown, with pointed deep brown warts. **Gills** white, crowded, free, forked, often staining brown. **Stem** stout, rather short, pale brown with dark warty-scaly zones at base. **Ring** soft, skirt-like, white. **Spores** elliptic, 6–8 X 3–4 µm, dextrinoid. *Inedible.* In deciduous woodlands, gardens, usually on calcareous soils, autumn, uncommon.

*Lepiota aspera*

Spores 6–8 × 3–4 µm
dextrinoid

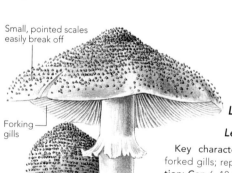

## *Lepiota cristata* (Stinking Parasol) ☣

**Key characters** dark brown cap with small concentric scales, strong unpleasant smell. **Description: Cap** 2–6 cm, white with a dark brown or reddish-brown umbo and tiny concentric brown scales. **Gills** white, crowded, free. **Stem** slender, pale brown. **Ring** very thin, often soon disappearing. **Spores** white, bullet-shaped, dextrinoid, 6–8 X 3–4 μm. *Possibly poisonous.* **Occurring** in short grass in fields, gardens, woodlands etc., summer and autumn, common. **Notes** this small, rather attractively marked species is easily recognized by the unpleasant odour.

*Lepiota cristata*

Spores 6–8 × 3–4 μm

Cap surface breaks up into felty patches

## *Lepiota clypeolaria*

**Key characters** zones of velvety scales on cap; slender stem woolly-floccose below. **Description: Cap** 3–8 cm, convex with umbo, soon expanding; pale ochre to reddish brown, then cracking into rings of scales, finer at margin. **Gills** white, free, soft. **Stem** has ring-like zone below which it is woolly-floccose, pale cream. **Odour** slightly gas-like. **Spores** white, fusiform, 12–19 X 5–6 μm. *Edibility uncertain, best avoided.* **Occurring** in mixed woods, autumn, frequent.

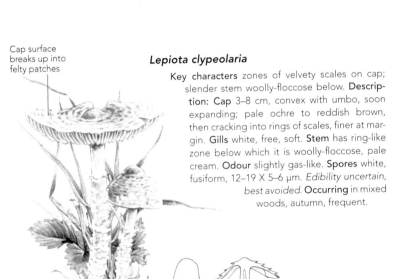

*Lepiota clypeolaria*

Spores 12–19 × 5–6 μm

## *Lepiota brunneoincarnata* 💀

**Key characters** small but stocky; cap minutely scaly with rose or wine-red flush. **Description:** Cap 3–5 cm, slightly umbonate, reddish brown with flush of pink; densely scaly at centre, less so at margin, scales darker brown. **Gills** cream or white, free. **Stem** flushed pale reddish brown below; squamulose-scaly up to the ring-like zone, bare above. **Spores** white, ovate, dextrinoid, 6–9 X 4–5 μm. **Odour** slightly fruity. *Poisonous, possibly deadly.* **Occurring** in woodland clearings, gardens and roadsides, uncommon to occasional, autumn.

Spores 6–9 × 4–5 μm

*Lepiota brunneoincarnata*

## *Lepiota bucknalli* 💀

**Key characters** stem blue or lavender; strong odour of coal-gas. **Description:** Cap 2–4 cm, slightly umbonate, white or pale grey, with a minutely granular surface; margin often with tiny toothed fringe. **Gills** white, free. **Stem** thin, lavender-blue or violet becoming dark blue below; surface powdery-granular. **Ring** absent. **Spores** white, bullet-shaped, 7–9 X 3–4 μm, dextrinoid. *Edibility not known, possibly poisonous.* **Occurring** in broadleaf woods on chalk or limestone, autumn, rare. **Notes** this uniquely coloured species is easily recognized if you are lucky enough to see one!

Smells of coal-gas

Spores 7–9 × 3–4 μm dextrinoid

*Lepiota bucknalli*

### Leucoagaricus leucothites
### (= Leucoagarius naucina)

*Leucoagaricus leucothites*

White, free gills

**Key characters** looks like a field mushroom, but spores white. **Description: Cap** 6–10 cm, convex then expanding, white to pale cream; smooth and silky, slightly granular or suede-like with age and breaking into small patches. **Gills** crowded, free, white then pale pink with age. **Stem** white, smooth, base not usually bulbous. **Ring** thin, high on stem, white. **Spores** white, ovate, 7–9 X 5–6 µm. *Edibility doubtful, best avoided – can also be mistaken for a deadly Amanita.* **Occurring** in fields, gardens, woodland clearings, autumn, uncommon.

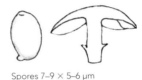

Spores 7–9 × 5–6 µm

## CYSTODERMA

### Cystoderma amianthinum

*Cystoderma amianthinum*

Widely spaced gills

Fragile ring points upward

**Key characters** granular cap and stem; yellow to orange-ochre colours; specific chemical test. **Description: Cap** 2–5 cm, slightly umbonate; usually radially wrinkled, and minutely granulose. **Gills** white, adnate. **Stem** colour as cap; granulose up to a fine ring zone. **Spores** white, 5–7 X 3–4 µm, amyloid. **Chemical test:** potassium hydroxide on cap cuticle = rust-brown. *Edible but not recommended.* **Occurring** in conifer or mixed heathy woodlands, autumn, common.

Spores 5–7 × 3–4 µm
amyloid

Cystoderma
carcharias

Stem covered
in tiny rose-
coloured warts
below the ring

## Cystoderma carcharias

**Key characters** main features as in the preceding species but pinkish-grey colour; specific chemical test. **Description: Cap** 2–4 cm, pinkish-grey to flesh-pink; margin toothed. **Gills** white, adnate. **Stem** colour as cap. **Ring** usually more prominent than in previous species. **Spores** white, 4–6 X 3–4 μm, amyloid. **Chemical test**: potassium hydroxide on cap = no reaction, not brown. *Edibile, but not recommended*. **Occurring** in conifer woodlands, autumn, frequent.

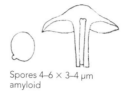

Spores 4–6 × 3–4 μm
amyloid

## MELANOPHYLLUM

### Melanophyllum echinatum
### (= Lepiota haematosperma)

**Key characters** gills blood then brownish red; spores grey-brown, drying reddish. **Description: Cap** 1–3 cm, minutely granulose; deep brown with margin toothed. **Stem** pale reddish brown, finely granular; flesh red. **Spores** ovate, 4–6 X 2–4 μm. *Edibility suspect, best avoided*. **Occurring** in woods and gardens on bare soil, autumn, uncommon.

Melanophyllum
echinatum

Spores 4–6 × 2–4 μm

# AGARICUS

*Agaricus campestris*

### Agaricus campestris (Field Mushroom)

Key characters in grassy fields; gills bright pink in young "buttons", then dark brown.

Description: Cap 5–10 cm, convex, slow to expand; smooth to slightly scaly-fibrillose; white to pale brown. Stem short, white with a thin ring which often disappears. Flesh white. Spores brown, 7–8 X 4–5 µm. *One of the best edible species*. Occurring in grassy fields, roadsides and gardens, summer and autumn, common.

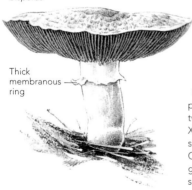

Thin, white, fragile ring

Spores 7–8 × 4–5 µm

*Agaricus bisporus*

### Agaricus bisporus (Cultivated Mushroom)

Key characters on soil; fibrillose cap, narrow ring on stem. Description: Cap 5–10 cm, pale brown with fine radiating fibrils. Gills dull pink then dark brown, crowded. Stem rather longer than in the Field Mushroom, white with rather prominent narrow ring. Spores brown, only two per basidium (hence *bisporus*), 6–8 X 5–6 µm. *Edible and excellent*. Notes this species is considered to be the ancestor of the Cultivated Mushroom. Occurring roadsides, gardens, manure heaps etc.; always on rich soil, summer to autumn, uncommon.

Thick membranous ring

Gills blackish brown when mature

Spores 6–8 × 5–6 µm

## *Agaricus impudicus (= A. variegans)*

**Key characters** cap with flattened centre, broad brown scales; flesh smells of rubber. **Description: Cap** 5–15 cm, convex, flattened-depressed at centre; cream to pale ochre with broad, radiating brown scales. **Gills** pale pink, then dark brown. **Stem** slightly longer than cap diameter, white with woolly scales below. **Ring** large, pendent. **Flesh**, when cut, with strong smell like fresh rubber exactly as in *Lepiota cristata*. **Spores** 4–5 X 3–4µm. *Edible but not recommended.* **Occurring** in mixed woodlands, summer and autumn, occasional to common. **Notes** a medium-sized species rather like a stout, brown-scaled Field Mushroom.

*Agaricus impudicus*

Spores 4–5 × 3–4 µm

## *Agaricus augustus*

**Key characters** large size, with yellow-orange cap, finely scaled; stem woolly. **Description: Cap** 6–20 cm, convex, then flattening; pale creamy-yellow to bright tawny orange or brown with small concentric rust-hazel fibrillose scales; edge with tattered remnants of veil. **Gills** broad, almost white, soon brown. **Stem** tall, stout, white; covered below ring with floccose, woolly scales. **Ring** large, pendent, skirt-like, scaly on underside. **Spores** ovate, 7–10 X 5–6 µm. *Edible and delicious.* **Occurring** in mixed woodlands, summer and autumn, frequent.

Cap covered with brown scales

Gills greyish to chocolate brown, never pink

Spores 7–10 × 5–6 µm

*Agaricus augustus*

71

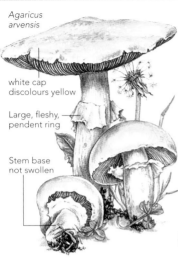

*Agaricus arvensis*

white cap discolours yellow

Large, fleshy, pendent ring

Stem base not swollen

## Agaricus arvensis (Horse Mushroom)

**Key characters** usually large and stout; cap yellowing; cogwheel-like flakes on underside of ring, growing in open grass. **Description:** Cap 7–15 cm, convex with flattened centre when young, then broadly expanded, white, smooth, staining dull brass-yellow when bruised. **Gills** broad, free, pale pink then dark brown when mature. **Stem** tall, robust, smooth below the ring, only slightly bulbous at base. **Spores** larger 7–10 X 4–5 µm. *Edible and delicious.* **Occurring** outside woodlands in fields, pathsides, etc. **Notes** very similar to *A. sylvicola* in form, colour, gills, ring, etc. but larger and more robust.

Spores 7–10 × 4–5 µm
ovoid

## Agaricus bitorquis

**Key characters** flat cap with thick flesh; very narrow, crowded gills. **Description: Cap** 6–15 cm, soon noticeably flattened with margin slightly inrolled; smooth or slightly cracking; white, then discoloured pale brown. **Gills** very narrow and crowded, dull pink, then deep reddish brown. **Stem** short and stout; thick veil sheathing the base, rather like a volva. **Ring** often thick, narrow, high on stem. **Flesh** very thick in cap, white, slowly becoming slightly brownish. **Spores** brown, subglobose, 5–7 X 4–5 µm. *Edible and delicious.* **Occurring** on roadsides and woodland edges; in towns often forces up paving stones; summer and autumn, rather common.

Cap smooth, not scaly

Stem has 2 rings

*Agaricus bitorquis*

Spores 5–7 × 4–5 µm

## Agaricus silvicola (= A. abruptibulbus of European authors)

*Agaricus silvicola*

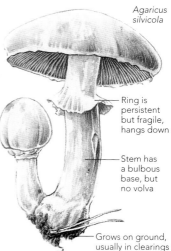

**Key characters** small to medium size; yellowing cuticle; smooth bulbous stem; in woodlands. **Description: Cap** 6–12 cm, convex with broadly expanded margin; white then slowly yellowish with age or bruising. **Gills** grey-white (never bright pink), then soon dark brown, free, crowded. **Stem** rather tall and slender with bulbous base, smooth below the ring. **Ring** large, thin and pendent, of two distinct membranes, the lower often toothed like a cogwheel. **Spores** 5–6 × 3–4 μm. **Odour** faint of anise. *Edible and delicious.* **Occurring** in mixed woods, autumn, common.

Ring is persistent but fragile, hangs down

Stem has a bulbous base, but no volva

Grows on ground, usually in clearings

Spores 5–6 × 3–4 μm

## Agaricus xanthodermus (Yellow Stainer) ☣

*Agaricus xanthodermus*

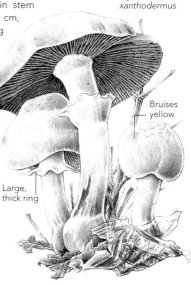

**Key characters** flesh staining vivid yellow in stem when cut, inky smell. **Description: Cap** 8–15 cm, white to greyish brown; cuticle often becoming coarsely cracked, sometimes even scaly; centre flattened to slightly depressed, cap skin scratches bright yellow. **Gills** at first pale pink, then grey-brown, free, crowded. **Stem** white, smooth, base bulbous. **Ring** large, pendent, double. **Spores** brown 5–6 × 4 μm. Odour of ink (very noticeable if cooked by mistake). *Poisonous to many, edible to others; should not be experimented with.* **Occurring** in fields, gardens and hedgerows, summer and autumn, frequent to common. **Notes** This is the commonest white mushroom that stains intense yellow in stem and cap.

Bruises yellow

Large, thick ring

Spores 5–6 × 4 μm

73

*Agaricus semotus*

Old caps become reddish

Spores 4–6 × 3–4 µm

### Agaricus semotus
### (= A. dulcidulus of some authors) 🍄☠

**Key characters** small, with purple colours in ivory cap, with fine radiating lines. **Description: Cap** 3–7 cm, ivory white to pale hazel brown with darker, very fine scales overall; usually with a flush of purple at centre, convex with flattened centre. **Gills** at first pale pink, then grey-brown. **Stem** white, smooth, bulbous; discolouring brown. **Ring** large, pendent, double. Flesh turning dull chrome-yellow but at base of stem only. **Spores** brown 4–6 X 3–4 µm. *Poisonous to some people; to be avoided.* **Occurring** in woodland clearings and margins, summer and autumn, uncommon.

### Agaricus moelleri 🍄☠
### (= A. placomyces of European authors,
### = A. praeclaresquamosus)

*Agaricus moelleri*

Sooty-brown scales on cap surface

All parts bruise yellow

**Key characters** cap finely black-scaled, stem base (not cap) flesh goes bright yellow when cut. **Description: Cap** 8–15 cm, pale ivory with fine radiating blackish fibrils or tiny scales; silky texture; often yellowing with age or bruising. **Gills** at first pale pink, then grey-brown, free, crowded. **Stem** tall, white, staining yellow in the bulbous base. **Ring** thin, flaring. **Flesh** white, only dull yellow when cut, only bright chrome-yellow in stem base. **Spores** 4–5 × 3 µm. *Edibility not known; probably toxic and best avoided.* **Occurring** in mixed woodlands, autumn, uncommon. **Notes** the closely related *A. phaeolepidotus* also in woodlands, rare, and is similar in nearly all respects but has unchanging flesh.

Spores 4–5 × 3 µm

## *Agaricus pseudovillaticus (= A.vaporarius)*

**Key characters** dull brown colours; thick, felty scales; stem very stout; often deeply rooted. **Description:** Cap 5–10 cm, dull grey-brown with thick, coarse scales; convex at first and only slowly flattening. **Gills** at first pale grey-pink, then dark brown, free. **Stem** very thick in proportion to length, often deeply rooting and pointed with thick shaggy veil tissue clinging to lower half. **Ring** thick, felty, often torn or missing. **Flesh** slowly reddening when cut. **Spores** 6–7 X 4–6 μm. *Edible but not highly recommended.* **Occurring** in woods or roadsides, in soil or leaf-litter, often in very large clumps with only the top of the caps visible, summer to autumn, uncommon.

*Agaricus pseudovillaticus*

Spores 6–7 × 4–6 μm

## *Agaricus silvaticus (= A. haemorrhoidarius)* (Scaly Wood Mushroom)

**Key characters** cap with red-brown scales; stem white; flesh reddening. **Description:** Cap 5–9 cm, convex then flattened, pale brown or almost white in some forms (especially under pines), with darker brown to reddish brown, finely pointed scales. **Gills** crowded, rather narrow, pale pink then soon brown. **Stem** rather slender, swollen at base, white; smooth to slightly scaly below the ring. **Ring** thin, floppy, woolly-scaly on underside. **Flesh** when cut white then soon pale to bright red, especially in cap and outer flesh of stem. **Spores** brown, ovate, 5–6 X 3–4 μm. *Edible and excellent.* **Occurring** in mixed woodlands in leaf-litter or needles of pines, autumn, common. **Notes** the similar *A. langei* has a tall, stout, non-bulbous stem, and cap with broad scales, strongly reddish brown; its ring soon vanishes.

*Agaricus silvaticus*

Deeply rooted in pine needles

Spores 5–6 × 3–4 μm

75

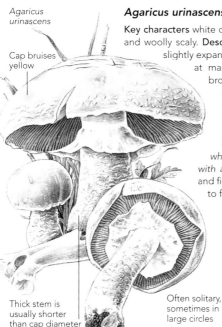

*Agaricus urinascens*

Cap bruises yellow

Thick stem is usually shorter than cap diameter

Often solitary, sometimes in large circles

### Agaricus urinascens (= A. macrosporus)

**Key characters** white cap often very large, stem short, stout and woolly scaly. **Description:** Cap 10–25 cm, convex then slightly expanded; smooth at first then slightly scaly at margin. **Gills** whitish grey then slowly brown; crowded, rather narrow. **Stem** stout, rather short, white; rough, woolly-scaly below the large, soft ring. **Flesh** white to slightly orange-pink when cut. **Spores** elliptic, brown, 8–12 X 5–7 µm. *Edible and good when young, becomes rather ill-smelling with age.* **Occurring** in open pasture land and fields, summer and autumn, occasional to frequent, favouring calcareous soils.

Spores 8–12 × 5–7 µm

### Agaricus benesii (= A. squamuliferus)

**Key characters** stocky, white, finely scaly mushroom with flesh turning bright red. **Description:** Cap 4–10 cm, convex then expanding; white becoming brownish with age, surface disrupting into fine scales. **Gills** crowded, free, dull pink then brown. **Stem** rather stout, white, slightly woolly scaly below the ring. **Ring** pendent,

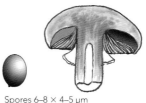

*Agaricus benesii*

Spores 6–8 × 4–5 µm

thin. **Flesh** white, turning bright red when scratched. **Spores** ovate, brown, 6–8 X 4–5 μm. *Edible and delicious.* **Occurring** at woodland margins and clearings, along roadsides, summer to autumn, uncommon. **Notes** this species is almost unique in being white (not brown, scaly) but with flesh of cap and stem rapidly turning bright red when cut (not yellow).

## *Agaricus phaeolepidotus* (☠)

**Key characters** cap smooth, silky, with faint, flattened scales; stem very smooth; flesh colour unchanging. **Description: Cap** 6–10 cm, convex with a flattened central 'boss'; pale cinnamon-brown with darker scales. **Gills** crowded, pale greyish pink then brown, never bright pink. **Stem** long, smooth, never scaly, white. **Flesh** white, unchanging, or slightly very pale ochre-yellow at base. **Spores** 5–6 X 3–4 μm. *Edibility doubtful, as a member of the* A. xanthodermus *group, which is mildly poisonous, this species is best avoided.* **Occurring** in deciduous woodlands on grassy soil, on straw or compost, autumn, uncommon. **Notes** it somewhat resembles some red-staining, scaly wood mushrooms, e.g. *A. silvaticus* (see above), but is smoother and has unchanging flesh.

*Agaricus phaeolepidotus*

Spores 5–6 × 3–4 μm

# COPRINACEAE

This distinctive family has characteristic very dark spores, and gills from free to adnexed or adnate and often (*Coprinus* species, the Ink Caps) deliquescing to liquid when mature. There is often a well developed veil and occasionally a ring. Many grow on dung (when they may vary considerably in size) and rotten wood. They are on the whole rather delicate, small and dull-coloured.

## COPRINUS

### Coprinus atramentarius ☠

*Coprinus atramentarius*

**Key characters** cap grey and slightly scaly; stem with ridged bulb at base, sometimes rooting. **Description: Cap** 2–6 cm, broadly conical-ovate then expanding to bell-shaped; pale brownish grey, darker and slightly scaly at centre. **Gills** narrow, crowded, free; pale grey, soon black and dissolving. **Stem** white, elongating as cap expands, tapering upwards. **Spores** black, ovate, 7–10 X 5–6 μm. *Toxic, to be avoided* This species is quite tasty and apparently harmless unless consumed with alcohol, when rather alarming symptoms occur of facial flushing, nausea and palpitations. **Occurring** in clusters in gardens, roadsides, near old stumps or on bare soil, summer and autumn, common.

Spores 7–10 × 5–6 μm

Covered with recurved, fibrous scales

### Coprinus comatus
### (Shaggy Mane, Shaggy Ink Cap, Lawyer's Wig)

**Key characters** tall, white, shaggy cap; slender stem with ring black, dissolving gills. **Description: Cap** 5–15 cm high, cylindrical then narrowly bell-shaped; white to pale brown at centre; very shaggy with woolly scales. **Gills** crowded, narrow, almost free; white then pink, then black, dissolving from margin until almost entire cap is gone. **Stem** tall (10–20 cm), smooth, white. **Ring** narrow, easily movable. **Spores** blackish-purple, elliptic, 13–14 X 7–9 μm. *Delicious and delicately flavoured when*

*Coprinus comatus*

Spores 13–14 × 7–9 μ

*young.* **Occurring** on grassland, roadsides, playing fields etc., especially on turf over soil recently disturbed, spring to autumn, common.

Coprinus
micaceus

### *Coprinus micaceus* (Glistening Ink Cap)

**Key characters** cap date-brown, grooved; with scattered "crystals" on surface when young. **Description: Cap** 3–6 cm, yellow to date-brown, ovate-conical, grooved, sparkling with tiny crystalline granules. **Gills** white, then almost black, rapidly autodigesting (deliquescing) to black liquid. **Stem** medium to long, thin, white and smooth. **Spores** lemon-shaped, 7–12 X 6–7 μm. *Edible but best avoided.* **Occurring** in large clumps on deciduous stumps, spring to autumn, common.

Spores 7–12 × 6–7 μm
with germ-pore

Coprinus
lagopus

### *Coprinus lagopus*

**Key characters** very tall stem; cap woolly-hairy, white; usually solitary. **Description: Cap** 2–5 cm, cylindrical-ovate, white, woolly-hairy, thin and papery, then rolling upwards from the margin as the grey gills dissolve and contract. **Stem** short at first then rapidly elongating. **Spores** 10–12 X 5–8 μm. *Edible but not worth considering.* **Occurring** in woodlands, roadsides etc., on woody debris, summer to autumn, frequent.

Gills soon
deliquescent

Spores 10–12 × 5–8 μm

79

Always in
large numbers

*Coprinus
disseminatus*

## Coprinus disseminatus
### (Fairies' Bonnets)

**Key characters** caps very small, strongly grooved; grows in large clusters. **Description: Cap** 1–2 cm, ovate, then expanded; thin membranous, grooved (more strongly than the larger *C. micaceus*); grey or pale ochre, not autodigesting. **Gills** white, then grey. **Stem** thin, short, finely hairy. **Spores** 8–11 X 4–5 µm. *Not poisonous, but too small to eat.* **Occurring** on stumps of deciduous trees, summer to autumn, common.

Spores 8–11 × 4–5 µm

*Coprinus
niveus*

## Coprinus niveus

**Key characters** beautiful snow-white toadstools on dung. **Description: Cap** 1–4 cm, tall-ovate, soon expanding to bell-shaped, texture chalky-scurfy, dissolving away from the margin inwards. **Gills** grey, then black, soon autodigesting. **Stem** long, thin, white, texture as cap; no ring. **Spores** lemon-shaped, 12–18 X 10–12 µm. *Edibility unknown.* **Occurring** always on cow or horse dung, summer and autumn, common.

Spores 12–18 × 10–12 µm

# LACRYMARIA

## Lacrymaria lacrymabunda
## (= Hypholoma velutinum)
### (Weeping Widow)

**Key characters** yellow-brown fibrillose cap; black weeping gills. **Description: Cap** 4–10 cm, convex, often with a low umbo, covered (especially when young) with woolly fibrils, veil remnants especially at margin; pale clay to ochre-brown, sometimes pale orange. **Gills** crowded, sinuate, dark brown to black; edges white with small droplets when fresh and rapidly developing. **Stem** quite thick, with woolly fibrils up to ring-like zone. **Spores** almost black, lemon-shaped and warty, 10–12 X 6–7 μm. *Edible but best avoided.* **Occurring** on road- and pathsides, in gardens and fields. Summer and autumn. Very common.

*Lacrymaria lacrymabunda*

Remains of cortina at cap edge

Spores 10–12 × 6–7 μm

Cap has a dark brown centre

Lower half of stem covered with brown, recurved scales

Ring has a double layer

Grows in tufts on and around conifer stumps

*Psathyrella caput-medusae*

# PSATHYRELLA

## Psathyrella caput-medusae

**Key characters** cap pale with broad, dark scales; lower stem scaly; on conifer stumps. **Description: Cap** 3–6 cm, convex then expanded, almost white with deep brown centre and scales on outer half. **Gills** adnate, pale grey then dark brown. **Stem** stout, white, smooth above the thick, flaring ring, with dark brown scales on lower half. **Spores** 10–12 X 4–5 μm. *Edibility uncertain.* **Occurring** on or around conifer stumps or sometimes on sawdust, autumn, rare to occasional.

Spores 10–12 × 4–5 μm

81

## Psathyrella candolleana

**Key characters** almost white caps, very fragile; in tufts on deciduous stumps. **Description: Cap** 3–8 cm, convex, then expanded, pale buff to white; smooth, but with tiny tooth-like veil remnants at margin. **Gills** adnate, pale greyish lilac, then deep brown. **Stem** thin, very fragile white, usually growing in clumps. **Spores** 7–8 X 4–5 µm. *Edibility uncertain but too fragile and thin in any case.* **Occurring** on stumps and buried wood of broadleaf trees, widespread summer and autumn, common.

Spores 7–8 × 4–5 µm

*Psathyrella candolleana*

*Psathyrella piluliformis*

Smooth — white stem

## Psathyrella piluliformis (= P. hydrophila)

**Key characters** cap changing colour on drying faint ring zone on stem; in clusters on deciduous stumps. **Description: Cap** 3–8 cm, convex soon almost flat; smooth, dark date-brown when moist; rapidly drying to pale buff, edge bears remains of a cobwebby veil. **Gills** adnate pale grey then deep brown. **Stem** white smooth, very fragile. **Spores** 5–7 X 3–4 µm *Edibility uncertain.* **Occurring** often in large clusters on fallen logs and stumps of broadleaf trees, summer to autumn, common.

Spores 5–7 × 3–4 µm

## *Psathyrella multipedata*

**Key characters** tall thin stems all coming from one common "root". **Description: Cap** 1–3 cm, conical, then expanded; date-brown when moist, drying out to clay-buff; margin striate. **Gills** adnate, grey, then dark purple-brown. **Stem** long, thin, fused at base with many others into a rooting "tap-root". **Spores** 6–10 X 4–5 μm. *Edibility uncertain.* **Occurring** along pathsides in woods and road edges, autumn, uncommon.

*Psathyrella multipedata*

Spores 6–10 × 4–5 μm

## *Psathyrella conopilea*

**Key characters** usually solitary; tall, thin, with conical brown cap. **Description: Cap** 2–5 cm, date-brown when moist, pale buff when dry, conical. **Gills** adnate, grey-brown, then dark purple-brown. **Stem** long, thin, white and smooth, no ring, solitary. **Spores** 12–16 X 7–8 μm. *Edibility uncertain.* **Occurring** on soil in woods and gardens, summer to autumn, widespread and common. **Notes** red-brown hairs on cap visible under a hand-lens distinguish this from similar species.

Conical cap

Spores 12–16 × 7–8 μm

*Psathyrella conopilea*

Gills brown and mottled

*Panaeolina foenisecii*

## PANAEOLINA

### Panaeolina (= Panaeolus) foenisecii

**Key characters** common in garden lawns; small, often zoned brown cap. **Description: Cap** 1–3 cm, globose to convex, dark brown when moist, pale cinnamon on drying – centre often dries first, producing a bicoloured or zoned appearance. **Gills** adnate, pale to dark brown, colouring unevenly ("mottled"). **Stem** thin, smooth, brown. **Spores** black, lemon-shaped, warty, 12–15 X 7–8 µm. *Has caused mild poisoning in children.* **Occurring** in lawns, fields and grassy roadsides everywhere, summer and autumn, very common.

Spores 12–15 × 7–8 µm

## STROPHARIACEAE

This family contains some brightly coloured and beautiful fungi, including some blue and green species – both rare colours in toadstools. Nearly all have brown to purple-brown or blackish spores and are found on dead wood, wood chips or soil containing woody organic matter, or on dung. Very few are considered edible, while some (particularly in Psilocybe and Stropharia) are decidedly poisonous and/or contain hallucinogenic toxins. Other distinguishing characteristics are the adnate to sinuate gill attachments, and, usually, a veil present as a marginal veil and/or ring. Genera included here are Hypholoma, Panaeolus, Pholiota, Stropharia and Psilocybe.

*Panaeolus semiovatus*

## PANAEOLUS

### Panaeolus semiovatus (= Anellaria separata)

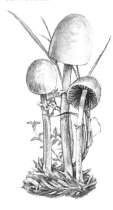

**Key characters** on dung; cap slimy, grey-brown, bell-shaped; distinct ring. **Description: Cap** 3–6 (–8), globose, then bell-shaped; smooth, pale greyish tan or buff; viscid (tacky) when moist. **Gills** adnate, mottled greyish, then black. **Stem** tall to very tall (6–16 cm), rigid, smooth, pale tan below and white above the erect membranous ring (ring sometimes torn or absent). **Spores** black, 18 X 10 µm. *Edibility uncertain; best avoided.* **Occurring** on horse dung in fields, summer to autumn, common.

Spores 18 X 10 µm

## *Panaeolus papilionaceous (= P. sphinctrinus)* ☣

**Key characters** conical grey cap with marginal "teeth".
**Description:** Cap 2–4 cm, conical, smooth; grey to greyish
brown, margin with distinct tooth-like (denticulate) fringe of
veil remnants, particularly when young. **Gills** adnate, "mottled", greyish, then almost black, edge white. **Stem** long,
thin, smooth, colour of cap; white-powdered at apex. **Spores**
black, lemon-shaped, 14–18 X 10–12 µm. *Edibility doubtful:
some related species are poisonous, sometimes hallucina-
tory.* **Occurring** in fields on or around dung, all year, common. **Notes** a very distinctive species if the colour and the
small "teeth" are both typical; occasional specimens with
the teeth missing and/or of darker
colour may prove misleading.

Dark
grey
cap

Spores 14–18 × 10–12 µm

*Panaeolus
papilionaceous*

# *HYPHOLOMA*

## *Hypholoma fasciculare* (Sulphur Tuft) ☣

**Key characters** yellow cap and sulphur-yellow gills (when
young); on deciduous wood. **Description:** Cap 4–8 cm, convex
to slightly umbonate; smooth, bright sulphur-yellow with a
tint of orange at the centre; margin with traces of veil
remnants. **Gills** sinuate, sometimes adnate; sulphur-yellow
then soon greenish and finally dark purple-brown. **Stem**
long, fibrous, pale yellow, brownish at base with
a ring zone above. **Spores** purple-brown,
5–7 X 3–5 µm. **Flesh** yellow and very
bitter. *Inedible; has a gastro-enteric irritant.* **Occurring** often in spectacular large
clumps, on stumps, logs or diseased
deciduous trees, throughout the year,
very common.

*Hypholoma
fasciculare*

Young gills
greenish

Spores 5–7 × 3–5 µm

## *Hypholoma lateritium* (= *H. sublateritium*)
### (Brick Caps, Red Caps)

*Hypholoma lateritium*

Young gills greenish

Picture to update and reposition spore in p/s

**Key characters** cap and stem large with reddish-brick (never sulphur) colours; on deciduous trees, usually later than other species. **Description:** Cap 4–10 cm, convex, then flattened; smooth, rich brick-red with paler margin; often with yellowish veil remnants at edge. **Gills** sinuate, pale yellow, then greyish lilac. **Stem** long but stouter than previous species, fibrous, pale brick-red, and with ring zone. **Spores** rich brownish lilac, 6–7 X 3–5 µm. *Usually considered inedible, although definitely eaten in the U.S.A.; there are possibly two differing strains.* **Occurring** in large clumps on deciduous trees and stumps, late autumn, frequent. **Notes** this large, attractively coloured species usually appears later than the other Hypholomas mentioned here.

Spores 6–7 × 3–5 µm

## *Hypholoma capnoides*
### (Conifer Sulphur Tuft)

Gills never yellow

Silky, shiny stem

*Hypholoma capnoides*

**Key characters** cap pale ochre-yellow; gills whitish when young; mild taste; on conifers. **Description:** Cap 4–10 cm, convex then flattened, dull, more ochre-yellow, paler at margin. **Gills** whitish at first then greyish lilac, not yellow-green, finally a dark purple-brown. **Stem** slender, pale yellow, darker brown at base, with a fine ring zone at the apex. Taste mild. Spores 7–9 X 4–5 µm. *Edibility uncertain; best avoided.* **Occurring** in large tufts on fallen conifer wood and stumps, late autumn, uncommon.

Spores 7–9 × 4–5 µm

## *Hypholoma udum*

**Key characters** stem tall and thin; cap umbonate, reddish ochre; spores purple-brown. **Description: Cap** 1–2 cm, convex to bell-shaped with an umbo at the centre; dull reddish ochre, smooth, slightly viscid. **Gills** adnexed, pale yellow-olive, then dark brown. **Stem** long, thin, pale reddish-ochre. **Spores** 14–18 × 6–7 µm. *Edibility doubtful; best avoided.* **Occurring** in bogs, marshes, etc., in *Sphagnum* moss, autumn, common. **Notes** typical of a number of small slender marsh-loving species of *Hypholoma* which are difficult to tell apart.

Spores 14–18 × 6–7 µm

*Hypholoma udum*

# *PSILOCYBE*

## *Psilocybe semilanceata* (Liberty Cap) ☠

**Key characters** sharply pointed cap; pale yellow colours, blueing flesh. **Description: Cap** 1–2 cm high, rounded-conical, margin incurved when young; with acute conical point, smooth, viscid, cuticle easily separable, pale ochre-yellow to buff with greenish tints at margin. **Gills** adnate, purple-brown. **Stem** tall, thin, wavy, white above, becoming pale yellow below; staining dark blue at base when picked. **Spores** purple-brown, 12–14 × 7 µm. *Poisonous; it contains varying amounts of hallucinogenic chemicals.* **Occurring** in grass in fields, gardens, roadsides etc., often in quite large numbers but not in tufts, late autumn, common.

*Psilocybe semilanceata*

Spores 12–14 × 7 µm

## *STROPHARIA*

### *Stropharia aeruginosa* (Verdigris Agaric)

Slimy cap

*Stropharia
aeruginosa*

**Key characters** vivid blue-green slimy cap; white scales, robust stature. **Description: Cap** 3–8 cm, convex with a low umbo, smooth and very viscid; rich blue-green slowly fading to pale yellow-green; with prominent white woolly veil remnants on cap when young. **Gills** broad, adnate, purple-brown. **Stem** stout, pale to dark blue-green, woolly-scaly below the prominent narrow ring, smooth above. **Spores** purple-brown, 7–9 X 4–5 µm. *Edibility suspect; possibly toxic.* **Occurring** in grass in woods, gardens and hedgerows, summer and autumn, uncommon. **Notes** the next species – *S. caerulea* – is by far the commonest blue-green *Stropharia*.

Spores 7–9 × 4–5 µm

### *Stropharia caerulea* (= *S. cyanea*)

*Stropharia
caerulea*

**Key characters** colours paler and bluer than Verdigris Agaric, soon washed out, few scales. **Description: Cap** 1–5 (8) cm, convex, flattening with very slight umbo, smooth, viscid; pale blue-green, fading rapidly to yellowish-buff, with very few if any white scales. **Gills** adnate, pale purple-brown. **Stem** slender, blue-green to pale yellow with blue in lower half. **Ring** thin, often almost absent. **Spores** purple-brown, 8–9 X 4–5 µm. *Possibly poisonous.* **Occurring** in gardens, woodland edges, often under nettles, or on garden mulch, disturbed soils, summer to autumn, common.

Spores 8–9 × 4–5 µm

## *Stropharia squamosa* (= Hypholoma squamosum)

**Key characters** cap convex with tiny scales; tall stem scaly below ring; spores purple-brown. **Description: Cap** 2–6 cm, convex, smooth with tiny scattered brown scales; pale ochre-yellow. **Gills** adnate, pale yellow, soon purple-brown. **Stem** tall, thin, pale ochre with scaly bands below, smooth above. **Ring** flaring, often torn. **Spores** 11–15 X 6–8 µm. *Edibility suspect.* **Occurring** on soil in beech woods containing wood chips or fallen twigs, autumn, uncommon to occasional.

*Stropharia squamosa*

Spores 11–15 × 6–8 µm

## *Stropharia semiglobata* (Dung Roundhead)

**Key characters** distinctive hemispherical cap and tall thin stem; on dung. **Description: Cap** 1–4 cm, hemispherical to slightly umbonate, not flattening with age; pale yellow to ochre, smooth, viscid. **Gills** broadly adnate, almost triangular, dark purple-brown. **Stem** long, thin, pale yellowish; below the ring viscid, then dry and shiny. **Ring** very thin, narrow, sometimes imperfect or absent. **Spores** dark brown, 18–20 X 10 µm. *Not edible.* **Occurring** on dung or dung-enriched grass, summer and autumn, common. **Notes** this easily recognized species is very variable in size.

*Stropharia semiglobata*

Spores 18–20 × 10 µm

### *Stropharia coronilla*

Crowded adnate gills

Narrow ring radially grooved above

*Stropharia coronilla*

**Key characters** mushroom-like shape with pale yellow cap; grooved ring. **Description:** Cap 2–4 cm, convex, then expanded, pale straw to ochre-yellow; smooth, not viscid as in previous species or only slightly so in wet weather. **Gills** adnate, almost sinuate, purple-brown. **Stem** short, stoutish, white or pale yellow, especially below ring. **Ring** thicker and more prominent than in *Stropharia semiglobata*, radially grooved above. **Spores** purple-brown, 8–9 X 4–5 μm. *Edible but not recommended: confusion is possible with other toxic species.* **Occurring** in fields, pastures and among dune-grasses, summer and autumn, frequent. **Notes** commonly confused with *Agaricus* species but the gills are attached, not free.

Spores 8–9 × 4–5 μm

### *Stropharia hornemannii* (= *S. depilata*)

*Stropharia hornemannii*

**Key characters** large glutinous yellow-brown cap; flesh smells unpleasant. **Description:** Cap 5–15 cm, convex then flattened with a low umbo, very viscid glutinous; pale ochre-yellow to darker brownish yellow, sometimes flushed violet when young. **Gills** adnate to sinuate, purple-brown. **Stem** medium to long, stoutish, white or pale straw-yellow, woolly-scaly up to the ring. **Ring** large, pendent. **Spores** purple-brown, 11–14 X 6–8 μm. *Not edible; probably poisonous.* **Occurring** on fallen twigs or sawdust of conifers, usually in boggy areas, autumn, uncommon to locally frequent.

Spores 11–14 × 6–8 μm

## CORTINARIACEAE

Perhaps the largest and most variable family of agarics, this group contains species of all sizes, habits and appearances from robust, clustered tree-dwellers to tiny, delicate swamp fungi. *Cortinarius* is thought to be the largest genus in the world, with many hundreds of species. Many are exceptionally beautiful and many unfortunately are rare. All the genera included here have a curtain-like veil (cortina), tawny orange or brown (often rust-brown) spores, and other anatomical features more difficult to observe.

# PHOLIOTA

*Pholiota aurivella*

Slimy cap —

Dry stem, with small, fibrillose scales —

Grows on upper tree branches

Spores 8–9 × 4–6 µm

## Pholiota aurivella (= P. cerifera)

**Key characters** often in the upper parts of trees (usually beech); large glutinous orange cap, scaly stem. **Description:** Cap 5–18 cm, convex, then soon flattened; glutinous-viscid, rich golden-yellow or orange, with darker adpressed scales, also glutinous. **Gills** broad, crowded, sinuate; pale yellow then rust-brown. **Stem** with ring zone, stout, often long and rooting; pale yellow-orange, not slimy, extremely tough and fibrous. **Spores** elliptic, rust-brown, 8–9 X 4–6 µm. Flesh tough. *Not edible.* **Occurring** clustered or solitary, usually on standing trees but also on fallen logs or stumps, summer to autumn, common. **Notes** a large, easily recognized species. The similar but much rarer *P. adiposa*, usually at base of trees or on stumps, has cap and stem slimy and more prominent warts.

## Pholiota gummosa (= P. ochrochlora)

**Key characters** glutinous pale greenish-yellow cap; stem white, floccose and sticky. **Description:** Cap 3–5 cm, distinctly viscid-glutinous, pale greenish yellow, with tiny white woolly scales soon vanishing. **Stem** white, then yellow in lower half, rust-brown at base, also floccose. **Spores** rust-brown, elliptic, 5–7 X 3–4 µm. *Edibilty unknown; best avoided.* **Occurring** on stumps but more often on buried wood, or in grassy areas, in small clusters, summer and autumn, frequent.

*Pholiota gummosa*

Spores 5–7 × 3–4 µm

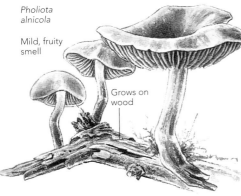

*Pholiota alnicola*

Mild, fruity smell

Grows on wood

Spores 7–9 × 4–6 μm

### Pholiota alnicola

**Key characters** in clusters at base of birch or willow; in late autumn; cap bright yellow with almost dry cuticle; pleasant odour. **Description: Cap** 4–12 cm, globose, then convex with low umbo; smooth, only slightly viscid; bright primrose to sulphur-yellow, sometimes slightly greenish at edge. **Gills** adnate, pale yellow, soon ochre to pale rust-brown. **Stem** long, often curved or twisted fibrous, pale yellow above becoming rust-brown below. No ring, but faint white veil at stem apex and on cap margin. **Flesh** from mild to bitter, tough with a strong, pleasant aromatic smell. **Spores** elliptic, rust brown, 7–9 X 4–6 μm. *Not edible.* **Occurring** often in large clumps around the base of birch trees, more rarely alders, willow or oaks, late autumn, frequent. The form on willow (variety *salicicola*) has very bitter flesh and is a duller yellow.

Smooth, sticky cap

*Pholiota highlandensis*

### Pholiota highlandensis (= P. carbonaria)
(Charcoal Pholiota)

**Key characters** always clustered on burnt soils in woodland cap small, orange-brown, slimy. **Description: Cap** 2–6 cm convex, viscid when moist, dry and shining in dry weather; rich orange-yellow to tawny ochre. **Gills** adnate, pale clay then dull brown. **Stem** dull yellow or orange browner at base; viscid below ring zone, slightly scaly. **Spores** 7–8 X 3–4 μm. *Inedible.* **Occurring** often in very large numbers, within a year or two of forest fires, bonfires etc., summer and autumn, common.

Spores 7–8 × 3–4 μm
ellipsoid

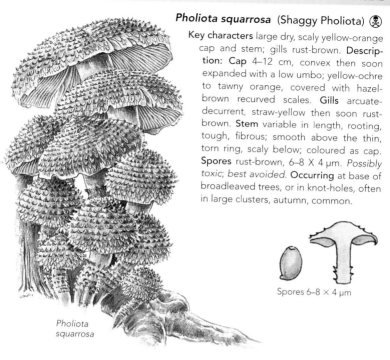

### *Pholiota squarrosa* (Shaggy Pholiota) ☒

**Key characters** large dry, scaly yellow-orange cap and stem; gills rust-brown. **Description: Cap** 4–12 cm, convex then soon expanded with a low umbo; yellow-ochre to tawny orange, covered with hazel-brown recurved scales. **Gills** arcuate-decurrent, straw-yellow then soon rust-brown. **Stem** variable in length, rooting, tough, fibrous; smooth above the thin, torn ring, scaly below; coloured as cap. **Spores** rust-brown, 6–8 × 4 μm. *Possibly toxic; best avoided.* **Occurring** at base of broadleaved trees, or in knot-holes, often in large clusters, autumn, common.

Spores 6–8 × 4 μm

*Pholiota squarrosa*

### *Pholiota flammans*

**Key characters** cap golden-yellow with paler scales; on conifer stumps and logs. **Description: Cap** 3–8 cm, convex then expanded with slight umbo, brilliant chrome to tawny yellow with paler yellow recurved scales. **Gills** crowded, adnexed, pale sulphur-yellow then soon rust-brown. **Stem** bright yellow with recurved scales below the thin ring, smooth above. **Spores** rust-brown, 4–5 × 2–3 μm. *Edibility doubtful; best avoided.* **Occurring** usually in small clumps, or solitary, on fallen conifer logs, stumps, etc., autumn, occasional to frequent.

*Pholiota flammans*

Very scaly

Spores 4–5 × 2–3 μm

93

*Pholiota myosotis*

### Pholiota myosotis

**Key characters** olive-brown viscid cap, long pale stem, usually in *Sphagnum* bogs. **Description: Cap** 2–4 cm olive-green to yellowish brown, convex then flattening or depressed at centre; smooth, viscid, paler at margin. **Gills** adnate, olive-green then rust-brown. **Stem** often very tall (7–15 cm) and slender with faint ring zone, fibrillose, dull olive-yellow with whitish powdery apex. **Spores** rust-brown, almond-shaped with small germ pore, 14–21 X 7–10 µm *Edibility doubtful, best avoided.*
**Occurring** most commonly in *Sphagnum* bogs, wet ditches etc., commonest in the north but locally common in the south also, summer to autumn, infrequent.

Spores 14–21 × 7–10 µm

## ROZITES

### Rozites caperata

**Key characters** pale clay-cinnamon cap with white "frosting", white stem; clay-coloured gills. **Description: Cap** 5–10 cm convex then soon expanded with umbo; pale ochre-yellow or brown cap with a coating of white, finely scattered veil-like minute crystals. **Gills** pale clay-brown, adnexed. **Stem** white, smooth or with thin belt of white veil. **Ring** fleshy, double, often torn, sometimes missing. **Spores** brown, finely warted, 11–14 X 7–9 µm. *Edible but not highly recommended.* **Occurring** in mixed woodlands with heathy vegetation on acid soils, autumn, commoner in Scotland and Scandinavia, occasional.

Cap covered by loose, cottony veil

Ring on stem is thick, fleshy and persistent

*Rozites caperata*

Spores 11–14 × 7–9 µm

# INOCYBE

*Inocybe* is a very distinctive genus usually easily recognized by the radially fibrillose cap and fibrous stem, dull cigar-brown spores and often pungent smell. Most are dangerously poisonous, containing muscarine compounds.

*Inocybe perlata*

## Inocybe perlata ☣

**Key characters** dull ochre cap with inturned margin; stout blackening stem. **Description: Cap** 3–10 cm, soon expanded with low umbo, smooth, with an abruptly incurved margin; pale ochre streaked with slightly darker fibrils. **Gills** crowded, adnate, cigar-brown with white edge. **Stem** rather stout (4–8 cm); white to cream-buff but darker, blackening below; finely fibrillose, not bulbous. **Spores** dull brown, elliptical, 9–12 × 6–8 μm. *As with all Inocybes, possibly dangerously poisonous.* **Occurring** at edges of woodlands, along grassy paths, roadsides etc., autumn, uncommon.

Spores 9–12 × 6–8 μm

## Inocybe erubescens (= I. patouillardii) ☣

**Key characters** white bell-shaped cap and white stem, bruising bright pinkish red; olive-brown gills. **Description: Cap** 3–8 cm, white to ivory-white, conical then bell-shaped, smooth or finely fibrillose; margin of cap often split; staining red. **Gills** whitish then pale olive-brown. **Stem** stout, tough, fibrous, white, usually not bulbous. **Spores** dull brown, bean-shaped, 10–13 × 5–7 μm. **Odour** strong, fruity or pungent. *Dangerously poisonous, even fatal.* **Occurring** in deciduous woods, especially beech on calcareous soils, summer and autumn, rare to occasional. **Notes** all parts of this fungus stain bright pinkish red when handled or bruised.

*Inocybe erubescens*

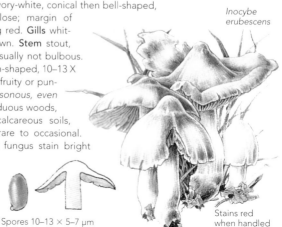

Spores 10–13 × 5–7 μm

Stains red when handled

95

### Inocybe geophylla (Common White Inocybe) 🕱

**Key characters** small white, umbonate cap and white stem clay-brown gills; sickly smell. **Description:** Cap 1–3 cm convex then soon expanded and umbonate, smooth, silky; white, slightly discoloured when older. **Gills** cream at first then dull brown. **Stem** thin, smooth, white, not bulbous. **Spores** dull brown, 8–10 X 5–6 µm. **Odour** sickly, sweetish *Poisonous; contains dangerous muscarine compounds.* **Occurring** in mixed woodlands, in leaf-litter often in small troops, autumn, common.

*Inocybe geophylla*

Spores 8–10 × 5–6 µm

*Inocybe geophylla*

### Inocybe geophylla var. lilacina 🕱

**Key characters** identical in all respects to the preceding except for the beautiful clear lilac coloration overall. **Notes:** can be distinguished from the similarly coloured Amethyst Deceiver – *Laccaria amethystina* – by its clay-brown gills.

Spores 8–10 × 5–6 µm

## *Inocybe rimosa (= I. fastigiata)* ☠

**Key characters** conical, fibrous, yellow-brown cap, strong, mouldy or soapy smell. **Description: Cap** 2–8 cm, conical then expanded and umbonate, fibrous, splitting at margin; yellowish brown. **Gills** pale clay then dull brown. **Stem** often tall and slender (4–10cm), not bulbous, whitish to ochre-yellow, fribrillose. **Spores** dull brown, bean-shaped, 8–14 X 4–7 µm. **Odour** sour, of mouldy bread or soap. *Poisonous; contains dangerous muscarine compounds.* **Occurring** in small groups in broadleaf woods, especially beech, summer to autumn, common.

*Inocybe rimosa*

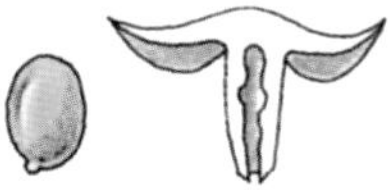
Spores 8–14 × 4–7 µm

## *Inocybe godeyi* ☠

**Key characters** white to cream, silky cap, bulbous stem and reddening flesh. **Description: Cap** 2–5 cm, conical, white to cream, silky-fibrous. **Gills** crowded, adnexed, whitish then pale clay, edge white. **Stem** white, slender, with a distinct basal bulb. **Flesh** white, staining reddish when bruised. **Odour** earthy or mealy. **Spores** dull brown, almond-shaped, 9–11 X 5–7 µm. *Poisonous; contains dangerous muscarine compounds.* **Occurring** in leaf-litter in broadleaf woods, autumn, uncommon. **Notes** often mistaken for the rarer *I. erubescens*, which is white and also stains red but does not have a bulbous stem base.

*Inocybe godeyi*

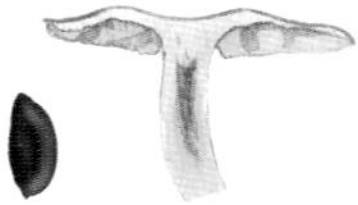
Spores 9–11 × 5–7 µm

*Inocybe adaequata*

## Inocybe adaequata (= I. jurana) ⊗

**Key characters** cap, stem and flesh with distinct flush of deep wine-purple. **Description: Cap** 4–8 cm, conical then expanded with blunt umbo; fibrillose, pale brown with dark wine-purple flush. **Gills** crowded, whitish then olive-brown, edge white. **Stem** stout, fibrous, usually not bulbous; white flushed with darker wine-purple fibrils, especially at base. **Flesh** also with flush of purple. **Spores** dull brown, bean-shaped, 10–15 × 5–7 µm. *Edibility uncertain; probably poisonous.* **Occurring** in leaf-litter in mixed woodlands, often deeply sunk in calcareous soil, autumn, uncommon.

Spores 10–15 × 5–7 µm

*Inocybe griseolilacina*

## Inocybe griseolilacina ⊗

**Key characters** brown tomentose cap with lilac stem. **Description: Cap** 1–3 cm, convex with papillate (nipple-shaped) umbo; pale brown, finely shaggy tomentose. **Gills** white then dull brown. **Stem** thin, pale lilac, finely floccose, not bulbous. **Spores** dull brown, elliptic, 8–10 × 5–6 µm. *Poisonous, contains dangerous muscarine compounds.* **Occurring** in leaf-litter in broadleaf woods, occasionally coniferous woods or along roadsides and tracks, summer to autumn, occasional.

Spores 8–10 × 5–6 µm

## Inocybe maculata 🕱

**Key characters** conical, fibrillose brown cap with patches of white veil; stem white then soon discoloured brown. **Description: Cap** 4–8 cm, usually sharply conical; fibrous, cigar-brown with pale creamy white veil patches at centre. **Gills** pale whitish then cigar-brown. **Stem** fibrillose, slender, with a slightly bulbous base. **Spores** dull brown, bean-shaped, 9–11 X 4–6 μm. **Odour** rather pungent, strong. *Poisonous, contains dangerous muscarine compounds.* **Occurring** in leaf-litter in deciduous woods and on pathsides, autumn, frequent.

Cracked cup

*Inocybe maculata*

Spores 9–11 × 4–6 μm

## Inocybe cookei 🕱

**Key characters** straw-yellow umbonate cap; marginate white bulb on stem. **Description: Cap** 2–5 cm, expanded with distinct umbo; smooth at centre, fibrillose and cracking at margin; pale straw-yellow. **Gills** whitish then dull clay-brown. **Stem** above bulb paler than cap, smooth. **Spores** dull brown, bean-shaped, 7–8 X 4–5 μm. *Poisonous; contains dangerous muscarine compounds.* **Occurring** on soil in mixed woods, autumn, frequent. **Notes** the rather similar *I. praetervisa* has irregular, lumpy spores.

Spores 7–8 × 4–5 μm

*Inocybe cookei*

### Inocybe asterospora 🧠

**Key characters** obtusely umbonate cap; marginate bulb to stem; distinctive spore shape. **Description: Cap** 3–5 cm conical-rounded, umbonate, dark brown, yellowish brown fibrillose with paler flesh exposed between the brown fibres. **Gills** adnexed, crowded, grey then cinnamon-brown. **Stem** pale brown with a distinctly marginate whitish bulb. **Spore** almost star-shaped (not oblong) with 5–8 conical knobs, 9–12 X 8–10 μm. *Poisonous.* **Occurring** in mixed woods by paths especially on clay soils, autumn, frequent. Similar in most respects to the more common *I. napipes* but that species has more elongate, less star-shaped spores.

Fibrillose cap

*Inocybe asterospora*

Spores 9–12 X 8–10 μm

### Inocybe bongardii 🧠

**Key characters** pale buff-brown scaly cap; tall stem, white flushed reddish; strong fruity odour, especially of ripe pears. **Description: Cap** 3–7 cm, convex to bell-shaped, fibrillose with scattered minute scales; pale brown with a flesh tint. **Gills** broad, whitish, soon olive-cinnamon. **Stem** tall, rather stout, fibrillose. **Flesh** stains reddish. **Spores** dull brown, bean-shaped, 10–13 X 5–7 μm. *Poisonous.* **Occurring** at edges and pathsides of mixed woods, summer and autumn, uncommon. **Notes** the similar *I. fraudans* (= *I. piriodora*) has the same odour but lacks the cap scales and is generally paler.

*Inocybe bongardii*

Tall, thick, fibrillose stem

Spores 10–13 X 5–7 μm

## Inocybe lanuginosa

**Key characters** dark brown woolly-scaly cap; woolly-scaly stem. **Description: Cap** 2–5 cm, convex then flattened, dark sepia-brown, woolly-scaly. **Gills** whitish then dull brown. **Stem** dark brown, woolly-fleecy below a ring zone, without a bulbous base. **Spores** oblong, nodulose, with 5–6 blunt knobs, 9–10 X 6–7 µm. *Poisonous.* **Occurring** in damp leaf-litter and marshy areas in coniferous woods, autumn, common.

Inocybe
lanuginosa

Spores 9–10 × 6–7 µm

## Inocybe cincinnata (= I. obscuroides) 

**Key characters** pale cigar-brown rather scaly cap with entirely lilac-violet, short stem. **Description: Cap** 2–4 cm, convex then expanded with low umbo, occasionally pale lilac at margin; woolly-fibrillose with minute, dark brown concentric scales, erect at centre, more fibrillose at margin. **Gills** whitish with lilac tint, soon cigar-brown. **Stem** not bulbous, lacking fibrils or scales, deep violet-lilac, paler buff at base. **Spores** dull brown, elliptic, 8–10 X 5–6 µm. **Odour** strong, pungent. *Poisonous.* **Occurring** leaf-litter in mixed woods, autumn, uncommon. **Notes:** the related *I. griseolilacina* has a longer, fibrillose-scaly slender stem and paler, evenly scaled cap.

Inocybe
cincinnata

Spores 8–10 × 5–6 µm

## *HEBELOMA*

### *Hebeloma mesophaeum*

*Hebeloma mesophaeum*

**Key characters** date-brown cap with distinct paler margin, ring-like veil on stem. **Description: Cap** 2–5 cm, convex then flattened, slightly viscid, clay-brown to date-brown, paler at margin. **Gills** sinuate, dull ochre-brown, fairly crowded. **Stem** whitish to brown, slender, with cottony woolly filaments on surface and a distinct ring-zone. **Flesh** dark brown in stem base. **Spores** elliptic, 9–11 X 4–5 μm. *Edibility doubtful; best avoided*; has bitter taste. **Occurring** in heathy woodlands near birch or conifers, summer to autumn, common.

Spores 9–11 × 4–5 μm

### *Hebeloma radicosum*

**Key characters** stem deeply rooting, scaly; marzipan smell. **Description: Cap** 5–10 cm, convex then umbonate, clay brown; smooth and slightly viscid with faint, slightly darker flattened scales scattered on surface. **Gills** sinuate, whitish then clay-brown. **Stem** stout and bulbous when young but soon elongating, difficult to pick due to the rooting base, with scaly bands or belts below the distinct ring zone. **Spores** dull brown, elliptic, 8–9 X 5 μm. **Odour** of marzipan especially strong in gills when bruised. *Edibility doubtful; best avoided.* **Occurring** associated with underground rodent and mole nests, autumn, uncommon.

Sticky cap

*Hebeloma radicosum*

Spores 8–9 × 5 μm

## *Hebeloma crustuliniforme* (Poison Pie) ☠️

**Key characters** pale buff coloration; stout stem; often strong smell of radish. **Description:** Cap 3–6 cm, convex then expanded with low umbo, margin inrolled when young; cuticle smooth and slightly viscid when moist. **Gills** sinuate, whitish then dull clay-brown, exuding droplets in wet weather. **Stem** variable but usually rather short, stout, white with "powdery" apex. **Spores** cigar-brown, almond-shaped, 10–12 X 5–7 µm. *Poisonous; may cause vomiting, cramp and diarrhoea.* **Occurring** in mixed woods, gardens and hedgerows, usually with birch and other broadleaf trees, late autumn, common.

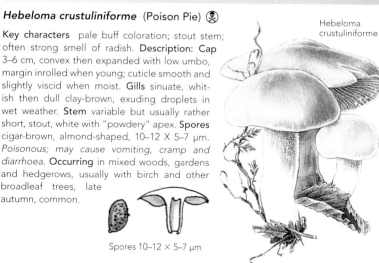

Hebeloma crustuliniforme

Spores 10–12 × 5–7 µm

## *Hebeloma sinapizans* ☠️

**Key characters** large pink-brown cap; stem with scaly zones. **Description:** Cap 5–15 cm, convex then soon flattened, smooth and usually dry; pale tan to fleshy-buff. **Gills** sinuate, narrow, whitish then dull brown. **Stem** tall, stout, slightly bulbous; white with floccose-scaly zones. **Spores** ovate, 10–13 X 6–8 µm. *Poisonous; causes gastro-intestinal upsets.* **Occurring** in mixed woods, hedgerows, etc., autumn, may be locally common on calcareous soils.

Slightly sticky cap

Finely toothed gill edge

Section always shows V-shaped flesh at top of stem cavity

Spores 10–13 × 6–8 µm

Hebeloma sinapizans

103

### Hebeloma sacchariolens

*Hebeloma sacchariolens*

**Key characters** buff-cream cap; strong sweet or sickly smell. **Description: Cap** 2–5 cm, convex then flattened; smooth and slightly sticky; cream-white to dull buff or brown with age. **Gills** sinuate, whitish then clay-brown to cigar-brown. **Stem** white, darker reddish-brown below. **Spores** ovate 8–9 X 4–5 µm. **Odour** strong, sweet, of fruit bubblegum, or soap. *Edibility doubtful; best avoided.* **Occurring** in mixed woods and heaths, usually in small groups, autumn, common and widespread.

Spores 8–9 × 4–5 µm

## CORTINARIUS

All members of *Cortinarius* have rust-brown spores but the genus is often divided into groups (subgenera) according to certain features: *Myxacium*, medium to large species with viscid caps and stems; *Phlegmacium*, large fleshy species with viscid or moist caps but dry stems; *Cortinarius*, medium to large, with dry, scaly to moist caps, and dry stems, sometimes robust; *Dermocybe*, small to medium-sized, rarely large, caps dry, silky or fibrillose, often yellow, orange to reddish, or greenish-yellow, stems slender and dry; *Sericeocybe*, small to medium-sized, caps silky-fibrillose, not hygrophanous (changing colour as dries), sometimes sticky in wet weather and then often robust, stem bulbous; and *Telamonia*, small, usually distinctly hygrophanous.

*Cortinarius delibutus*

### Cortinarius (Myxacium) delibutus

**Key characters** clear yellow cap and stem, both viscid, young gills and stem apex bluish violet. **Description: Cap** 5–10 cm, convex then expanded

Spores 7–9 × 6–7 µm

104

smooth, sticky; clear golden to brownish yellow. **Gills** sinuate, bluish-lilac when young then soon rust-brown. **Stem** tall, slender and slightly bulbous; pale yellow below and sticky below the distinct ring zone. **Spores** subglobose, 7–9 X 6–7 μm. *Inedible; taste bitter.* **Occurring** under birch and aspen on boggy soil, autumn, occasional to common and widespread.

## Cortinarius (Myxacium) mucifluoides (= C. pseudosalor)

**Key characters** shiny, dull yellow-ochre to brown; slimy violet-tinted tapered stem. **Description: Cap** 3–10 cm, rounded-conical then expanded, sticky when wet, dull ochre-brown to yellowish. **Gills** broad, adnate, pale violaceous then soon rust-brown, strongly interconnected with cross-veins. **Stem** cylindrical, tapering, slightly rooting; sticky below an apical ring zone and often strongly tinted violet below with belt-like zones. **Spores** wartyrough, rust-brown, 12–15 X 7–8 μm. **Odour** of honey in the flesh of the stem base. *Edibility uncertain and best avoided.* **Occurring** under beeches especially on clay soils, summer and autumn, common and widespread in southern England.

*Cortinarius mucifluoides*

Spores 12–15 × 7–8 μm

## Cortinarius (Myxacium) ochroleucus

**Key characters** pale cream-ochre cap and stem; only very slightly sticky; taste bitter. **Description: Cap** 3–8 cm, convex with a low umbo, pale cream to ochre; smooth, silky-fibrillose to slightly sticky. **Gills** pale yellow-ochre then rust-brown. **Stem** tapering, almost white, slightly sticky, becoming dry and silky. **Spores** 7–8 X 4–5 μm. *Not recommended for eating; very bitter-tasting.* **Occurring** in beech woods on clay soils, autumn, uncommon.

*Cortinarius ochroleucus*

Spores 7–8 × 4–5 μm

Tapering stem base

*Cortinarius elegantissimus*

## Cortinarius (Phlegmacium) elegantissimus

**Key characters** bright golden colours; strong aromatic smell; stem with large flattened basal bulb. **Description** Cap 4–10 cm, convex then expanded; sticky when wet, bright golden orange, smooth. **Gills** yellow when young then soon rust-brown. **Stem** rather tall, stout, with large basal bulb; fibrillose sulphur-yellow below, becoming paler above. **Flesh** sulphur-yellow in stem base, almost white above and in cap. **Spores** lemon-shaped, 12–15 X 7–8 µm. **Odour** strong, aromatic. *Edibility doubtful, best avoided.* **Occurring** under beeches on chalky soil, late autumn, occasional to frequent, often in rings around trees.

Spores 12–15 × 7–8 µm

*Cortinarius glaucopus*

## Cortinarius (Phlegmacium) glaucopus

**Key characters** smooth, sticky, rusty-brown cap (greenish when young); stem apex and young gills bluish; marginate bulb. **Description: Cap** 6–12 cm, convex then soon flattening; fleshy, edge wavy; smooth, slightly sticky, greenish to ochre then rust-brown, but variable. **Gills** crowded, sinuate, azure-blue then soon brownish. **Stem** rather short, swollen at base with marginate bulb; ochre or brownish below, lilac-blue at apex; fibrillose with clinging veil remnants, often stained rust brown with spores. **Spores** elliptic, 9–10 X 5–6 µm. *Edibility uncertain; best avoided.* **Occurring** in mixed woods, sometimes in large numbers on calcareous soils, late autumn, occasional to frequent.

Spores 9–10 × 5–6 µm

## *Cortinarius (Phlegmacium) caerulescens*

**Key characters** dark bluish-violet cap; stem
with basal bulb; deep bluish gills.
**Description: Cap** 5–8 cm, convex
then expanded and slightly
umbonate, deep bluish-violet
then fading to ochre at centre,
slightly sticky. **Gills** deep bluish
at first then rust-brown. **Stem**
cylindrical with prominent
basal bulb, violet-blue with
pale yellowish bulb. **Flesh** soft,
lavender. **Spores** 9–11 X 5–7 μm.
*Edibility uncertain; best avoided.*
**Occurring** in mixed woods on chalky
soils, autumn, occasional.

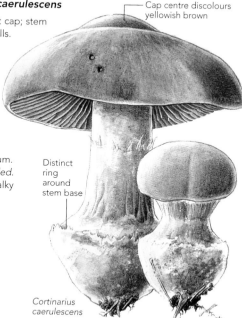

Cap centre discolours
yellowish brown

Distinct
ring
around
stem base

*Cortinarius
caerulescens*

Spores 9–11 × 5–7 μm

## *Cortinarius (Phlegmacium) purpurascens*

**Key characters** sticky date-brown cap with bluish-violet stem;
flesh bruising deep violet. **Description: Cap** 6–15 cm,
convex then expanded and flattened; yellowish to
dark date-brown, occasionally with violet tint
at margin, quite sticky. **Gills** deep violet at first
then cinnamon to rust-brown. **Stem** rather stout,
bulbous, often with a clearly marginate bulb but
variable; fibrillose, pale violet bruising or scratching deep violet; ring zone at apex. **Spores** 8–11 X
5–7 μm. *Edibility uncertain, best avoided.* **Occurring**
in mixed woods, especially conifers or birch, summer to autumn, frequent to common everywhere.

*Cortinarius
purpurascens*

Spores 8–11 × 5–7 μm
non-amyloid

107

Pale violet cap fades with age

Silky cortina leaves a ring-like zone on stem

Stem has a swollen base

*Cortinarius alboviolaceus*

### Cortinarius (Sericeocybe) alboviolaceus

**Key characters** pale lilac-white colours over-all. **Description: Cap** 3–8 cm, convex then expanded and umbonate, silky-fibrillose; pale bluish lilac when fresh, fading to white or greyish with age. **Gills** greyish lilac then rust-brown, rather broad, distant. **Stem** swollen, clavate, bluish lilac above, paler below reaching up to a cobweb-like veil. **Flesh** bluish, especially in stem. **Spores** ovate, 7–9 X 6–7 μm. *Edibility uncertain; best avoided.* **Occurring** under beech and oak; autumn, frequent to common and widespread everywhere.

Spores 7–9 × 6–7 μm

*Cortinarius armillatus*

Stem with 1 or more red zones

Broad, widely spaced gills

### Cortinarius (Sericeocybe) armillatus
(Red-banded Cortinarius)

**Key characters** brick-red cap; pale stem with red belts **Description: Cap** 5–12 cm, convex then expanded and flattened; dry, fibrillose, brick-red to tawny orange when old. **Gills** whitish then cinnamon-brown. **Stem** tall, swollen-clavate; pale whitish brown with three or four reddish belts running obliquely round. **Spores** almond-shaped, 9–12 X 5–6 μm. *Edible but not recommended.* **Occurring** under birch in bracken and heath vegetation, summer and autumn, frequent to common and widespread everywhere.

Spores 9–12 × 5–6 μm

## *Cortinarius (Sericeocybe) anomalus*

**Key characters** gills and stem apex violet when young, stem with faint yellowish bands. **Description: Cap** 3–7 cm, convex-umbonate then soon flattened; smooth or very slightly fibrillose; dull greyish-clay or reddish brown, with a slight violet tint when young. **Gills** at first pale violet then soon cinnamon brown. **Stem** long, clavate; violet at apex when young, pale yellowish cream below; surface with pale yellow-cream bands visible at certain angles. **Spores** ovate, 7–9 X 6–7 μm. *Edibility uncertain; best avoided.* **Occurring** in leaf-litter of birch, beech or oaks, autumn, common everywhere.

*Cortinarius anomalus*

Gills turn rusty brown

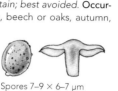

Spores 7–9 × 6–7 μm

## *Cortinarius (Sericeocybe) pholideus*

**Key characters** hazel-brown scaly cap and stem; stem with lilac tints when young. **Description: Cap** 3–8 cm, dark brown, convex with low umbo, covered with minute recurved, pointed scales, darker than surface underneath. **Gills** crowded, broad, lilac at first then soon cinnamon-brown. **Stem** tall, rather slender, lower half with scales like cap, upper half at first tinged lilac from the cortina. **Spores** elliptical, 6–7 X 4–5 μm. *Edibility doubtful; best avoided.* **Occurring** in leaf-litter under birches, autumn, occasional to frequent and widespread.

Tiny scales point upwards

Gills and stem apex at first blue-violet

Spores 6–7 × 4–5 μm

*Cortinarius pholideus*

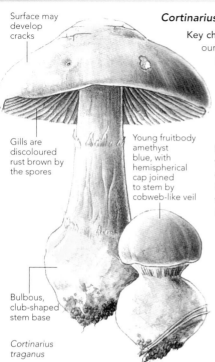

Surface may develop cracks

Gills are discoloured rust brown by the spores

Young fruitbody amethyst blue, with hemispherical cap joined to stem by cobweb-like veil

Bulbous, club-shaped stem base

*Cortinarius traganus*

### Cortinarius (Sericeocybe) traganus

**Key characters** stout lilac-blue fungus, discolouring patchily to ochre; strong goaty-gas smell. **Description: Cap** 5–10 cm, convex to broadly umbonate, thick-fleshed, dry, smooth, silky; often cracking, pale bluish-lilac fading to yellowish ochre. **Gills** broad, adnexed, widely spaced; ochre-yellow then rust-cinnamon. **Stem** stout, clavate-bulbous, lilac-blue to violet with remains of woolly veil around base and middle. **Flesh** in cap ochre-yellow, becoming darker in stem to rust-brown at base. **Odour** very strong of goats or acetylene gas. **Spores** elliptic, 8–10 X 5–6 µm. *Inedible.* **Occurring** in northern conifer woods, autumn, occasional to frequent.

Spores 8–10 × 5–6 µm

### Cortinarius (Cortinarius) violaceus

**Key characters** entire fruitbody an intense deep violet; velvety-scaly cap. **Description: Cap** 5–15 cm, convex then expanded; dry, velvety, deep and intense violet to violet-black. **Gills** broad, distant, violet then rust-brown. **Stem** tall, fibrillose, swollen at base, also violet. **Spores** 11–14 X 7–9 µm. **Odour** distinctive of cedar wood. *Edible but best avoided.* **Occurring** in mixed woodlands, especially birch, autumn, rare to uncommon, very localised although widespread.

*Cortinarius violaceus*

Spores 11–14 × 7–9 µm

## *Cortinarius (Cortinarius) orellanus* ☠

**Key characters** rounded, orange or orange-brown cap and often spindle-shaped yellow stem; gills widely spaced. **Description: Cap** 3–5 cm, convex, and often umbonate, dry, fibrillose, with slightly scurfy-scaly surface; the minute scales are a darker more olive brown than the rest of the cap. **Gills** widely spaced, broad, yellowish orange then soon cinnamon-brown. **Stem** often spindle-shaped, occasionally clavate; yellowish, fibrillose, cobweb-like cortina visible between cap and stem when young. **Spores** subglobose, 8–11 X 5–8 µm. *Highly poisonous, even fatal, apparently often many days after eating the fungus.* **Occurring** in mixed woodlands, especially birch and oaks, autumn, uncommon to rare, mainly found in the west of Britain and Europe.

*Cortinarius orellanus*

Spores 8–11 × 5–8 µm

## *Cortinarius (Telamonia) torvus* (Sheathed Cortinarius)

**Key characters** swollen stem with white, stocking-like sheath. **Description: Cap** 4–10 cm, dry, silky-fibrillose; reddish brown to dark brown. **Gills** dull violet when young and finally cinnamon-brown, widely spaced. **Stem** quite tall, swollen below, pale violet above, brownish cream below with a white sheath of stocking-like veil on lower half, with cobweb-like veil above. **Spores** elliptic, 8–10 X 5–6 µm. *Edibility doubtful; best avoided.* **Occurring** under mixed woods of beech and oak, autumn, uncommon.

Dry cap

Spores 8–10 × 5–6 µm

*Cortinarius torvus*

*Cortinarius hinnuleus*

## Cortinarius (Telamonia) hinnuleus

**Key characters** umbonate ochre cap; stem white-zoned; strong earthy smell or of gas. **Description: Cap** 3–6 cm, convex with broad umbo; smooth, dry, often radially wrinkled; yellow-ochre to dull brown, paler at edge. **Gills** ochre then soon rust-brown; broad and very widely spaced. **Stem** equal or tapering downwards, pale whitish ochre, a distinct white belt-like zone around middle and a cobweb-like cortina above this. **Spores** ovate, 6–9 X 4–5 μm. *Edibility very doubtful; best avoided.* **Occurring** in grass under deciduous trees, especially oak, often in large troops, summer to autumn, occasional to common.

Spores 6–9 × 4–5 μm

*Cortinarius decipiens*

## Cortinarius (Telamonia) decipiens

**Key characters** small bay-brown cap, pale silvery-lilac stem. **Description: Cap** 1–4 cm, bell-shaped, with central umbo or point, bay-brown, drying paler, smooth and silky. **Gills** thin, cinnamon to rust-brown. **Stem,** slender and elegant, pale silvery-lilac with faint ring-zone at the apex. **Spores** elliptic 8–9 x 5–6 μm. *Edibility uncertain; best avoided.* **Occurring** in damp places under birch and willow, summer to late autumn, common and widespread.

Pale, shiny stem

Spores 8–9 × 5–6 μm

# GYMNOPILUS

## Gymnopilus penetrans

**Key characters** small yellow-orange caps and stems; gills spotted rust-brown. **Description:** Cap 1–5 cm, convex then expanded; dry, slightly scaly-fibrillose to almost smooth; golden tawny with paler veil remnants at margin. **Gills** thin and crowded, golden yellow but soon with rust-coloured stains. **Stem** rather short, slender, yellow-orange, paler above and usually with white base; with a very faint ring zone of veil at apex. **Spores** rich orange, elliptic, slightly warty, 7–8 X 4–5 µm. *Inedible; usually very bitter.* **Occurring** on twigs, chips or logs of birches and conifers, summer and autumn, common or even abundant.

Smooth, dry cap surface

Grows on fallen twigs and stumps

*Gymnopilus penetrans*

Spores 7–8 × 4–5 µm

## Gymnopilus junonius (= Pholiota spectabilis)

**Key characters** large orange cap and stem with thick ring; in clumps. **Description:** Cap 5–15 cm, convex then expanded; dry, fibrillose, sometimes slightly scaly; rich bright orange. **Gills** thin, narrow and crowded, yellow then rust-orange. **Stem** large, swollen below and tapering at base, fibrillose-scaly, orange with a membranous ring at apex. **Spores** ovate, rust-orange, 8–10 X 5–6 µm. *Inedible and possibly hallucinogenic; flesh extremely tough and fibrous as well as very bitter.* **Occurring** at the base of deciduous trees or on stumps and logs, summer and autumn, common. This is one of the commonest and most spectacular of the fungi found on wood.

*Gymnopilus junonius*

Gills are yellow at first, then rust-coloured

Spores 8–10 × 5–6 µm

# CREPIDOTUS

## Crepidotus mollis

*Crepidotus mollis*

Tiny lateral stem

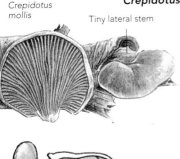

Spores 6–8 × 4–6 μm

**Key characters** gelatinous shell- or kidney-shaped cap with tiny lateral stem. **Description: Cap** 2–7 cm, pale ochre to almost white when dry, with a thick gelatinous cuticle, shell or kidney-shaped. **Gills** crowded, thin, clay-brown to cinnamon. **Stem** very short, almost absent, lateral from the rear edge of the cap. The whole fungus is horizontal, bracket-like. **Spores** clay-brown, smooth, 6–8 × 4–6 μm. *Edibility uncertain; best avoided.* **Occurring** on stumps and logs of deciduous trees, especially oaks, summer and autumn, common everywhere.

# KUEHNEROMYCES

## Kuehneromyces (= Galerina, = Pholiota) mutabilis

**Key characters** brown cap changes colour as it dries, often bicoloured; stem scaly; in clumps. **Description: Cap** 3–8 cm, convex then flattened with a low umbo, smooth; rich date-brown when wet then drying out a pale chamois-leather colour, usually with the umbo retaining the darker, moist colouring long after the rest has dried; may have a darker margin. **Gills** adnate, pale ochre then cinnamon-brown. **Stem** dark brown and scaly below the ring, paler and smooth above. **Ring** membranous, flaring, usually rust-brown from spore deposit. **Spores** ovate, 6–8 × 4–5 μm. *Edible and excellent, but note that this species is found in clumps – similar but solitary species can be poisonous.* **Occurring** on stumps of deciduous trees, summer and autumn, common and widespread.

*Kuehneromyces mutabilis*

Spores 6–8 × 4–5 μm

# GALERINA

## Galerina sphagnorum

**Key characters** small cap, striate at edge; pale orange colours; always in *Sphagnum* moss. **Description: Cap** 1–3 cm, hemispherical, with central pimple or umbo, yellow-brown to orange, smooth with striated edge. **Gills** broad, distant, adnate, pale tawny yellow then rust-brown. **Stem** slender, smooth, pale yellow-brown, often wavy-irregular. **Spores** rust-brown, slightly warty, 8–12 X 5–7 µm. *Edibility uncertain but too small to be worth considering.* **Occurring** in *Sphagnum* moss in bogs and heaths, spring to autumn, common. **Notes:** there are a few very similar species, also found in mosses, which are difficult to separate without a microscope.

*Galerina sphagnorum*

Spores 8–12 × 5–7 µm

# PHAEOLEPIOTA

## Phaeolepiota (= Pholiota) aurea

**Key characters** large scurfy-granular orange cap; tall granular orange stem with large ring. **Description: Cap** 5–20 cm, convex then flattened with low umbo, tawny to golden orange-brown, with a granular, scurfy surface. **Gills** adnexed, pale ochre-yellow then rust-coloured. **Stem** tall, with a sheath- or stocking-like granular veil covering stem and flaring outwards to form the large ring, tawny brown; stem apex smooth, paler. **Spores** ochre, smooth, warty, 11–14 X 4–5 µm. *Edible but poor; not recommended.* **Occurring** on bare soil, grass or herbage in mixed woodlands, often along pathsides in large troops, autumn, rare to occasional mostly in southern England and central Europe.

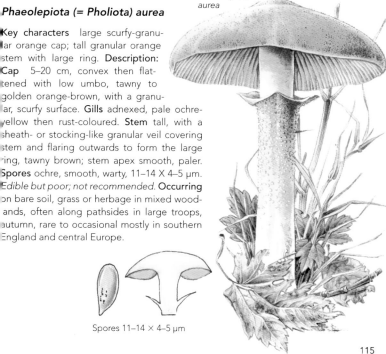

*Phaeolepiota aurea*

Spores 11–14 × 4–5 µm

## *ENTOLOMATACEAE*

The fungi of this large group all have a pink coloration to the spore deposit. The spores are unusual in being very angular and polygonal, rather like some crystals in geological deposits. Gill attachment varies between genera from sinuate or emarginate to adnate. Some colours not usually found within the fungi (blue, violet, green) are commonly found in this attractive family. Many former genera are now included in one large genus – Entoloma, although the latter is divided into several subgenera. None are recommended for the table and some species are decidedly toxic, causing severe gastro-intestinal disturbance.

### *ENTOLOMA*

#### *Entoloma sinuatum*  (= *E. lividum*)
(Livid Entoloma) ☠

**Key characters** large wavy-edged yellow-grey cap; gills yellowish then pink. **Description: Cap** 5–20 cm, pale yellowish grey to fawn cap, which is smooth and evenly coloured margin at first inrolled and then expanded and wavy. **Stem** rather stout, about the same length as cap diameter, white **Spores** 9–11 X 8–9 μm. *Poisonous, causing severe sickness and diarrhoea, but rarely fatal.* **Occurring** in woodland clearings, in deciduous woods in early autumn and rather uncommon. **Notes:** similar in many respects to the more common *E clypeatum* illustrated below, but the latter differs in its darker cap and greyish-pink gills.

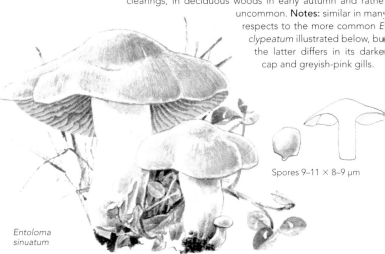

Spores 9–11 × 8–9 μm

*Entoloma sinuatum*

## Entoloma clypeatum

**Key characters** under fruit or rose bushes; irregularly shaped and unevenly coloured cap. **Description: Cap** 3–7 cm, expanded with an obtuse umbo, edge of cap often wavy, irregular; olive-grey to yellowish brown with darker, irregular streaks. **Gills** sinuate, pale grey then soon flesh-pink. **Stem** short, stout, white, flesh fibrous. **Spores** 9–12 X 7–9 μm. *Edibility uncertain; best avoided, as there are similar and very dangerous poisonous species.* **Odour** floury, of new meal or of cucumber. **Occurring** in fields and gardens, associated with rose bushes and fruit trees, spring, summer and sometimes early autumn, occasional to frequent.

*Entoloma clypeatum*

Spores 9–12 × 7–9 μm

*Entoloma porphyrophaeum*

## Entoloma porphyrophaeum

**Key characters** tall, fibrous, with wine-purple tints in the brown cap and stem. **Description: Cap** 3–8 cm, bell-shaped then expanded, umbonate; fibrillose, brown with distinct wine-coloured, lavendar tint. **Gills** sinuate to emarginate (notched near stem), whitish brown then flesh pink. **Stem** tall, fibrous, often twisted, purplish brown with white base. **Spores** 10–13 X 6–7 μm. *Edibility doubtful; best avoided.* **Occurring** in fields and woodland clearings often in deep grass, summer and autumn, occasional.

Spores 10–13 × 6–7 μm

*Entoloma rhodopolium*

Spores 8–10 × 6–8 μm

## *Entoloma rhodopolium* 💀

**Description:** grey-brown cap drying much paler; white stem; smells and tastes like new meal. **Description:** Cap 3–7 cm, expanded and umbonate then flattened, margin slightly inrolled; greyish brown to yellowish brown but paler, ash-grey and silky when dry. **Gills** emarginate, white then flesh-pink. **Stem** slender, cylindrical, white to pale greyish, fibrous, fragile. **Spores** 8–10 × 6–8 μm. *Poisonous although not deadly; causes gastric upsets.* **Odour** of new meal or cucumber. **Occurring** in grass and leaf-litter in deciduous woods, summer and autumn, common and very widespread.

## *Entoloma rhodopolium forma nidorosum* 💀

**Key characters** greyish cap and slender stem; strong smell of bleach. **Description:** Cap 2–4 cm, rounded then flattened, sometimes depressed at centre; fragile, smooth and hygrophanous; pale fawn to grey-brown. **Gills** adnate, pale greyish then pink. **Stem** long, slender, fragile, almost white. **Spores** 8–10 × 6–8 μm polygonal. **Odour** usually strong of bleach or strong alkalis. *Poisonous.* **Occurring** in mixed woodlands in rather damp, boggy places, autumn, frequent. **Notes:** this distinctive form is often treated as a good species in its own right.

*Entoloma rhodopolium forma nidorosum*

Spores 8–10 × 6–8 μm polygonal

## Entoloma nitidum

**Key characters** conical-umbonate cap and stem both deep blue; in damp woods. **Description:** Cap 2–5 cm, conical then expanded and umbonate; fibrillose to minutely scaly at centre; deep indigo blue. **Gills** broad, emarginate, white then pink. **Stem** long, tapering and "rooting", fibrous; blue as cap but paler, whitish at base. **Spores** 7–9 X 6–8 μm. *Edibility uncertain; best avoided, as are all toadstools in this family.* **Occurring** on boggy soil under birch and pines, autumn, uncommon.

Cap often slightly scaly in the centre

*Entoloma nitidum*

Spores 7–9 × 6–8 μm

## Entoloma sericellum

**Key characters** small white cap and stem, pink gills, growing in grass. **Description:** Cap 2–3 cm, rounded to bell-shaped then soon flattened and depressed at centre; dry and smooth white to dull ivory. **Gills** broad, widely spaced, slightly decurrent, white then pale pink. **Stem** long, slender, white and translucent. **Spores** 9–12 X 5–8 μm, polygonal. *Edibility uncertain; best avoided.* **Occurring** in open fields and pastures, summer and autumn, occasional to frequent.

*Entoloma sericellum*

Spores 9–12 × 5–8 μm
polyagonal

## TRICHOLOMATACEAE

A very large and diverse group, most of this large family
have a white to cream or pale pinkish spore print but many
genera differ markedly in appearance, habitat, and chemical make-up. For example, Tricholoma consists entirely of
terrestrial, rather fleshy, fibrous species with sinuate gills
and white spores, while Panellus is found on trees and logs
with almost stemless brackets, and has pinkish clay spores.
These differences are reconciled by similarities in development and genetics.

## CLITOPILUS

### Clitopilus prunulus (The Miller)

*Clitopilus
prunulus*

**Key characters** soft white cap and stem with "kid-glove"
texture; pink spores; mealy smell. **Description:** Cap 2–8 cm, convex then expanded
and funnel-shaped, margin irregular, wavy,
white to pale cream, finely velvety. **Gills**
more or less decurrent, crowded, white
then pinkish. **Stem** from usually very short
to medium length, white, fibrous. **Spores**
fusiform with longitudinal ribs, pink, 10–14
X 4–6 μm. *Edible and good.* **Occurring** on
soil in mixed woodlands, autumn, common
everywhere.

Spores 10–14 × 4–6 μm

## TRICHOLOMA

### Tricholoma equestre (= T. flavovirens)

*Tricholoma
equestre*

**Key characters** greenish-yellow cap, centre reddish;
gills, stem sulphur-yellow; under conifers. **Description**
Cap 5–12 cm, convex then expanded with low umbo,
smooth, sometimes slightly sticky; sulphur to olive-yellow; minutely scaly, reddish towards the centre. **Gills**
rather crowded, sinuate-emarginate, sulphur yellow.
**Stem** stout, fibrillose, paler yellow. **Flesh** yellowish
with a slight mealy smell. **Spores** white, 5–8 X
4–5 μm. *Edible and widely eaten in Europe.*
**Notes**: the Death Cap (Amanita phalloides,
which sometimes has a similarly coloured cap,

Spores 5–8 × 4–5 μm

much softer-fleshed and has both a ring and volva.
**Occurring** in conifer woods, autumn, occasional in
Scotland, rarer further south.

## Tricholoma columbetta

**Key characters** pure almost dazzling
silky white, sometimes with small blue
stains when old; no odour. **Description:**
**Cap** 6–10 cm, convex then expanded
with a low umbo at centre, slightly
fibrillose at the margin, pure white. **Gills**
crowded, sinuate, white. **Stem** tall, fibrous,
rooting, pure white. **Spores** white, 5–7 X 4–5
µm. *Edible and good.* **Occurring** in leaf-litter of
beech woods, preferring calcare-
ous soils, autumn, occasional.

*Tricholoma
columbetta*

Satiny white
cap surface

Broad
white
gills

Spores 5–7 × 4–5 µm

Rooting
stem
base

## Tricholoma albobrunneum

Cap becomes sticky
in wet weather

**Key characters** slightly viscid chestnut-
brown cap; often bicoloured stem; under
conifers. **Description: Cap** 5–10 cm, convex
then expanded, margin incurved, often
scalloped; smooth and slightly viscid,
finely fibrillose, chestnut-brown. **Gills** sinuate-
emarginate, white, rather crowded, soon spotted
reddish-brown. **Stem** stout, cylindrical, fibrous;
white above, brownish below, often clearly
defined like a band. **Spores** white, elliptic, 4–6
X 4 µm. *Edibility uncertain, best avoided many
brown species of Tricholoma are toxic to some
degree.* **Occurring** in rings under conifers,
autumn, occasional to frequent.

Stem is
whitish
at apex,
red-brown
below

*Tricholoma
albobrunneum*

Grows
well in
sandy
soil

Spores 4–6 × 4 µm

121

Sticky cap

## *Tricholoma ustale* 🕱

**Key characters** brown cap and stem, reddish-spotted gills, strong mealy smell. **Description: Cap** 3–10 cm, convex then expanded with margin often incurved when young; slightly viscid, rich chestnut to bay-brown. **Gills** white, sinuate, becoming spotted with reddish-brown stains. **Stem** slender to medium thickness with tapering base, fibrillose; white above and pruinose, becoming darker brownish at base. **Flesh** reddening slightly. **Odour** strong, mealy-cucumber. **Spores** white, 5–6 X 3–4 µm. *Edibility doubtful; possibly toxic, not recommended.* **Occurring** in mixed broadleaf woods, autumn, occasional to frequent and widespread.

Whitish gills spot red

*Tricholoma ustale*

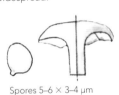

Spores 5–6 × 3–4 µm

## *Tricholoma fulvum (= T. flavobrunneum)*

**Key characters** reddish-brown streaky cap and stem; spotted gills, yellow stem flesh. **Description: Cap** 4–10 cm, convex and rather umbonate, then expanded; fibrillose or with radial streaks, viscid in damp weather; reddish brown. **Gills** sinuate, yellowish with brown spotting. **Stem** rather long, fibrillose, reddish brown. **Flesh** in stem yellow, in cap whitish, with mealy odour and taste. **Spores** white, 5–7 X 3–5 µm. *Edibility uncertain; best avoided.* **Occurring** usually under birches in peaty boggy soil, late summer to autumn, common everywhere.

*Tricholoma fulvum*

Pale yellow gills are spotted red

Unpleasant smell of rancid meal

Spores 5–7 × 3–5 µm

## Tricholoma orirubens

**Key characters** dark, almost black cap, scaly-squamulose; pink stains often (not always) on gills; strong floury smell and taste. **Description: Cap** 2–7 cm, convex then expanded usually with an umbo; deep grey to black with numerous fine scales. **Gills** sinuate, white often with black edging and frequently turning rose-pink where eaten by insects etc. or otherwise damaged. **Stem** smooth and white or sometimes with grey punctae. **Spores** white, 4–6 (7) × 3–4 µm. *Edible and good.* **Occurring** in coniferous woodlands, autumn, occasional to common.

*Tricholoma orirubens*

Spores 4–6(7) × 3–4 µm

## Tricholoma pardinum ☣

**Key characters** coarsely scaled grey-brown cap, often large; gills with olive tints, exuding droplets in damp weather. **Description: Cap** 9–20 cm, convex then expanded and broadly umbonate, margin inrolled; usually with rather large, woolly scales darker grey-brown on a pale brown or grey background. **Gills** sinuate, white to slightly yellowish, finally with olivaceous tints. **Stem** stout, fleshy, fibrous, with a white tomentose surface above becoming slightly darker, brownish, below. **Flesh** smells slightly of flour. **Spores** white, large, 8–10 × 5–6 µm. *Dangerously poisonous, although not usually deadly, causing severe gastro-enteritis.* **Occurring** in conifer woods chiefly in mountainous regions of continental Europe, not yet found in Britain, autumn, occasional.

*Tricholoma pardinum*

Spores 8–10 × 5–6 µm

123

*Tricholoma
portentosum*

## *Tricholoma portentosum*

**Key characters** dark smooth ca
with very fine fibrils; yellowis
gills and stem; stout build; n
distinctive smell. **Description**
Cap 5–10 cm, convex then soo
expanded and often umbonate
smooth with fine radiating fibril
dark greyish to greenish brown, darke
almost black, at centre, where the fibri
go black. **Gills** white or yellowish, sinuate
**Stem** stout, smooth white or tinged yellow
**Spores** white, 5–6 X 3–5 µm. *Edible an*
*delicious.* **Occurring** often below conifer
but sometimes under mature beeches, lat
autumn, uncommon to locally frequent.

Spores 5–6 × 3–5 µm

## *Tricholoma virgatum*

*Tricholoma
virgatum*

**Key characters** conical, grey cap with radiating fibres, sharp
bitter taste, gills with jagged edge. **Description: Cap** 5–7 cm
bell-shaped, usually with distinctly pointed centre; smooth
shiny, ash-grey with fine radiating darker fibres. **Gills** pale
greyish white with a jagged margin (use a hand-lens). **Stem**
rather slender; white at apex, often greyish at base wit
grey-white flesh. **Taste** of flesh sharp-bitter. **Spores** 5–
X 4–5 µm. *Edibility uncertain; best avoided.* **Occu**
**ring** in mixed woods in leaf-litter, late autumn, occa
sional to frequent and widespread.

Gills have
jagged
edge

Sharp,
bitter
taste

Spores 5–6 × 4–5 µm

## Tricholoma imbricatum

**Key characters** reddish-brown, umbonate cap with overlapping flattened scales, smooth cap margin. **Description: Cap** 4–10 cm, convex to conical, then expanded with broad umbo; dry, dull reddish brown to umber, surface cracking all over into rough overlapping (imbricate) scales; margin of cap is smooth. **Gills** sinuate, white then pale brownish, spotted darker brown. **Stem** rather stout, swelling at base, pale brown, fibrous; often rather hollow. **Spores** white, 5–7 X 3–5 µm. *Edibility uncertain; best avoided.* **Occurring** always below pines, on sandy soils, late autumn, frequent to common and widespread.

Cap surface dry, scaly

Slightly rooting base

*Tricholoma imbricatum*

Spores 5–7 × 3–5 µm

## Tricholoma saponaceum
## (Soap-scented Tricholoma)

**Key characters** cap colours variable, often pale but normally blackish at centre; pinkish flush in stem and gills; distinctive smell of cheap soap. **Description: Cap** 3–10 cm, convex then expanded and broadly umbonate; smooth, dry or very slightly squamulose at centre; colour very variable, pale grey, even white, to olivaceous or brown, usually blackish at centre. **Gills** sinuate, rather distant; white or tinged sulphuryellow or greenish, often speckled with reddish spots. **Stem** rather stout, tapering and rooting, fibrous; white or same colour as cap, often slightly scaly. **Spores** white, 5–6 X 3–4 µm. *Edibility uncertain; best avoided.* **Occurring** in mixed woods on soil and leaf-litter, often in small clumps, summer and autumn, common and widespread.

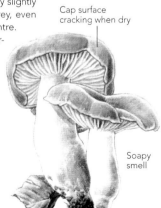

Cap surface cracking when dry

Soapy smell

*Tricholoma saponaceum*

Spores 5–6 × 3–4 µm

125

*Tricholoma sejunctum*

## Tricholoma sejunctum

**Key characters** yellow-green fibrillose cap; white gills an stem flushed yellow; floury smell. **Description:** Ca 5–10 cm, convex then expanded and ofte sharply umbonate; pale to greenish yellow wi darker radiating fibrils and streaks; smoo or slightly squamulose, viscid in wet weat er. **Gills** rather distant, broad, strongly sin ate; white or with yellow tints. **Stem** fibrou tough, often rather wavy and irregular shape; white with pale yellowish tints. **Tas** also floury but then bitter. **Spores** white, 5–7 4–5 μm. *Not edible; has unpleasant taste an can cause upsets.* **Occurring** mainly decid ous woodlands, summer to autumn, occ sional to frequent.

Spores 5–7 × 4–5 μm

## Tricholoma sulphureum (Sulphurous Tricholoma)

*Tricholoma sulphureum*

**Key characters** bright sulphur-yellow in all parts; very stron smell of coal gas. **Description:** Cap 3–8 cm, convex the expanded and broadly umbonate; smoot dry; clear sulphur-yellow to slightl brownish at centre. **Gills** distan broad and thick, sinuate-emarginat sulphur-yellow. **Stem** rather lon fibrous and tapering, sulphu yellow. **Odour** very strong an unpleasant of coal gas. **Spores** whit 8–11 X 5–6 μm. *Not edible.* **Occurring** usua under oaks, autumn, occasional to common

Thick, spaced gills

Spores 8–11 × 5–6 μm

## Tricholoma argyraceum

**Key characters** greyish, minutely squamulose cap; often yellowish tints in gills and stem; floury smell and taste. **Description: Cap** 4–8 cm, convex then expanded and umbonate; brownish grey and squamulose-fibrillose all over; edge with remains of fine veil, sometimes yellowish at edge. **Gills** rather crowded, sinuate; white or greyish, ageing yellowish. **Stem** white, yellowish or greyish, smooth, rather slender. **Spores** white, 5–6 X 3–4 μm. *Edible*. **Occurring** usually under beech, especially on chalky soils but also conifers, autumn, frequent to common. **Notes:** The closely related *T. terreum* (mixed woods, common, edible) differs by its rather darker blackish-grey cap, greyish gills, lack of the floury odour and taste, and larger spores 6–7 X 4–5 μm.

Gills stain yellow

*Tricholoma argyraceum*

Spores 5–6 × 3–4 μm

## Tricholoma cingulatum

**Key characters** small, usually under willows; persistent cottony ring; slightly floury smell and taste. **Description: Cap** 2–6 cm, convex then expanded and slightly umbonate; brownish grey and minutely velvety-squamulose. **Gills** distant, sinuate, white. **Stem** rather long, slender, white and slightly fibrillose, with a distinct and persistent cottony ring near apex. **Spores** white, 4–6 X 2–4 μm. *Edible*. **Occurring** under willows (*Salix*), summer to autumn, occasional to locally frequent.

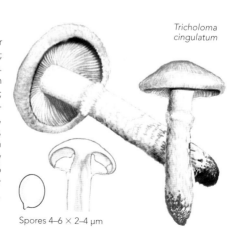

*Tricholoma cingulatum*

Spores 4–6 × 2–4 μm

127

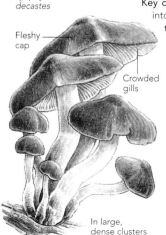

Cap with thick flesh and inrolled margin

Gills very crowded

*Calocybe gambosa*

## Calocybe gambosa (St George's Mushroom)

**Key characters** only in spring and early summer; all parts creamy-white; strong floury taste and smell. **Description:** Cap 4–12 cm, convex then expanded with wavy, irregular margin; smooth, never scaly or fibrillose; ivory-white to pale buff. **Gills** sinuate to slightly decurrent when cap expanded; very crowded; white to cream. **Stem** short and stout, flesh fibrous; ivory-white. The floury taste and smell disappear on cooking. **Spores** white, 5–6 X 3–4 µm. *Edible and delicious.* **Occurring** in fields, woodland margins and roadsides, frequent to common everywhere. **Notes:** This is one of the best edible species and cannot easily be confused, except perhaps with the rare, poisonous, red-staining *Inocybe erubescens* which can appear early and bears a very superficial resemblance.

Spores 5–6 × 3–4 µm

## *LYOPHYLLUM*

### Lyophyllum decastes

*Lyophyllum decastes*

Fleshy cap

Crowded gills

In large, dense clusters

**Key characters** in dense clusters with stem bases fused into one common base; grey to brown caps. **Description:** Cap 4–10 cm, convex then expanded, margin incurved and usually wavy; smooth, dry, minutely fibrillose; grey-brown to yellow-brown, very tough. **Gills** crowded, adnate to decurrent, white to greyish. **Stem** tough, fibrous, many joining together at the base; white or greyish, floccose-pruinose at apex. **Spores** white, globular, 6 X 5–6 µm. *Edible and quite good.* **Occurring** in woods, on pathsides and disturbed soils, autumn, common. **Notes:** one of a small number of species difficult to tell apart; perhaps the most distinctive is *L. loricatum* with a very shiny, brown, elastic cap cuticle.

Spores 6 × 5–6 µm

## Lyophyllum connatum  (= Clitocybe connata)

**Key characters** in smallish clusters, bases of stems fused but distinct; chalk-white colour; specific chemical test. **Description: Cap** 4–10 cm, convex then expanded, margin incurved and wavy; smooth, dry; pure chalk-white. **Gills** crowded, narrow, adnate-decurrent, white to yellowish. **Stems** white, long and slender; although the stems are adjoining they are not springing from one common base. **Spores** white, elliptic, 6–7 X 3–4 μm. **Chemical test:** ferrous sulphate on gills = violet in one minute. *Edible but not recommended.* Easily confused with poisonous species of Clitocybe. **Occurring** in clumps (usually smaller than the previous species) but often in long rows along pathsides, grassy places in woodlands, autumn, uncommon (commoner in the north).

Smooth white cap

Grows in tufts

*Lyophyllum connatum*

Spores 6–7 × 3–4 μm

# MELANOLEUCA

## Melanoleuca grammopodia

**Key characters** very large umbonate cap; rather pale brown colours; often in large circles. **Description: Cap** 6–25 cm, convex then expanded and umbonate, grey-brown to yellow-brown, hygrophanous, umbo usually darker. **Gills** crowded, sinuate-adnate, white then pale cream. **Stem** tall, rather stout, straight, slightly bulbous; whitish with brownish fibrils. **Flesh** white to pale brown. **Odour** strong, rather unpleasant. **Spores** white, elliptic, with warts, amyloid (turning blue-black) with iodine, 8–10 X 5–6 μm. *Edibility uncertain, best avoided.* **Occurring** in woodland clearings, meadows etc., often in large rings, especially in mountainous districts, autumn, occasional.

Spores 8–10 × 5–6 μm

*Melanoleuca grammopodia*

*Melanoleuca cognata*

### Melanoleuca cognata

**Key characters** rather yellowish or tan coloration; stem tall; gills ochre-tan. **Description:** Cap 5–10 cm, convex then expanded and umbonate, smooth, ochre-yellow to tan, paler when dry. **Gills** becoming clearly pale ochre or tan when mature, sinuate-adnate, crowded. **Stem** tall, straight, slightly bulbous, colour as in cap but with darker fibrils. **Flesh** white to pale ochre, with pleasant odour. **Spores** white, elliptic, with amyloid warts, 7–9 X 5–6 µm. *Edible and quite tasty.* **Occurring** in conifer woods on paths and clearings, autumn, uncommon.

Spores 7–9 × 5–6 µm

### Melanoleuca brevipes

**Key characters** large dark brown umbonate cap, short, stout stem. **Description:** Cap 5–8 cm, convex then expanded and umbonate; dark umber brown when moist, hygrophanous, becoming pale grey-brown on drying. **Gills** whitish or with very pale grey tints; crowded, sinuate-adnate. **Stem** stout, straight; shorter than cap diameter, dark grey-brown with darker fibrils. **Flesh** white. **Spores** white, elliptic, with amyloid warts, 8–11 X 5–6 µm. *Edible but not highly recommended.* **Occurring** in groups or singly alongside paths (often cinder paths), pastures and meadows, summer to autumn, occasional to frequent.

*Melanoleuca brevipes*

Short stem

Spores 8–11 × 5–6 µm

## *Melanoleuca adstringens* (= *M. melaleuca* in part)

*Melanoleuca adstringens*

**Key characters** cap umbonate, deep brown but hygrophanous; stem with black flesh at the base. **Description: Cap** 4–10 cm, convex then expanding and usually slightly umbonate; smooth; deep brown when moist, drying almost grey-buff. **Gills** broad, crowded, sinuate-adnate, white. **Stem** rather tall, straight, slightly swollen at base; whitish (when dry) to brown, with darker, brown fibrils. **Flesh** white then dark blackish brown in stem base. **Odour** pleasant. **Spores** pale cream, elliptic, with minute amyloid warts, 8 X 4–5 μm. *Edible but not recommended.* Like many *Melanoleuca* species this has characteristic microscopic harpoon-shaped sterile cells (cystidia) among the basidia on the gill edge. **Occurring** in mixed woods, especially pathsides, fields and meadows, late autumn, common everywhere. **Notes:** often called *M. melaleuca* but that species has white flesh in the stem base and lacks harpoon cystidia on the gill edge.

Gills white, sinuate

Spores 8 × 4–5 μm

## *LEPISTA*

### *Lepista nuda* (Wood Blewits)

**Key characters** lilac or violet colours in cap, gills and stem; robust stature. **Description: Cap** 4–10 cm, convex then expanded, flattened or slightly umbonate; smooth, greasy; lilac to reddish violet, browner with age. **Gills** crowded, sinuate-adnate then slightly decurrent; soft, lilac, easily separable from cap tissue. **Stem** usually rather short, stoutish, fibrous, lilac-violet. **Spores** flesh-pink in a deposit, 6–8 X 4–5 μm. *Edible and delicious.* Sold in country markets it is one of the very best species, but one to which a very few people report stomach upsets, either through under-cooking or perhaps allergic reaction: try only a little the first time. **Occurring** in woods along paths, gardens and compost heaps, late autumn to winter, common everywhere.

Lilac-grey cap discolours grey or brownish

Crowded gills

Stem may be slender or robust

*Lepista nuda*

Flesh white with a lilac tint; varies from thin to thick in texture

Spores 6–8 × 4–5 μm

131

*Lepista saeva*

Violet stem

## *Lepista saeva*
### (Common Field Blewit, Blue-leg)

**Key characters** cap and gills without lilac colours; stout stem bluish lilac. **Description: Cap** 4–10 cm, convex then expanded, margin inrolled; smooth, dry, pale buff or clay to greyish. **Gills** crowded, adnate-decurrent; white or pinkish-buff, never lilac. **Stem** short, stout, fibrillose, clear bluish lilac. **Spores** flesh-pink, 7–9 X 4–5 μm. *Edible and delicious.* One of the best and best-known species, it is one to which a few people are allergic. **Occurring** in grassy meadows and pastures, late autumn to early winter, frequent to common.

Spores 7–9 × 4–5 μm

## *Lepista irina*

*Lepista irina*

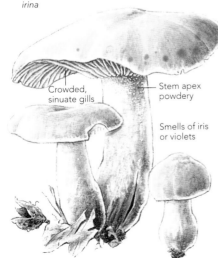

Crowded, sinuate gills

Stem apex powdery

Smells of iris or violets

**Key characters** cap, gills and stem lacking lilac tints; sweet smell of violets or mock orange. **Description: Cap** 6–12 cm, convex-umbonate then expanded, pale cream-buff with browner centre, smooth. **Gills** crowded, sinuate, yellowish cream. **Stem** stout, often swollen at base, whitish but bruising brown. **Odour** strong of iris or violets, sometimes a little over-powering. **Spores** flesh-pink, 7–8 X 3–4 μm. *Edible and delicious.* **Occurring** in open meadows and fields, late autumn to winter, occasional to frequent. **Notes** Extremely similar to the two previous species, but completely lacking lilac or violet tints.

Spores 7–8 × 3–4 μm

## Lepista (= Clitocybe) flaccida

Lepista flaccida

**Key characters** funnel-shaped caps, tan to rich orange; texture rather floppy, leathery. **Description: Cap** 5–10 cm, convex then rapidly funnel-shaped; soft, leathery, reddish tan to rich orange (this latter colour form is sometimes called *C. inversa* and treated as a separate species). **Gills** crowded, deeply decurrent; pale, whitish to tan. **Stem** rather slender above, slightly swollen below, smooth; tan to orange. **Spores** pink, minutely prickly-warty, 4–5 X 3–4 μm. *Edible but not very good; best avoided.* **Occurring** in mixed woodlands in leaf-litter, often in large fairy-rings, late autumn, frequent to common. **Notes:** often placed in the genus *Clitocybe* but recent studies place this with the Blewits, in the genus *Lepista*.

Earthy smell develops with age

Spores 4–5 × 3–4 μm

# ASTEROPHORA

## Asterophora (= Nyctalis) parasitica

**Key characters** small mushroom only on old fruitbodies of *Russula* and *Lactarius*. **Description: Cap** 1–3 cm, convex then flattened; smooth, silky, grey; slightly striate at margin. **Gills** thick, distant, whitish then soon covered in a brownish powder-like deposit, which is composed of special spores called chlamydospores (the similar *A. lycoperdoides* turns powdery all over). **Stem** slender, white, smooth. **Odour** repulsive, pungent. **Spores** buff, 5–6 X 3–4 μm, but usually replaced by the asexually produced chlamydospores, 15 X 10 μm. *Not edible.* **Occurring** on old, rotting fruitbodies of large *Russula* and *Lactarius* species, autumn, occasional.

Asterophora parasitica

Spores 5–6 × 3–4 μm

## *CLITOCYBE*

### *Clitocybe nebularis* (Clouded Agaric)

Large and robust, often in rings

*Clitocybe nebularis*

**Key characters** in rings; umbonate, fleshy grey, often large caps; pale gills. **Description:** Cap 5–20 cm, convex with inrolled margin, then expanding and broadly umbonate, finally slightly depressed; smooth, not fibrillose, pale grey to greyish fawn often with a white, woolly powdery "bloom". **Gills** crowded, arched-decurrent; white then pale cream. **Stem** usually rather short, stout, fibrous, tough; greyish with white swollen base. **Spores** cream, 6–8 X 3–5 μm. *Edibility variable; best avoided.* It is suspected in some cases of mild poisoning. **Occurring** often in large circles in leaf-litter of deciduous and conifer woods, late autumn, very common.

Spores 6–8 × 3–5 μm

### *Clitocybe clavipes* (Club Foot)

**Key characters** umbonate to depressed, grey-brown cap; gills a distinct pale yellow; stem swollen, spongy. **Description:** Cap 4–10 cm, convex then expanded and umbonate, slightly depressed with age; smooth, greyish brown to buff. **Gills** thick, soft, deeply decurrent, pale cream with a distinct primrose-yellow hue. **Stem** very bulbous, club-shaped, soft, spongy, hairy at base, fibrillose; pale grey. **Spores** white, 4–5 X 3–4 μm. *Edible but not recommended.* **Occurring** in leaf-litter or needles of mixed woods, autumn, common.

*Clitocybe clavipes*

Spores 4–5 × 3–4 μm

## Clitocybe geotropa

**Key characters** large depressed and umbonate pale tan cap; tall stem. **Description: Cap** 10–20 cm, beginning convex with a small umbo then rapidly expanding to slightly funnel-shaped still with umbo; pale buff to ochre, smooth. **Gills** rather crowded, decurrent; white then pinkish buff. **Stem** longer than cap diameter, stout, fibrous, clavate; colour as cap, base downy-hairy. **Spores** white, 6–8 X 5–6 μm. *Edible and delicious.* **Occurring** in woodland clearings and margins, especially on chalky soils, autumn, occasional to frequent.

Smells of iris or violets

Stem apex powdery

*Clitocybe geotropa*

Spores 6–8 × 5–6 μm

## Clitocybe gibba (= C. infundibuliformis) (Common Funnel-cap)

**Key characters** thin, pale pinkish-tan, funnel-shaped cap; slender stem. **Description: Cap** 3–8 cm, rapidly funnel-shaped; thin-fleshed, smooth, pale pinkish buff to yellow-ochre. **Gills** deeply decurrent, crowded; white to pale buff. **Stem** rather long, slender, swollen below, rather tough; pale buff. **Spores** white, tear-drop shaped, 6–7 X 3–4 μm. *Edible and quite good.* **Occurring** in leaf-litter or grass in deciduous woodlands and heaths, summer to autumn, frequent to common. **Notes:** this rather attractive species is easily recognized by the thin, pale caps, pleasant slightly acidic smell and rather slender stature.

*Clitocybe gibba*

Very thin flesh

Spores 6–7 × 3–4 μm

135

### *Clitocybe odora* (Aniseed Toadstool, Anise Cap)

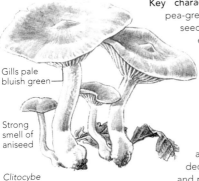

Gills pale
bluish green

Strong
smell of
aniseed

*Clitocybe
odora*

**Key characters** whole toadstool blue-green or pea-green and with clear strong smell of aniseed. **Description:** Cap 3–7 cm, convex then expanded and slightly umbonate, margin wavy, irregular; cuticle smooth, dry; pale green to blue-green. **Gills** narrow, adnate-decurrent, pale blue-green. **Stem** rather short, slender, smooth to fibrillose; swollen and woolly at base; pale blue-green. **Spores** white, elliptic, 6–8 X 3–4 µm. *Edible and delicious.* Use as flavouring or with small pieces added to a dish. **Occurring** in leaf-litter of deciduous woods, especially on roadsides and paths, autumn, frequent to common everywhere.

Spores 6–8 × 3–4 µm

### *Clitocybe rivulosa* (= *C. dealbata*) ☠

Cap greyish,
wrinkled

**Key characters** small white cap with delicate bloom usually in zones; stem fibrous, often twisted. **Description:** Cap 2–6 cm, convex then expanded and slightly depressed, margin incurved; white to pale pinkish-tan surface with frosted appearance, often zoned or spotted in rings. **Gills** crowded, thin, decurrent or adnate, white to cream. **Stem** usually shorter than cap diameter, slender, smooth; woolly at base; fibrous and often noticeably twisted; white to pale buff. No distinctive odour. **Spores** white, elliptic, 3–5 X 2–4 µm. *Dangerously poisonous, even deadly, causes muscarine poisoning.* **Occurring** in fields, roadsides and gardens in lawns, summer and autumn, frequent to common.

*Clitocybe
rivulosa*

Spores 3–5 × 2–4 µm

### Clitocybe vibecina (= C. langei)

**Key characters** small hygrophanous (changing colour when wet) grey-brown to pale tan cap; greyish gills; floury smell and taste. **Description:** Cap 2–4 cm, convex then expanded and slightly depressed; smooth, dark grey-brown when wet; paler, often bicoloured when partially dry; striate at margin when wet. **Gills** rather close, narrow, decurrent, greyish. **Stem** slender, smooth, pale greyish tan. **Spores** white, tear-drop shaped, 5–7 X 2–3 μm. *Edibility uncertain, best avoided.* **Occurring** in conifer woods and under bracken by birches, late autumn to winter, common.

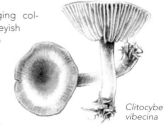

*Clitocybe vibecina*

Strong smell of rancid flour

Spores 5–7 × 2–3 μm

## LEUCOPAXILLUS

### Leucopaxillus giganteus (= Clitocybe gigantea)

**Key characters** huge white caps with downy margins; gills and stem also white; often in rings. **Description:** Cap 10–30 cm, soon funnel-shaped; margin inrolled, woolly-pubescent; ivory-white, often rather rough and cracked or scaly at very centre. **Gills** crowded, decurrent, forking. **Stem** white, short, stout, tough and fibrillose. **Spores** white, amyloid, 6–8 X 3–6 μm. *Edibility uncertain; best avoided.* **Occurring** in large rings in pastures, hedgerows, killing nearby grass, summer to autumn, occasional to frequent. **Notes:** this species is now removed from *Clitocybe* into the separate genus *Leucopaxillus* because of its differing anatomy and amyloid spores.

*Leucopaxillus giganteus*

Grows in groups or rings

Spores 6–8 × 3–6 μm

137

Dry, velvety surface

Thin, crowded, forking gills

*Hygrophoropsis aurantiaca*

Spores 7–8 × 4 µm

## HYGROPHOROPSIS

### *Hygrophoropsis aurantiaca* (False Chanterelle)

**Key characters** in heathy woods of birch and pine; orange-yellow cap and blunt orange gills. **Description: Cap** 3–6 cm, convex then expanded and funnel-shaped, margin inrolled; slightly downy; bright orange-yellow to almost cream-colour when on open heaths. **Gills** crowded, thin with blunt edges, repeatedly forked, decurrent; orange or pale yellow; soft and easily separable from cap flesh. **Stem** soft, sometimes swollen, smooth; orange above and darker brown below. **Spores** white, elliptic, 7–8 X 4 µm, dextrinoid. *Usually considered poisonous; although actually edible.* **Occurring** in open woods of birch or pine or in heathland, summer and autumn, common or even abundant. **Notes:** it is often mistaken for the true Chanterelle (*Cantharellus cibarius*), which however lacks true gills, having rounded gill-like wrinkles on the cap undersurface.

## LACCARIA

### *Laccaria laccata* (Deceiver)

**Key characters** can be extremely deceptive, but reddish brown colours, fibrous stem and pinkish gills are typical. **Description: Cap** 2–4 cm, convex then expanded and slightly depressed; reddish brown to tan on drying; smooth to slightly scaly at centre. **Gills** thick, distant, adnate; pinkish to reddish brown, dusted with white spores when mature. **Stem** slender, tough, fibrous; colour as cap. **Spores** white, globose, spiny, 7–8 µm. *Edible and quite tasty although rather small.* **Occurring** in troops in very mixed habitats from dark woodlands to paths or open heaths, summer and autumn, abundant. **Notes:** The very similar species *L. bicolor* has a reddish-brown cap with lilac gills and bright lilac-violet woolly stem base; uncommon.

Long, twisting stem

*Laccaria laccata*

Spores 7–8 µm

Laccaria proxima

Powdery gills

## Laccaria proxima

**Key characters** pinkish-brown scurfy-scaly cap, tall, fibrous pink stem, spores elliptic. **Description:** Cap 2–7 cm, convex then flattened to slghtly depressed, pinkish brown with fine scurfy scales at centre. **Gills** thick, widely spaced, pale pink, adnate. **Stem** 5–12 cm tall, slender, tough, pink with darker fibres. **Odour** fairly strong of radish. *Edible.* **Occurring** in rather damp, often marshy places, summer to autumn, frequent to common. **Notes:** This variable species is similar in many respects to *L. laccata* but distinguishable by its different build, spores 7–10 X 6–8 µm, and habitat.

Spores 7–10 × 6–8 µm

## Laccaria amethystina (Violet Deceiver)

**Key characters** unmistakable deep amethyst cap and stem (but paler when dry). **Description:** Cap 2–3 cm, convex then expanded and slightly depressed; intense deep amethyst or violet when moist, but hygrophanous, so paler greyish pink to bluish when dry. **Gills** deep violet, adnate, dusted with white spores when mature. **Stem** slender, fibrous, colour as cap. **Spores** white, globose, with tiny non-amyloid spines, 9–11 µm. *Edible but rather too small for the table.* **Occurring** in damp, rather shady woods, on stream sides, etc., autumn, common.

Laccaria amethystina

Spores 9–11 µm

139

*Omphalina
ericetorum*

Spores 8–10 × 5–6 µm

### *Omphalina ericetorum*

**Key characters** cap small, top-shaped with scalloped edge; stem apex darker; many species rather similar. **Description** Cap 0.5–2 cm, convex then soon flattened and slightly depressed; edge scalloped, with radial grooves to centre; pale yellow-brown to olive. **Gills** white to yellowish, adnate-decurrent, distant. **Stem** slender, smooth, colour as cap; darker at apex, woolly at base. **Spores** white, elliptic, 8–10 X 5–6 µm. *Edibility uncertain; best avoided. Far too small to be of any importance.* **Occurring** in troops, on heathy soils, peaty areas in woods etc, autumn, common.

## *COLLYBIA*

### *Collybia butyracea*
(Greasy Cap, Butter Cap)

**Key characters** usually umbonate cap with "greasy" texture and darker umbo; stem club-shaped. **Description:** Cap 3–8 cm, convex then expanding with low umbo, smooth and very greasy when moist; greyish brown to reddish or olive, fading when dry but usually with umbo and margin darker. **Gills** whitish, crowded, free from stem. **Stem** often rather swollen at base, tapering upwards, smooth but with woolly-hairy base; colour as cap. **Odour** is slightly rancid. **Spores** white, elliptic, 6–7 X 3–4 µm. *Edible but not particularly delicious.* **Occurring** in mixed woods in leaf-litter, autumn, common.

Cap has dark,
oily centre spot

*Collybia
butyracea*

Spores 6–7 × 3–4 µm

## Collybia dryophila

**Key characters** pale yellowish colours; thin brownish stem, tough and flexible, with slightly woolly base. **Description:** Cap 2–4 cm, convex then soon flattened, thin-fleshed, often wrinkled; colour very variable, reddish tan or pale buffy-tan to yellowish or even white. **Gills** white to distinctly yellowish; narrow, crowded, free to adnexed. **Stem** thin, tough but flexible, smooth and only slightly woolly-hairy at base; light reddish brown. **Spores** white, elliptic, 5–6 X 3–4 µm. *Edible* but small. **Occurring** in small groups in mixed woodlands (especially oaks in leaf-litter, summer to autumn, often abundant.

*Collybia dryophila*

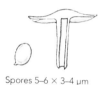

Spores 5–6 × 3–4 µm

## Collybia confluens

**Key characters** growing in dense tufts, stems finely hairy, often flattened. **Description:** Cap 2–4 cm, convex then expanded, pinkish brown, drying to buff, rather thin-fleshed and soft. **Gills** very crowded, adnate, whitish to pinkish buff. **Stem** pale tan, pinkish or purplish lower down, finely hairy or fuzzy, often flattened. **Spores** white, elliptic 7–9 X 3–4 µm. *Edible but worthless.* **Occurring** in dense clusters in mixed woods, usually beech or oak, summer to autumn, occasional to frequent.

*Collybia confluens*

Tufted, with stem bases joined

Spores 7–9 × 3–4 µm

*Collybia erythropus*

Stem and cap contrast markedly in colour

## *Collybia erythropus* (= *C. marasmioides*, = *C. bresadolae*)

**Key characters** strong contrast between very pale cap and deep red to brownish-red stem. **Description:** **Cap** 2–3 cm, convex then soon flattened, smooth, dry, slightly wrinkled; pale buff-tan to almost white when dry. **Gills** free, not crowded, whitish to flesh colour. **Stem** slender, often flattened, smooth and shining, dark glossy maroon red to red-brown. **Spores** white, pip-shaped, 6 X 2–3 µm. *Edible but too small and thin to be worth collecting.* **Occurring** in deciduous woodlands in leaf-litter or on wood, autumn, frequent.

Spores 6 × 2–3 µm

## *Collybia maculata* (Spotted tough shank)

**Key characters** tough, sinewy, pure white with rust-brown spots and stains. **Description:** **Cap** 4–10 cm, convex then soon flattening; dry and smooth; pure white at first then soon spotted and stained with rust-coloured spots, finally completely reddish brown. **Gills** very crowded, free; edge minutely toothed; whitish then soon spotted reddish brown. **Stem** rather tall, slender to stout, smooth to fibrillose, very tough and often rooting; white then spotted like cap. **Spores** pinkish-cream, almost spherical, 4–5 X 5 µm. *Not edible; very tough and rather bitter.* **Occurring** often in large rings in leaf-litter of broadleafed and coniferous woods, summer and autumn, very common.

*Collybia maculata*

Tall, fibrous stem with rooting base

Large groups embedded in deep litter, frequently under bracken

Spores 4–5 × 5 µm

## Collybia fusipes (Spindle shank)

**Key characters** always clustered at base of deciduous trees or stumps, swollen, spindle-shaped stem; red-brown colours. **Description: Cap** 3–6 cm, convex then slightly expanding with broad umbo; smooth, dry to slightly greasy in wet weather; dull brick-red to deep brown, paler tan when dry. **Gills** broad, thick, not crowded, edge often crinkled, with interconnecting veins between gills; whitish then pale brown with darker reddish spots. **Stem** usually rooting, several fused together at base; very variable in length and width, often grossly swollen and spindle-shaped, splitting into deep cracks in dry weather; colour as cap only paler. **Flesh** very tough, pliant. **Spores** white, elliptic, 5–6 X 3–4 μm. *Edible but very tough.* **Occurring** in clusters at base of trees and stumps, usually beech or oak, summer and autumn, common.

*Collybia
fusipes*

Spores 5–6 × 3–4 μm

## Collybia peronata (Wood Woolly-foot)

**Key characters** rather dull, tan cap; yellowish stem with thick woolly-hairy base. **Description: Cap** 3–6 cm, convex then expanded and flattened, yellowish tan to earth-brown. **Gills** rather distant, pale yellowish buff. **Stem** pale yellow, distinctly woolly-hairy at base often binding leaf-litter together. **Spores** white, pip-shaped, 7–9 X 3–4 μm. *Inedible,* it has a distinctly peppery taste when chewed for a minute or two. **Occurring** in clumps in deciduous woods, autumn, common. **Notes:** The related *C. fuscopurpurea,* found in beech woods and much less common, is distinguished by the dark reddish brown to deep purplish-brown cap, and stem with yellower hairs on lower half.

*Collybia
peronata*

Spores 7–9 × 3–4 μm

Woolly
stem base

## MARASMIUS

### Marasmius rotula

Gills joined to a "collar"

**Key characters** black wiry stem; whitish, strongly grooved cap; gills attached to "collar". **Description** Cap 0.5–1.5 cm, rounded with centre flattened and strongly radially grooved, white to cream. **Gills** distant connecting to "collar" around the stem apex like spokes of a wheel. **Stem** very slender, smooth, shining, black. **Spores** white, pip-shaped, 7–10 X 3–5 µm. *Too fragile to consider eating.* **Occurring** on decaying sticks and roots in mixed woodlands, autumn, common. **Notes:** two rather shorter, but equally small-capped species are *Micromphale foetidum*, stocky, dull grey-brown, on branches of beech, with unpleasant smell, and *Marasmius ramealis*, a tiny pinkish-white species found in large numbers on twigs.

*Marasmius rotula*

Spores 7–10 × 3–5 µm

### Marasmius androsaceus (Horse-hair Fungus)

**Key characters** long slender stems like horse-hair; reddish-brown caps. **Description:** Cap 0.5–1 cm, rounded to flattened with central depression, rather wrinkled with radial grooves; dull reddish brown. **Gills** rather narrow, adnate, sparse, colour as cap. **Stem** extremely slender, hair-like, black, shining. **Spores** white, pip-shaped, 6–9 X 3–4 µm. *Inedible; far too fragile and small to consider worth eating.* **Occurring** the stems arise directly from the thin, wire-like black mycelium which travels through and around the material on which it grows. On twigs, needles and debris of conifers, also heather, autumn, frequent.

*Marasmius androsaceus*

Spores 6–9 × 3–4 µm

# Marasmius oreades
## (Fairy Ring Toadstool)

Marasmius
oreades

**Key characters** buff-coloured, often umbonate caps; widely spaced gills, in rings in grass. **Description: Cap** 2–5 cm, convex then soon expanded with a broad umbo, margin often slightly grooved particularly in old, wet specimens; ochre-tan to pinkish buff. **Stem** short to medium length, smooth, colour as cap but white, woolly, below, tough and leathery. **Spores** white, pip-shaped, 9–11 X 5–6 µm. *Edible and delicious.* Care must be taken to avoid picking some of the poisonous *Clitocybe* species which can grow along with it such as *C. rivulosa.* **Occurring** in large rings in lawns, fields and grassy clearings or paths in woods, summer and autumn, common everywhere.

Grows in large
numbers forming
fairy rings

Spores 9–11 × 5–6 µm

# Marasmius alliaceus (Garlic Mushroom)

**Key characters** tall, black, slender stem; strong smell of garlic when bruised. **Description: Cap** 2–4 cm, convex then soon expanding with slightly radially grooved margin; pale grey-ish to clay-brown. **Gills** whitish, adnexed, rather distant. **Stem** tall, slender, rooting; finely velvety, black. **Spores** white, ovate, 9–12 X 6–7 µm. *Inedible.* Has been used by some for garlic flavouring but not really recommended. **Occurring** in leaf-litter and twigs of deciduous woods, especially beech, autumn, occasional. **Notes:** similar is *M. scorodonius,* also with a garlic odour but smaller and with reddish-brown colours, in grass.

Marasmius
alliaceus

Strong smell
of garlic

Spores 9–12 × 6–7 µm

### *Flammulina velutipes* (Velvet shank)

Sticky, shiny cap

Dark, velvety stem

Grows tufted on wood, as a wound parasite

*Flammulina velutipes*

**Key characters** appears in the winter month cap yellowish orange; stem velvety, dark **Description: Cap** 2–6 cm, convex the soon expanding, fleshy; bright yellowish t orange, darker at centre when wet, and wit rather moist, slippery texture. **Gills** whit to pale yellowish, adnexed, broad. **Stem** varying in length and thickness, dense tufted, curving upwards; rich reddish brow to almost black, and velvety at base. **Spore** white, elliptic, 7–10 X 3–4 μm. *Edible an delicious; recommended.* **Occurring** on dea or decaying deciduous timber, common, appears when few other fungi are present

Spores 7–10 × 3–4 μm

### *Tricholomopsis rutilans*

*Tricholomopsis rutilans*

Sulphur-yellow gills

**Key characters** vividly coloured yellow cap covered by pu plish squamules, and yellow gills. **Description: Cap** 4–12 cm convex then expanded, rich golden-yellow overlaid with da purplish flecks and scales, darker and more densely scaled a centre. **Gills** broad, distant, adnexed, golden-yellow. **Stem** pale yellowish with some purplish scales but paler an less squamulose; rather stout, without myceli strands. **Spores** white, ovate, 5–7 X 4–5 μm *Edibility uncertain; best avoided.* **Occurring** on stumps and logs of conifers, summer an autumn, common everywhere. **Notes:** th beautiful species is similar to *T. decora*, whic is also found on conifers, but in norther regions, and is rather paler with brownish, no purplish, squamules.

Spores 5–7 × 4–5 μm

## *Megacollybia (= Tricholomopsis) platyphylla*

**Key characters** cap and stem greyish, fibrillose; broad, distant gills; prominent mycelial strands at base of stem. **Description:** Cap 4–10 cm, soon flattened; smooth, dry, radially fibrillose, dull greyish to yellowish brown. **Gills** very broad, very distant, adnexed to free, whitish. **Stem** rather short, straight and thick; dry, fibrillose, colour as cap or whitish. **Spores** white, 6–8 X 6–7 µm. *Not edible because of toughness and rather bitter flesh.* **Occurring** on stumps, logs or buried timber of deciduous wood, attached by bootlace-like white mycelial strands, summer and autumn, common.

*Megacollybia platyphylla*

Stem white, fibrillose

Mycelial cords well developed

## *Armillaria mellea* (Honey Fungus, Honey Tuft)

**Key characters** tufted on wood; tapered stems with thick ring; scaly cap centre. **Description:** Cap 4–12 cm, convex then expanded with low umbo, minutely scaly, especially at centre; colour variable, honey-yellow to slightly greenish yellow with minute darker brown scales scattered at centre. **Gills** whitish, then pinkish brown often spotted darker brown; adnate or slightly decurrent. **Stem** long, tapered at base and fused lightly to other stems at base; colour as cap or paler, whitish. **Ring** conspicuous, thick, yellow-white. Black bootlace-like mycelial strands attached to stem bases travel throughout stump, under tree bark, etc. **Spores** pale cream, elliptic, 9–10 X 5–7 µm. **Flesh** smells rather strong, taste often very bitter, burning. *Edible when cooked (removes bitterness).* Considered delicious by many. **Occurring** on a wide variety of coniferous and deciduous timber and shrubs, usually in large clumps; a serious parasite, autumn, common everywhere. **Notes:** the closely related *A. gallica* (= *A.bulbosa*) usually grows on the ground on buried wood, is a more pinkish brown and has a swollen, club-shaped stem with thin, cottony ring. It is even more common than *A. mellea*.

Spores 6–8 × 6–7 µm

Scaly cap and stem

Decurrent gills

Spores 9–10 × 5–7 µm

Spreads by black, bootlace rhizomorphs under bark

*Armillaria mellea*

### *Armillaria tabescens*

*Armillaria tabescens*

No ring on stem

Darker towards base

**Key characters** yellow-brown squamulose caps, slender ringless stems in dense clumps. **Description: Cap** 4–12 cm, convex then flattened and slightly depressed, yellowish to reddish brown, with dark brown tiny squamules at centre. **Gills** moderately crowded, adnate, slightly decurrent, pale tawny brown. **Stem** slender, tapering, pale yellow-brown, fibrous, without any trace of a ring. **Spores** white, ovate, 8–10 X 5–7 μm. *Edible when cooked.* **Occurring** on deciduous timber especially oaks, early summer to early autumn (almost always before the true Honey Fungus), uncommon fruting more commonly in warmer years, more frequent in southern regions.

Spores 8–10 × 5–7 μm

### *Oudemansiella mucida* (Porcelain Fungus)

*Oudemansiella mucida*

Slimy caps

On dead trunks and branches of beech

**Key characters** unmistakable glistening white caps on beechwood; short stem with thin ring. **Description: Cap** 3–6 cm, convex then flattened with umbo; pure, glistening white to greyish, extremely slimy. **Gills** white, broad, distant, adnexed. **Stem** slender, very tough, whitish to grey, fibrillose, with a thin ring at the top. **Spores** white, ovate, 13–18 X 12–16 μm. *Edible but not recommended.* **Occurring** often in large numbers on beech trunks and logs, autumn, frequent to common.

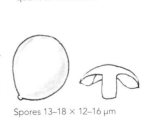

Spores 13–18 × 12–16 μm

## *Xerula (= Oudemansiella) radicata* (Rooting Shank)

**Key characters** very tall straight stem, deeply rooting; slimy wrinkled cap. **Description: Cap** 3–8 cm, convex to bell-shaped then expanding with central umbo, margin wrinkled; very slimy when wet; clay-brown to ochre, darker at centre, radially wrinkled. **Gills** white, broad, distant, adnexed, edge often brown. **Stem** soon very tall, to 20 cm, slender, tapering upwards; whitish, darker below, fibrillose, striate, and with strong "tap-root". **Spores** white, ovate, 12–16 X 10–12 µm. *Edible but not recommended.* **Occurring** around stumps or buried timber, autumn, common. **Notes:** the similar but rare *X. pudens* is darker brown with velvety, not slimy, cap and stem.

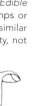

*Xerula radicata*

Spores 12–6 × 10–12 µm

# MYCENA

## *Mycena flavoalba*

**Key characters** pale yellow-white caps, growing in troops in lawns. **Description: Cap** 1–2 cm, convex, then flattened, pale primrose yellow with darker centre, minutely striate. **Gills** adnate with a decurrent tooth, white; broad, distant. **Stem** very slender, smooth, pale yellow, fading. **Spores** ellipsoid, white, 6–8 X 3–4 µm. *Edible, however, it is too small to consider as food.* **Occurring** in scattered troops in lawns and open meadows of short grass, summer to autumn, frequent to common.

*Mycena flavoalba*

Spores 6–8 × 3–4 µm

149

*Mycena
leptocephala*

## Mycena leptocephala

**Key characters** dark greyish colours; strong smell of domestic bleach or nitric acid. **Description: Cap** 0.5–1.5 cm, convex-conical then expanding, dark grey-brown to pale grey; smooth, deeply striate when moist. **Gills** whitish to grey, adnate-ascending. **Stem** slender, smooth, shining, pale grey. **Spores** white, elliptic, 8–10 X 6–7 µm. *Edibility doubtful, best avoided.* **Occurring** often solitary or in very small troops or clusters in open grass or on soil, autumn, common and widespread.

Spores 8–10 X 6–7 µm

## Mycena epipterygia

**Key characters** cap and stem slimy, yellowish green. **Description: Cap** 1–2 cm, convex then bell-shaped; smooth, slimy with striate margin: pale yellowish brown. **Gills** white, adnate. **Stem** slender, smooth and slimy; bright yellow to greenish yellow, the slimy skin is easily removed. **Spores** white, elliptic, 8–11 X 4–5 µm. *Inedible.* **Occurring** on litter of conifer woods or heaths, summer and autumn, common.

Spores 8–11 X 4–5 µm

*Mycena
epipterygia*

## *Mycena galericulata* (Bonnet Mycena)

**Key characters** cap pinkish grey, relatively large; gills pinkish with cross-veins. **Description: Cap** 2–5 cm, conical to bell-shaped then expanded with umbo; very variable in colour from pale grey to pinkish brown or olivaceous; striate at margin. **Gills** white to pinkish, rather thick with noticeable cross-veining at base. **Stem** long, slender, smooth; hairy at base, rooting; colour as cap or yellower. **Spores** white, elliptic, 10–11 X 6–8 µm. *Inedible.* **Occurring** in clumps on deciduous wood, stems often fused together, all year, common everywhere.

Inter-veining between gills

*Mycena galericulata*

Spores 10–11 × 6–8 µm

## *Mycena crocata*

**Key characters** dull grey-brown cap with saffron stem containing bright orange-red latex. **Description: Cap** 1–2 cm, conical then expanded, campanulate; greyish brown to olive, often paler, almost white; smooth with slightly striate margin. **Gills** white, adnate, staining orange-red. **Stem** long, slender, smooth and shining, saffron-orange, base rooting and hairy; paler above. **Flesh** releases a carrot-red juice when broken. **Spores** white, elliptic, 9–11 X 6–7 µm. *Edibility doubtful, best avoided.* **Occurring** in leaf-litter and twigs in beech woods, especially on chalky soils, autumn, uncommon to occasional.

Bruises saffron

*Mycena crocata*

Spores 9–11 × 6–7 µm

*Mycena
inclinata*

Dense clusters
on oak stumps

Spores 8–10 × 6–8 μm

## Mycena inclinata

**Key characters** always on oaks; brown cap with dentate margins; stem reddish below white above; strong odour when fresh **Description: Cap** 1–3 cm, convex then expanded; strongly striate; margin toothed, protruding beyond gills; pale to rich brown, becoming paler, almost white at margin. **Gills** whitish to grey, adnate, crowded. **Stem** long, slender, smooth; rich reddish brown and hairy at base fading to white in upper half. **Odour** often strong, rancid or soapy. **Spores** white, subglobose, 8–10 X 6–8 μm. *Inedible.* **Occurring** in large clumps on old or dead oak trees and stumps, autumn, common and widespread everywhere.

## Mycena polygramma

**Key characters** steel-grey colours; stem with faint white longitudinal raised lines. **Description: Cap** 2–4 cm, bell-shaped then expanded with umbo, margin striate; dark steel-grey, slightly yellowish with age. **Gills** white to greyish, often stained pink. **Stem** long, slender, rooting, smooth and rigid; steel-grey with minute, white, raised longitudinal lines. **Spores** white, elliptic, 9–12 X 6–8 μm. *Inedible.* **Occurring** in clusters or solitary on deciduous stumps and logs, buried wood, autumn, frequent.

*Mycena
polygramma*

Spores 9–12 × 6–8 μm

## *Mycena haematopus* (Bleeding Mycena)

**Key characters** deep red-brown cap, stem yields dark reddish juice. **Description:** Cap 1–3 cm, bell-shaped, greyish brown sometimes with white powdery bloom, striate at margin. **Gills** white then flesh-tinted to deeper reddish brown (red-edged in the similar *M. sanguinolenta*), adnate. **Stem** slender, rigid, fragile; colour as cap darkening below to reddish brown; when broken it yields a dark red-brown latex. **Spores** white, elliptic, 10 X 6 µm. *Inedible.* **Occurring** in clumps on stumps of deciduous trees, autumn, frequent.

*Mycena haematopus*

Blood-red juice in stem

Spores 10 × 6 µm

## *Mycena galopus*

**Key characters** grey-black to pure white colours; stem yields white latex. **Description:** Cap 1–2 cm, convex to bell-shaped then slightly expanding; strongly striate almost to centre; from dark greyish black to almost white in the variety *alba*; centre darker. **Gills** whitish, adnexed. **Stem** slender, smooth, polished, slightly hairy at base, colour as cap; when broken exudes drops of white, milk-like latex. **Spores** white, oblong-elliptic, 12–14 X 6–7 µm. *Inedible.* **Occurring** in leaf-litter, pine needles, twigs etc., of mixed woods, summer and autumn, common.

*Mycena galopus*

Stem exudes copious white milk if broken

Spores 12–14 × 6–7 µm

153

Pink or lilac cap
with striate margin

Smell of
radish

Mycena
pura

Spores 6–8 × 3–5 µm

## Mycena pura 💀

**Key characters** lilac-pink, purple or bluish colours
and strong smell of radish. **Description: Cap**
2–4 cm, conical then expanded with umbo;
smooth, margin striate; colour very variable,
white, violaceous, lilac to pink (as shown) fading
to greyish with age. **Gills** white to pinkish, adnate.
**Stem** rather stout, hollow, coloured as cap; base
woolly. **Flesh** with strong odour of radish when
bruised. **Spores** white, ovate, 6–8 X 3–5 µm
*Inedible and possibly toxic.* **Occurring** in leaf-litter in mixed woods, autumn, common. **Notes**
the similar beech-wood species *M. pelianthina*
also smells of radish and is of similar appearance
but has gill edges coloured dark purple, while *M.
rosea* (also in beech woods) is more robust and
a bright rose-pink.

Mycena
sanguinolenta

Very slender
stem exudes
red juice
when broken

## Mycena sanguinolenta

**Key characters** small, with reddish brown colours; red latex in flesh; gill edge red. **Description: Cap** 0.5–1 cm, convex to bell-shaped
striate at margin; reddish brown, darker at centre
**Gills** whitish or coloured as cap but paler; edge
dark-red when viewed under hand-lens (compare with *M. haematopus*). **Stem** very slender
colour as cap but paler; yields thin reddish
latex when broken. **Spores** white, elliptic, 8–9
X 4–6 µm. *Inedible.* **Occurring** usually in troops
not clumps, among mosses and fallen leaves
autumn, common and widespread.

Spores 8–9 × 4–6 µm

## *Mycena vitilis*

**Key characters** very small, tall and slender; cap sharply umbonate. **Description: Cap** 0.5–1.5 cm, conical then expanded with prominent umbo, striate to centre; grey-brown. **Gills** greyish, thin, adnate. **Stem** long, very slender, smooth; very pale, almost white; base rooting, binding the leaf-litter. **Spores** white, elliptic, 9–12 X 5–7 μm. *Inedible.* **Occurring** in leaf-litter in deciduous woods, usually not tufted, autumn, common.

Grey-brown, striate cap

Long, shiny stem

Spores 9–12 × 5–7 μm

*Mycena vitilis*

## *Macrocystidia cucumis*

*Macrocystidia cucumis*

**Key characters** pinkish cinnamon to dark red brown; flesh with strong fishy or cucumber odour. **Description: Cap** 2–5 cm, conical-campanulate, smooth, margin slightly striate; deep red brown and often pruinose. **Gills** crowded, emarginate, yellowish-flesh colour. **Stem** tough, velvety, short to medium length; deep reddish brown to almost black, paler at apex. **Spores** pale reddish brown, oblong-elliptic, 8–10 X 3–4 μm. *Inedible.* **Occurring** on bare soil in mixed woods, especially on pathsides, frequent also on wood mulch in gardens, autumn, occasional to abundant.

Spores 8–10 × 3–4 μm

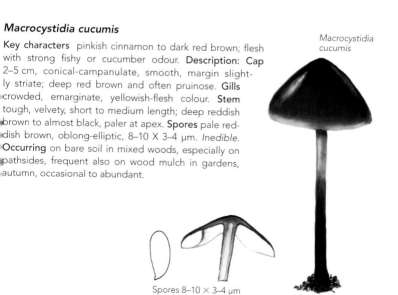

## *PLEUROTACEAE*

This family consists almost entirely of fungi growing on wood, and having usually rather tough, fleshy fruitbodies with either no stem or a rather off-centre (eccentric) stem. The spores are white to pale cream or pinkish. Some species are well-known edibles and one in particular, commonly called Shiitake (*Lentinula edodes*) is widely cultivated throughout the World.

### *PLEUROTUS*

#### *Pleurotus dryinus*
#### *(= corticatus)*

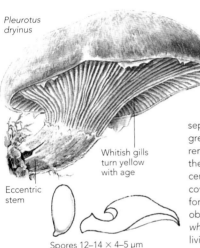

*Pleurotus dryinus*

Whitish gills turn yellow with age

Eccentric stem

Spores 12–14 × 4–5 μm

**Key characters** cap convex, with felty-woolly scales; stem with ring zone. **Description:** Cap 5–10 cm, convex then expanding, margin inrolled; flesh thick, surface soft and downy, separating into woolly flattened scales; pale greyish brown to cream. **Gills** deeply decurrent down to ring zone; thin, crowded, white then yellowish. **Stem** short, stout, usually off-centre (eccentric), with distinct veil at apex covering gills when young, soon rupturing to form ring zone; colour whitish. **Spores** white, oblong-cylindrical, 12–14 X 4–5 μm. *Edible when young.* **Occurring** on elms, usually old living trees rather than stumps, autumn, rare to occasional.

#### *Pleurotus cornucopiae*

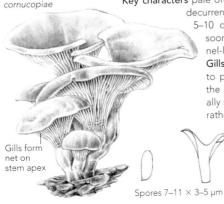

*Pleurotus cornucopiae*

Gills form net on stem apex

Spores 7–11 × 3–5 μm

**Key characters** pale often funnel-shaped cap; gills deeply decurrent, forking at base. **Description:** Cap 5–10 cm, convex when very young but soon flattened then depressed and funnel-like; smooth, white then pale ochre. **Gills** long, decurrent, crowded, whitish to pale ochre, forking where they join the stem. **Stem** variable in length, usually short 1–5 cm or even absent; thick rather eccentric whitish, base often tomentose. **Spores** white, ellipsoid, 7–11 x 3–5 μm. *Edible and good.* **Occurring** on deciduous logs, especially beech, summer to autumn, occasional.

## *Pleurotus ostreatus* (Oyster Mushroom)

*Pleurotus ostreatus*

Short stem

**Key characters** shell-shaped fruitbodies; cap smooth, bluish grey when young. **Description: Cap** 5–15 cm, rounded when very young then soon expanding and flattening to form flat, oyster-shell-shaped brackets, deep brown to bluish black or bluish grey when young but soon very pale buff to almost white with age. **Gills** deeply decurrent, thin, crowded, whitish cream. **Stem** absent or very short (except in the var. *salignus*) white, woolly. **Spores** pale lilac in thick deposit, elongated, 8–11 X 3–4 µm. *Edible and highly favoured by many.* **Occurring** often in large numbers on various deciduous trees (especially beech), autumn to winter, occasionally earlier, common and widespread everywhere. **Notes:** The variety *salignis* appears late in the year and has a long hairy stem, deep bluish-grey cap usually not fading, and gills also bluish. Considered a good species by some. The variety *columbinus* is distinguished by a peacock-blue cap. *P. pulmonarius* is often confused with *P. ostreatus* but occurs mostly in the summer to early autumn and is usually pale cream-buff ageing yellow and has smaller spores than *P. ostreatus*.

Spores 8–11 × 3–4 µm

## *Panellus serotinus*

**Key characters** olive-green to brownish with age, felty-tomentose; gills yellow; stem lateral. **Description: Cap** 3–10 cm, convex with inrolled margin then expanding, flattened, kidney-shaped to almost circular with lateral short stem; surface tomentose to smooth with age or when wet; deep olive-green to yellow-green, then brownish. **Gills** adnate, crowded, narrow, yellow. **Stem** short, thick, tomentose; yellowish with brown squamules, darker near cap. **Spores** white, cylindric-elongate, 4–6 X 1–2 µm, amyloid. *Edibility doubtful; to be avoided.* **Occurring** on trunks, fallen logs, etc. of deciduous trees, especially beech, late autumn throughout the winter, uncommon.

*Panellus serotinus*

Spores 4–6 × 1–2 µm

Flesh is soft and gelatinous

### *Panellus (= Panus) stipticus* 🕱

**Key characters** flattened, kidney-shaped, pale, clay-coloured caps; gills ochre; taste bitter. **Description:** Cap 1–5 cm, convex then flattened, kidney-shaped to semi-circular with lateral stem; surface at first slightly pruinose-scurfy then smooth; pale buff to clay-brown. **Gills** crowded, adnate, thin; pale ochre to cinnamon. **Stem** short, thin, tapering downwards, whitish, emerging from rear of cap. **Spores** white, elliptic, 4–6 X 2–3 µm, amyloid. *Not edible, possibly toxic.* **Occurring** on dead wood of deciduous trees, all year, common and widespread.

*Panellus stipticus*

Stem broadest at point of attachment

Spores 4–6 × 2–3 µm

### *Panus torulosus*

**Key characters** very tough flesh; downy cap and stem with lilac flush when young. **Description:** Cap 5–10 cm, often very irregular, lobed, wavy at margin, convex then soon funnel-shaped; very tomentose, downy; pale ochre with clear lilac-violet tints on cap and stem when young,

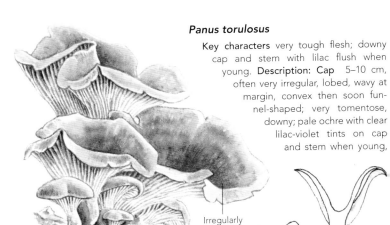

*Panus torulosus*

Irregularly funnel-shaped caps

Spores 5–6 × 3–4 µm

soon entirely ochre. **Gills** decurrent, narrow, crowded; pale ochre-brown often with lilac flush, soon flesh-colour. **Stem** very short to almost absent, often lateral; tomentose, violet then brown. **Flesh** tough, woody, often drying extremely hard. **Spores** white, cylindrical, 5–6 X 3–4 µm. *Not edible.* **Occurring** on stumps of deciduous trees, autumn, occasional to frequent.

## *Lentinus lepideus*

**Key characters** tough, broadly scaly cap; pale colours; edges of gills serrate. **Description: Cap** 5–12 cm, convex then slightly depressed at centre; skin cracking into broad, irregular scales; pale ochre or whitish yellow to brownish with scales darker, brown. **Gills** decurrent to slightly sinuate. distant, broad; with edge ragged and serrate; pale whitish yellow. **Stem** short to medium but rather variable in length and thickness; tough and fibrillose, often scalysquamulose; colour as cap. **Spores** white, elliptic, 10–15 X 4–6 µm. *Not edible.* **Occurring** on old coniferous timber, including old railway sleepers, occasionally in houses, autumn, uncommon to occasional. **Notes:** The closely related *L. tigrinus* has a more depressed, funnel-shaped cap, thinner flesh, densely but minutely squamulose-scaly cap and rather slender, tapering stem with ring-like zone at apex; found on deciduous wood, uncommon.

Gills have a toothed edge

*Lentinus lepideus*

Spores 10–15 X 4–6 µm

## BOLBITIACEAE

This family consists of three principal genera which have smooth, medium-brown spores with a prominent germ-pore, and the cells of the cap cuticle rounded. Many species have a ring, most are small, or even tiny. The robust *Agrocybe cylindracea* has for centuries been cultivated on poplar stumps and poles for food.

*Agrocybe erebia*

White ring finally turns brown

Spores 10–13 × 5–7 µm

### Agrocybe erebia

**Key characters** dark brown colours, dull brown spore print; thin ring on stem. **Description: Cap** 3–6 cm, convex then flattening with low umbo, margin often striate, deep umber-brown when moist, soon drying paler, clay-brown. **Gills** adnate, whitish, soon cigar-brown. **Stem** moderately stout, long, slightly fibrillose; whitish brown then darker. **Ring** prominent, pendent, grooved above, vanishing with age. **Spores** elliptic, 10–13 × 5–7 µm. *Edibility uncertain, best avoided.* **Occurring** on bare soil, sometimes leaf-litter, in deciduous woods, summer to autumn, frequent. **Notes:** *A. praecox* found in spring and early summer is of similar build and stature but pale cream overall; *A. molesta* (= *A.dura*), in spring, is stouter, tougher, pale cream with the cap often cracking; both are common.

*Agrocybe cylindracea*

### Agrocybe cylindracea  (= Pholiota aegerita)

**Key characters** smooth, wrinkled and cracked; ring on stem; in clumps on wood. **Description: Cap** 4–10 cm, convex then slightly expanded; silky surface often wrinkled and channelled, centre cracking; pale ochre-buff to clay-brown, paler, almost white at margin. **Gills** adnate-sinuate with decurrent tooth; pale ochre then dull cigar-brown. **Stem** fibrous, tapered downwards, white to pale clay. **Ring** high, thin, membranous, soon torn and vanishing. **Spores** dull brown, elliptic, 9–10 × 5–7 µm. *Edible and delicious.* **Occurring** on stumps and trunks of poplars, elms, occasionally other deciduous trees, autumn, occasional.

Spores 9–10 × 5–7µm

## Conocybe tenera

**Key characters** tall slender stem and conical cap; yellow-orange colours; spores pale
rust-brown. **Description: Cap** 2–4 cm, conical
then slightly expanded-campanulate; smooth,
ochre to orange-brown. **Gills** narrow, adnate
(to free), crowded, cinnamon. **Stem** smooth,
colour as cap. **Spores** oval, 10–12 X 5–7 μm.
*Not edible.* **Occurring** in grass in fields, woods
and roadsides, summer and autumn, common.
**Notes:** the related *C. lactea*, uncommon, in
grass, can be easily identified by its milk-white
cap and stem and cinnamon gills.

Conical cap does
not expand

*Conocybe
tenera*

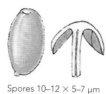

Spores 10–12 × 5–7 μm

## Bolbitius vitellinus

*Bolbitius
vitellinus*

**Key characters** bright egg-yellow cap, thin,
sticky, very fragile. **Description: Cap** 2–4 cm,
golden yellow then fading, deeply campanulate-
conical, soon expanded, flattened; margin striate; thin-fleshed, rapidly collapsing. **Gills** free,
thin, crowded, pale cinnamon. **Stem** tall, slender,
white to pale yellow, with woolly-powdery coating. **Spores** rust-brown, elliptic, 11–15 X 6–9 μm.
*Too small for eating.* **Occurring** on horse dung,
manured grass, sometimes wood chips, summer
and autumn, common everywhere.

Spores 11–15 × 6–9 μm

## HYGROPHORACEAE

This group – the Waxcaps – contains some of our most colourful and spectacular species. Bright reds, yellows, greens and orange are the rule rather than the exception in this family, which also includes pure white and the more usual greys and browns. Cap and stem are often very viscid. All species have thick, waxy gills, white spores and long basidia. The genus *Hygrophorus* was formerly divided into three groups: *Limacium*, with slimy cap, adnate-decurrent gills and slimy stem usually dotted at the apex; *Camarophyllus*, with dry cap, smooth, fibrous stem and gills free to decurrent; and *Hygrocybe* with thin, fragile, moist to viscid cap, smooth stem and gills free to decurrent. The last two are now considered to form the single genus *Hygrocybe*, usually associated with open grassland; *Limacium* now forms the genus *Hygrophorus*, associated with trees. Despite the often bright colours the hygrophori can be surprisingly difficult to identify. Recent studies have shown the existence of many more species than formerly recognized; precise notes of colours, viscidity, taste etc. are necessary for accurate identification.

*Hygrophorus hypothejus*

## HYGROPHORUS

### Hygrophorus hypothejus
(Winter Hygrophore)

**Key characters** cap slimy, olive-brown; gills yellow; stem pale; late in season. **Description: Cap** 2–6 cm, convex then expanding, depressed; radially fibrillose, yellowish grey to olive and slimy. **Gills** decurrent, brown and rather sparse, thick, waxy, yellow then saffron. **Stem** cylindric, whitish or pale yellowish olive, slimy below ring-like zone. **Spores** white, ovate, 7–10 X 4–5 μm. *Edible and quite good.* **Occurring** in pine woods, late autumn to early winter, common.

Spores 7–10 × 4–5 μm

162

## *Hygrophorus discoxanthus (= H. chrysaspis)*

**Key characters** slimy white cap and stem discolouring yellowish to reddish brown; specific chemical test. **Description: Cap** 2–5 cm, convex then expanded with low umbo; smooth and viscid, white then soon yellowish brown from centre outwards. **Gills** adnate-decurrent, thick, waxy; whitish often with a pale orange-pink hue, discolouring as cap. **Stem** fleshy, white, slimy; apex dotted with white scurf. **Odour** strong, fragrant to slightly sickly. **Spores** elliptic, white, 7–9 X 4–6 µm. **Chemical test:** flesh + potassium hydroxide = red-brown. *Not known to be poisonous but not recommended.* **Occurring** in beech woods, autumn, frequent. **Notes:** The very similar *H. chrysodons* is found principally under beech, also with strong odour; it has bright yellow flecks on the cap and stem, flesh does not discolour.

All surfaces discolour rusty brown

*Hygrophorus discoxanthus*

Spores 7–9 X 4–6 µm

## *Hygrophorus eburneus*

**Key characters** slimy white cap and stem, tapering stem base, with oaks. **Description: Cap** 2–10 cm, convex then expanded, broadly umbonate; smooth, very slimy; pure white. **Gills** adnate-decurrent, thick, waxy; white. **Stem** slender, tapering at base, slightly rooting, sticky, white. **Odour** not distinct. **Spores** white, ovate, 7–9 X 4–6 µm. *Edible but not recommended.* **Occurring** in beech woods, autumn, uncommon. **Notes:** The similar *H. cossus* has a strong smell of Goat Moth Caterpillar, a sweet, rather sickly odour and commonly grows with oaks.

*Hygrophorus eburneus*

Spores 7–9 X 4–6 µm

163

*Hygrophorus erubescens*

### Hygrophorus erubescens

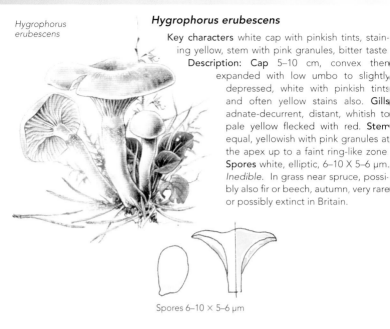

**Key characters** white cap with pinkish tints, staining yellow, stem with pink granules, bitter taste. **Description:** Cap 5–10 cm, convex then expanded with low umbo to slightly depressed, white with pinkish tints and often yellow stains also. **Gills** adnate-decurrent, distant, whitish to pale yellow flecked with red. **Stem** equal, yellowish with pink granules at the apex up to a faint ring-like zone. **Spores** white, elliptic, 6–10 X 5–6 µm. *Inedible.* In grass near spruce, possibly also fir or beech, autumn, very rare or possibly extinct in Britain.

Spores 6–10 × 5–6 µm

*Hygrocybe pratensis*

## HYGROCYBE

### Hygrocybe (Camarophyllus) pratensis

**Key characters** all parts yellow-buff (rarely white), top-shaped; gills deep, decurrent, with cross-veins. **Description:** Cap 2–6 cm, convex then expanded; dry, smooth, dull yellowish-buff to very pale buff (white in the var. *pallida*). **Gills** decurrent, deeply so with age, giving the top-shaped appearance; buff to tawny; thick and distant, often interconnected by veins at base. **Stem** rather stout, tapered at base, paler than cap. **Spores** white, elliptic, 7–8 X 5 µm. *Edible and quite good.* Occurring in open fields, pastures, autumn, common.

Spores 7–8 × 5 µm

## Hygrocybe ceracea

**Key characters** bright golden yellow, sticky cap and dry stem; adnate-decurrent gills. **Description: Cap** 1–5 cm, rounded to slightly depressed at centre, expanding with age; very sticky when moist; bright golden yellow, paler with age. **Gills** yellowish white or sometimes deep yellow-orange, broadly adnate-decurrent; soft, waxy. **Stem** medium to slender, often flattened and compressed; slightly tapered at base; dry and smooth; colour as cap or paler, white at base. **Spores** white, elliptic, 6–8 × 3–4 μm. *Inedible.* **Occurring** in unfertilized meadows and rough pastures, late autumn to winter, common and widespread. **Notes:** the very similar *H. chlorophana* has narrowly adnate, not decurrent gills.

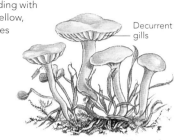

Decurrent gills

*Hygrocybe ceracea*

Spores 6–8 × 3–4μm

## Hygrocybe chlorophana

**Key characters** sticky cap and stem; constant yellow colours, especially in the adnexed gills. **Description: Cap** 2–7 cm, obtusely rounded, soon flattening; very viscid; bright lemon or chrome-yellow. **Gills** free to adnate (not decurrent), distant; waxy, whitish yellow, bright yellow to deeper yellow near cap flesh. **Stem** fragile, moist to greasy-sticky (persistently); smooth, bright yellow. **Spores** white, elliptic, 6–9 × 4–6 μm. *Edible but not recommended.* **Occurring** in fields and pastures, late autumn, frequent to common. **Notes:** Can be distinguished from several very similar yellowish hygrophori by the lemon-yellow gills, cap and stem without orange flush (sometimes a faint trace when young) and the persistent viscidity. *Hygrocybe ceracea* (above) has a soon dry, smooth stem and distinctly adnate-decurrent gills.

*Hygrocybe chlorophana*

Spores 6–9 × 4–6 μm

### Hygrocybe virginea (= H. nivea)

*Hygrocybe virginea*

**Key characters** cap waxy, small, white, top-shaped; no odour; in fields. **Description: Cap** 2–5 cm, convex, broadly domed, then expanded, top shaped; dry to slightly greasy, smooth, pure white to ivory; margin slightly striate. **Gills** decurrent, distant, white and waxy. **Stem** slender, tapered below, white. **Spores** white, elliptic, 7–8 X 4–5 µm. *Edible and quite good.* **Occurring** in open fields, pastures, woodland clearings, late autumn, frequent to common everywhere. **Notes:** the rather similar *H. russocoriacea* has a strong smell of cedar wood, a smaller and more ivory-coloured cap and larger spores.

Thick, distant gills

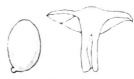

Spores 7–8 × 4–5 µm

### Hygrocybe calyptriformis

*Hygrocybe calyptriformis*

**Key characters** sharply pointed, splitting cap and pink colours. **Description: Cap** 2–5 cm, sharply pointed, margin expanding, often splitting into 3–4 large wings; smooth, dry, slightly fibrillose; clear pale rose-pink. **Gills** pale rose then whitish, waxy; distant, adnexed, very narrow at stem. **Stem** tall, graceful, fragile, striate-fibrillose, white to pale pinkish. **Spores** white, elliptic, 7–8 X 4–5 µm. *Edible but too rare to eat.* **Occurring** in unfertilized meadows, pastures, woodland margins, churchyards, late autumn to winter, very rare in Europe as a whole, locally frequent in Britain.

Cap and gills pink or lilac

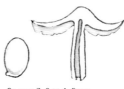

Spores 7–8 × 4–5 µm

## Hygrocybe coccinea (Common Scarlet Waxcap)

**Key characters** cap rather rounded, bell-shaped; bright blood-red to scarlet in all parts. **Description: Cap** 2–5 cm, moist then soon dry, smooth, convex to slightly flattened; bright scarlet or blood-red fading to orange or dull ochre when very old. **Gills** adnate-decurrent, broad, waxy; red with paler, orange margin. **Stem** stocky to rather slender, smooth, dry, slightly striate; paler scarlet to orange-ochre below. **Spores** white, elliptic, 7–9 X 4–5 μm. *Edible and quite good.* **Occurring** in fields, pastures, woodland margins, late autumn, locally frequent to common. **Notes:** similar species have more yellow or white in cap, stem or gills, or different cap shapes. *H. mucronella* has a convex to acutely conic cap, scarlet then orange, gills adnate-decurrent, deep yellow flushed orange-red at the base, and taste bitter, not mild.

Smooth, dry cap

*Hygrocybe coccinea*

Spores 7–9 ×4–5 μm

## Hygrocybe conica (= H. nigrescens) (Blackening Waxcap)

**Key characters** pointed cap; yellow-orange-red colours; white to pale yellow gills; all parts blackening. **Description: Cap** 1–5 cm, acutely conical, then expanded but retaining acute umbo; dry, fibrillose; orange or yellowish, sometimes with red flush; strongly blackening all over. **Gills** free to adnexed, waxy, white to pale yellow before greyish, then black (flushed red in the var. *conicoides* on sand dunes). **Stem** equal, slender, fibrillose; yellow and white at base, sometimes with red flush; blackening. **Spores** white, elliptic, 7–9 X 4–5 μm (3 μm larger on a frequent two-spored form). *Edible but not highly recommended.* **Notes:** extremely variable and a number of varieties and species have been described but all are treated here as this one, variable species.

*Hygrocybe conica*

Spores 7–9 × 4–5 μm

*Hygrocybe punicea*

*Hygrocybe punicea*

## *Hygrocybe punicea*

**Key characters** very large obtuse, irregular cap, blood-red colours, fibrous stem. **Description:** Cap 5–10 cm, bluntly rounded to bell-shaped, margin often lobed and irregular; smooth distinctly greasy-sticky; deep blood-red to cherry or crimson, soon fading to orange then pale yellow, finally whitish. **Gills** blood-red to purplish with yellow margin, then fading. **Stem** tall, rather stout, slightly viscid, coarsely fibrillose; red then soon yellowish but base persistently white. **Flesh** within stem also white. **Spores** white, elliptic, 8–12 X 4–6 µm. *Edible but rare and should not be eaten.* **Occurring** in unfertilized meadows, fields and churchyards, late autumn to winter, rare to occasional. **Notes:** perhaps the most magnificent of the waxcaps, its presence is considered a sign that the grassland is a potentially valuable waxcap site. *H. splendissima* differs in the often flattened or twisted stem, stem base rarely white, and a dry cap of a more carmine red.

Spores 8–12 × 4–6 µm

Cap umbo blue-green

*Hygrocybe psittacina*

## *Hygrocybe psittacina* (Parrot Toadstool)

**Key characters** very glutinous cap and stem; green-orange coloration (persistent at stem apex), gills adnate not decurrent. **Description: Cap** 2–5 cm, convex then expanded with broad umbo; smooth, very viscid with thick gluten; at first bright green because of the gluten but as this disappears changing to yellowish or reddish, finally purplish. **Gills** adnate, broad, thick; green, then yellowish with green at base. **Stem** slender, shortish; persistently green at apex and all over at first, then yellowish below; viscid, tough. **Spores** white, elliptic, 7–10 X

Spores 7–10 × 4–6 μm

4–6 μm. *Inedible.* **Occurring** in short turf in fields and pasture, late autumn, frequent. **Notes:** the similar but more orange-brown *H. laeta* may also have greenish colours but has decurrent, whitish to grey-violet gills.

## *Hygrocybe miniata*

**Key characters** flattened or depressed red cap with tiny scales; in grass. **Description: Cap** 1–5 cm, convex then flattening, often slightly depressed; dry, fibrillose or scurfy, soon torn into minute recurved scales especially at centre (use a hand-lens); deep blood-red to scarlet, then orange or ochre. **Gills** adnate, thick, orange-red to scarlet with yellow margin. **Stem** equal, slender, smooth; deep red-orange, paler at base. **Spores** white, elliptic-oblong, 7–10 X 5–6 μm. *Inedible.* **Occurring** in heathland, pastures or fields, summer to late autumn, uncommon to occasional. **Notes:** the similar *H. turunda* grows in wetter, boggy places in sphagnum tussocks, it has more orange or yellow cap colours, darker brownish scales at the centre; margin fringed or dentate.

Cap scurfy-scaly at centre

*Hygrocybe miniata*

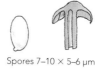

Spores 7–10 × 5–6 μm

# RUSSULACEAE

*Russula delica*

All Russulaceae have unusual flesh, the cells being a mixture of packets of round cells interwoven with long cells, the latter often containing latex. All have spores with warts or strong ridges and networks on the surface, which stain blue-black in iodine. The two principal genera, *Russula* and *Lactarius*, have, as a result of the mainly spherical cells, which make up the flesh, a distinctive granular, crumbly texture. The flesh of all *Lactarius* species when broken exudes a milky or coloured latex. Many species are widely sought after for food while others can be extremely hot to the taste when raw. Tasting a small (pea-sized) piece of flesh or gill or a drop of "milk" is an essential part of identification. Very few species are poisonous, although several are very indigestible or emetic if eaten in quantity.

Firm texture

Slightly fishy smell

Spores 8–12 × 7–9 μm

## RUSSULA

### Russula delica

**Key characters** white to cream, rather funnel-shaped; white gills, very firm, brittle stem. **Description: Cap** 5–15 cm, convex, soon expanded, soon funnel-shaped; rather velvety matt at first, especially at strongly inrolled margin. **Gills** fairly crowded, decurrent, cream, spotted brown. **Stem** rather short, hard. **Spores** white, ovate, 8–12 X 7–9 μm. **Taste** hot and bitter. **Odour** rather unpleasant. *Edible but not recommended.* **Occurring** in mixed woods, summer and autumn, common. **Notes** *R. chloroides* differs in having a faint blue tint at the stem apex just below the gills, which also have a bluish tint.

All parts blacken with age

Gills thick and widely spaced

### Russula nigricans

**Key characters** white cap and stem turning brown-black all over as if burnt; gills widely spaced staining red. **Description: Cap** 6–20 cm, convex then expanded and depressed, very firm, solid fleshed white then soon brown and finally coal-black as if burned. **Gills** very thick, broad, brittle, widely spaced, cream staining red. **Stem** short, stout, firm, white. **Flesh** white, soon red when scratched, finally black. **Spores** white, ovate 7–8

*Russula nigricans*

Spores 7–8 × 6–7 μm

6–7 µm. **Taste** slowly hot. *Inedible.* **Occurring**
 mixed woods, summer and autumn, very com-
 on. **Notes:** *R. densifolia* is extremely similar but
 iffers in its crowded gills.  *R. albonigra*, uncom-
 on, has gills quite crowded and flesh turning
 rectly black, no red stage.

## ussula foetens

 **ey characters**  cap large, viscid at first; unpleas-
 nt odour and taste. **Description: Cap**  5–15 cm,
 obust, very firm, convex then flattened; gluti-
 ous-viscid then dry, dull yellowish to honey-
 rown with brown flecks or scabs at margin, which
 strongly furrowed and striate.
 ills thick, distant; cream often
 iscoloured with rust-like spots.
 tem stout, firm, hollow, brittle;
 hitish to dull yellowish. **Odour**
 rong, oily or rancid. **Taste** of
 ills very hot, of stem almost

Spores 8–10 × 7–9 µm

 ild. **Spores** in deposit pale cream, subglobose, 8–10
 7–9 µm. *Not edible.* **Occurring** in mixed woods,
 ummer and autumn, frequent, especially in the
 orth. **Notes:**  The variety *subfoetens* is com-
 oner in the south, it has a milder taste, and
 e flesh turns yellow with strong alkalis. The
 elated *R. grata* is most easily distinguished by
 s odour of bitter almonds (marzipan).

## ussula heterophylla

 **ey characters**  cap various shades of green,
 rowded gills and small white spores. **Description:**
 ap  5–10 cm, convex then flattened, smooth,
 rass-green, olive to yellowish green or even
 rownish, with faint radial veins. **Gills** cream,
 rowded, greasy-flexible, often forking. **Stem**
 qual, fairly solid, white, brown-spotted with age.
 **pores** broadly elliptic, 5–7 × 4–6 µm (smallest of any
 ritish *Russula*). **Taste** mild to slightly hot. *Edible but*
 ot recommended. **Occurring** in deciduous woods,
 ummer to early autumn, frequent to common. **Notes:**
 ne of the first *Russula* species to appear in the sum-
 er. The similar  *R. aeruginea* has cream-yellow brittle
 ills and pale yellow spores, the grass-green cap is
 equently spotted with rust-brown.

Cap is
very slimy

*Russula
foetens*

*Russula
heterophylla*

Often grows
by the side
of paths

Spores 5–7 × 4–6 µm

171

*Russula
pseudointegra*

## Russula pseudointegra

**Key characters** large scarlet-red cap, firm, rather bitter flesh and odd smell.
**Description: Cap** 7–12 cm, convex then flattened, bright scarlet-red, sometimes pale almost white when washed out. **Gills** distant, thick, strong, interveined, deep ochre-yellow when mature. **Stem** rather stout, firm, white. **Flesh** with an odd smell slightly of menthol mixed with fruit. **Taste** is bitter and slightly hot. *Inedible* **Spores** ovate, 7–9 X 6–9 μm. **Occurring** usually under oak along grassy rides or tracks, summer to autumn, occasional to common and widespread.

Spores 7–9 × 6–9 μm

## Russula atropurpurea (= R. krombholtzii)

*Russula
atropurpurea*

**Key characters** cap deep purplish red with blackish centre, robust, firm build. **Description: Cap** 4–10 cm, convex then expanded, may be red or violaceous; often with very pale cream blotches, usually blackish at centre. **Gills** adnate to slightly decurrent, rather crowded, pale cream; with frequent, firm rust-like spots on edge. **Stem** white tinted brownish, rust to grey when damp and old. **Flesh** firm then spongy. **Spores** off-white, ovate, 7–9 X 6–7 μm. **Odour** fruity of stewed apples. **Taste** mild to slightly hot. *Edible and good.* **Occurring** in mixed woods, summer to autumn, abundant everywhere.

Spores 7–9 × 6–7 μm

## Russula puellaris

**Key characters** purplish-red small cap, all parts of fungus stain ochre-yellow with age. **Description: Cap** 2–5 cm, convex then slightly expanded, and finally depressed; reddish brown, reddish purple to yellowish brown. **Gills** narrow, crowded, fragile; yellowish cream colour. **Stem** equal, white, soft and spongy, soon staining deep yellow-ochre with age. **Spores** cream-yellow, subglobose, 7–9 X 6–8 µm. **Taste** mild. *Edible, but too fragile to be considered food.* **Occurring** in deciduous or conifer woods, autumn, occasional to common everywhere.

Fragile, becoming more yellow

*Russula puellaris*

Spores 7–9 × 6–8 µm

## Russula claroflava

**Key characters** in boggy birch woods; cap clear bright yellow, gills yellowish; flesh slowly blackish. **Description: Cap** 5–10 cm, convex then expanded, shining and moist at first then soon dry and smooth: margin often slightly striate; brilliant chrome to lemon-yellow, whole fungus slowly (5–10 hours) greying to black. **Gills** pale primrose yellow. **Stem** rather tall, equal, soft, white, flesh becoming grey then black. **Spores** 8–10 X 7–8 µm, ovate, in deposit rather deep cream. **Taste** mild to slightly hot, especially when young. *Edible and delicious.* **Occurring** under birches in wet areas, summer to autumn, frequent. Often confused with R. ochroleuca (see below) but distinguished by its habitat, much brighter yellow cap and yellowish gills; R. ochroleuca does not go grey-black.

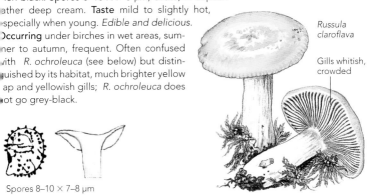

*Russula claroflava*

Gills whitish, crowded

Spores 8–10 × 7–8 µm

173

Cap always has central umbo

### Russula caerulea (= R. amara)

**Key characters** below pines; cap umbonate, de
violet, bluish purple to brownish purple. **Descr
tion: Cap** 4–8 cm, almost conical then expand
with blunt umbo (this is almost unique within t
genus), deep purple-violet to violet-brown. **G
crowded, pale ochre. **Stem** rather long, slenc
swollen at base, firm, white. **Spores** in depc
pale ochre, ovate, 8–10 X 7–9 µm. **Taste** of fle
and gills mild, cuticle bitter. *Edible but not r
ommended.* **Occurring** under pines, summer
autumn, occasional to common.

*Russula
caerulea*

Spores 8–10 × 7–9 µm

### Russula emetica (Sickener)

**Key characters** below pines in moss; cap bright scarlet; wh

*Russula
emetica*

gills and stem; very hot taste. **Description: Cap** 5–10 c
convex then expanded, bright clear scarlet or bloc
red, sometimes paling with age or after rain; cu
cle peels completely; margin soon sulca
**Gills** pure white to pale cream. **Stem** lor
slightly bulbous, soft, fragile, pure whi
**Spores** white in deposit, ovate, 9–11
7–9 µm. **Taste** extremely hot. *Inedible, c
cause vomiting when raw; apparently har
less when cooked; best avoided.* **Occurri
usually in damp, mossy ground under pin
autumn, common. **Notes:** The very simi
*R. mairei*, also scarlet, grows only in bee
woods, has the cuticle only half peelir
white gills with faint greenish-grey refle
tions, and an odour of honey or fruit.

Cap is scarlet in
peak condition

Gills and
stem both
white

Spores 9–11 × 7–9 µm

## Russula ochroleuca

**Key characters** cap dull ochre to green-ish yellow, stem white often flushed yellow. **Description: Cap** 4–10 cm, convex then flattened; margin sulcate with age, dull ochre-yellow, slightly greenish yellow. **Gills** pale cream, brittle, quite crowded. **Stem** firm, often soon hollow, white sometimes with yellowish crust at base, then greyish with age (but not blackening). **Spores** off-white in deposit, ovate, 8–10 X 7–8 μm. **Taste** mild to slightly hot. *Edible but not recommended.* **Occurring** in mixed woods, summer and autumn, common everywhere. This is one of the commonest of all toadstools.

*Russula ochroleuca*

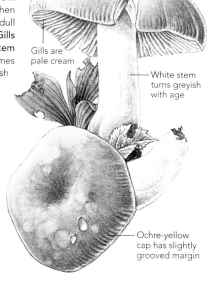

Gills are pale cream

White stem turns greyish with age

Ochre-yellow cap has slightly grooved margin

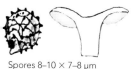

Spores 8–10 × 7–8 μm

## Russula fellea

**Key characters** overall straw-honey colour; odour of geranium. **Description: Cap** 4–8 cm, convex then expanded, fleshy, firm, margin slightly sulcate; ochre-yellow to straw but less dull than in *R. ochroleuca*. **Gills** pale straw-yellow to honey. **Stem** rather stout, firm, colour same as cap and gills. **Spores** in deposit pale cream, ovate, 7–9 X 6–7 μm. **Odour** of household geranium (*Pelargonium*) although often faint and not detectable by some. **Taste** very hot. *Edible when cooked but best avoided.* **Occurring** in beech woods, autumn, common.

*Russula fellea*

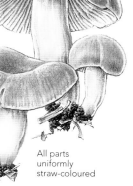

All parts uniformly straw-coloured

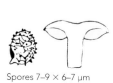

Spores 7–9 × 6–7 μm

## *Russula fragilis*

**Key characters** small, fragile, colours purplish (but variable); toothed gill-edge. **Description:** Cap 2–6 cm, convex then expanded and often depressed, very soft and fragile, margin furrowed: mixtures of purple, greenish, violet and black all common, centre usually darker. **Gills** white to pale cream, margin distinctly jagged-toothed when viewed under lens. **Stem** white, soft, fragile (difficult to pick intact). **Spores** white in deposit, subglobose, 7–9 × 6–8 μm. **Taste** very hot. *Edible when cooked but best avoided.* **Occurring** in mixed woods, summer and autumn, very common. **Notes:** Even if it is washed out and almost white, the gill edge is distinctive.

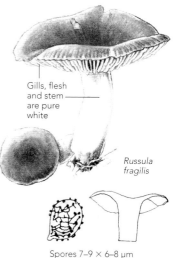

Gills, flesh and stem are pure white

*Russula fragilis*

Spores 7–9 × 6–8 μm

*Russula cyanoxantha*

Variable cap colour

Crowded, white gills

Stem remains white

Thick flesh, white or greyish, with mild taste

## *Russula cyanoxantha*

**Key characters** violet-green colours on cap; gills soft, flexible; specific chemical test. **Description:** Cap 5–15 cm, convex then expanding, sometimes depressed, firm-fleshed; colours very variable, usually some shade of violet to bluish green, often both in one cap. **Gills** narrow, fairly crowded, white, soft and greasy, "elastic" to the touch, not breaking. **Stem** rather stout, firm; white or with faint violet flushes. **Spores** white, elliptic, 7–9 × 6–7 μm. **Taste** mild. **Chemical test:** iron sulphate (FeSO₄) + flesh = no reaction to faintly green (the normal reaction is pink). *Edible and good.* **Occurring** in mixed woods, summer and autumn, common. **Notes:** the closely related *R. ionochlora*

Spores 7–9 × 6–7 μm

also edible, less common, has brittle, darker cream gills, spores cream, and flesh + iron sulphate = salmon pink.

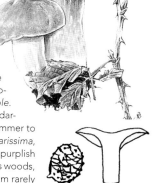

*Russula lepida*

## Russula lepida

**Key characters** very firm flesh; stem and cap deep rose-red to pink with white "bloom"; cedarwood taste. **Description: Cap** 4–10 cm, convex then flattened, very firm-fleshed; a beautiful vermillion red, sometimes fading to yellowish or white, cuticle hardly peeling. **Gills** crowded, narrow, off-white to cream, brittle. **Stem** equal, very firm to hard-fleshed, white or more often flushed pink like the cap. **Spores** white, sub-globose, 8–9 X 7–8 μm. **Taste** mild to bitter. *Inedible.* **Odour** slightly fruity, of menthol or distinctive of cedarwood, as in a pencil. **Occurring** in beech woods, summer to autumn, frequent. **Notes:** the closely related *R. amarissima*, uncommon, has a very bitter taste and rather more purplish red cap. *R. aurora* (= *R. rosea*), common in deciduous woods, differs in the cap not pruinose, flesh not so hard, stem rarely pink, cuticle peeling halfway to the cap centre, and without distinctive odour or taste.

Spores 8–9 × 7–8 μm

## Russula queletii

**Key characters** purple cap and stem (especially at base); gills cream; no reaction in ammonia test. **Description: Cap** 4–10 cm, convex then expanded, deep purple-red, red or purple-violet, to greenish at centre, firm, fleshy. **Gills** very slightly adnate-decurrent, white to pale lemon-yellow. **Stem** usually slightly swollen at base; pinkish-violet, pruinose. **Spores** pale cream-ochre, subglobose, 8–10 X 7–9 μm. **Odour** strong of apples. **Taste** hot. *Not edible, bitter when cooked.* **Occurring** below spruce, autumn, uncommon to occasional. **Notes:** The very similar *R. sardonia* has distinctly yellowish gills, and gills + ammonia = deep rose-red in 15 minutes.

*Russula queletii*

Fruity but unpleasant smell

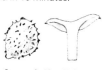

Spores 8–10 × 7–9 μm

177

*Russula virescens*

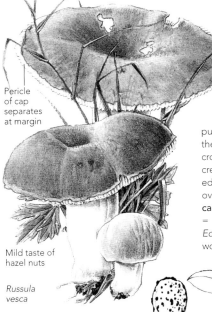

White stem

### Russula virescens

**Key characters** green cap cracking into little flattened platelets. **Description:** Cap 5–10 cm subglobose then convex and expanding, very fleshy, firm; pale verdigris to herbage green often paling to yellow or white, covered with flattened plaques as the cuticle breaks up. Gills crowded, brittle, white to cream. **Stem** rather short, stout, firm; white, slightly staining brown. **Spores** white, subglobose, 7–9 X 6–7 μm. **Taste** mild. *Edible and delicious.* **Occurring** in beech woods, summer and autumn, occasional to frequent.

Spores 7–9 × 6–7 μm

### Russula vesca

**Key characters** cap pinky brown to buff; cuticle retracting from margin, showing flesh below. **Description:** Cap 5–10 cm, convex then expanded, fleshy, firm, colour very variable, usually shades of pale reddish brown (colour of ham), buff, pinkish brown to flesh, olive or almost white; cuticle pulls back from the margin to expose the underlying white flesh. **Gills** narrow, crowded, forking near stem, white to pale cream. **Stem** firm, white, base often pointed, stained rust-brown. **Spores** white, ovate, 6–8 X 5–6 μm. **Taste** mild. **Chemical test:** iron sulphate ($FeSO_4$) on flesh = rapidly extremely deep salmon pink. *Edible and good.* **Occurring** in deciduous woods, summer and autumn, common.

Pericle of cap separates at margin

Mild taste of hazel nuts

*Russula vesca*

Spores 6–8 × 5–6 μm

## Russula graveolens
## (= R. xerampelina in part)

**Key characters** cap colour very variable, but the unique iron sulphate reaction (dark green) is constant. **Description: Cap** 5–15 cm, convex then expanded, fleshy, firm; colour extraordinarily variable, usually reddish brown to purplish but also mixtures of brown, green, red and purple or even yellow-ochre, usually rather dull looking; surface distinctly matt, colours often slightly "zoned". **Gills** broad, thick, pale cream to ochre. **Stem** usually rather stout, white soon staining dirty brown, surface rather "veined". **Spores** pale ochre, ovate, 8–11 X 6–9 µm. **Odour**, particularly when old or crushed, strong of crab, fish (herring) or shrimps. **Taste** mild. *Edible and good.* **Chemical test:** iron sulphate on flesh = deep green; this reaction makes an otherwise almost impossible "chameleon" easy to confirm. **Occurring** mainly under oaks, summer and autumn, common. **Notes:** the true *R. xerampelina* grows with pines and has a blood-red cap and stem, others characters are similar.

Cap is variable in colour

Smell of crab

*Russula graveolens*

Spores 8–11 × 6–9 µm

# LACTARIUS

## Lactarius blennius

**Key characters** cap slimy, olive-green marked with darker spots or zones; very hot latex. **Description: Cap** 4–8 cm, convex then rather flat, very slimy at first, especially after rain; pale greenish grey to olive-brown, slightly zoned and with depressed darker spots. **Gills** somewhat adnate, white to dull grey. **Latex** from cut gills white, fairly copious, slowly turns grey, extremely hot to taste. **Stem** rather short, stout, colour as cap, viscid. **Spores** cream, ovate, 7–8 X 6–7 µm. *Not edible.* **Occurring** in beech and oak woods, autumn, frequent. **Notes:** the rather rare *L. circellatus*, found under hornbeam, has a greyer, distinctly zonate cap, often very irregular in outline, and a very short stem.

slimy cap

*Lactarius blennius*

Spores 7–8 × 6–7 µm

### *Lactarius helvus*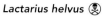

*Lactarius helvus*

**Key characters** cap pale cinnamon, minutely squamulose; smell sweet, spicy; milk mild. **Description: Cap** 5–10 cm, convex then soon flattened and often depressed to funnel-shaped; finely felty-squamulose, pale ochre, cinnamon-brown to yellow-brick. **Gills** slightly decurrent, thin, crowded; watery, yellowish-pink to cinnamon. **Latex** thin, scanty, mild. **Stem** rather soft, long, colour as cap. **Spores** pale ochre, subglobose, 7–9 X 5–6 µm. *Toxic raw and not recomended.* **Occurring** in damp birch woods in Britain but also under conifers, autumn, occasional.

Unusual smell of liquorice

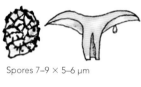

Spores 7–9 × 5–6 µm

### *Lactarius camphoratus*

**Key characters** small cap red-brown; strong scent of curry as it dries. **Description: Cap** 2–6 cm, convex then soon funnel-shaped, thin, deep reddish brown, wine brown. **Gills** slightly decurrent, fairly crowded, pale reddish-brown.

*Lactarius camphoratus*

**Latex** fairly abundant, white to watery, mild to taste. **Stem** firm, rather short, purplish brown. **Spores** white, subglobose, 6–7 X 6 µm. *Edible dried as a spice.* **Occurring** in mixed woods both broadleaf and conifers. autumn, common.

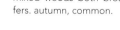

Spores 6–7 × 6 µm

## *Lactarius quietus*

**Key characters** only under oak; cap light brown, zoned; characteristic oily, sweet odour. **Description: Cap** 4–8, convex then expanded, dry, smooth; dull pale reddish-brown with darker concentric zones. **Gills** whitish to pale brown, adnate-decurrent, fairly crowded. **Latex** white, mild and sweet. **Odour** of sweet oil. **Stem** rather tall, firm, colour as cap. **Spores** cream, 7–9 × 6–7 µm. *Edible but not very good.* **Occurring** often in circles around oaks, summer and autumn, very common.

Oily smell

*Lactarius quietus*

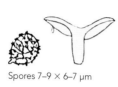

Spores 7–9 × 6–7 µm

## *Lactarius rufus*

**Key characters** cap foxy red, sharply umbonate; latex white, mild then slowly very hot. **Description: Cap** 4–8 cm, convex then soon expanded and often depressed, almost always with small sharp umbo; rich reddish foxy brown, texture slightly roughened. **Gills** adnate-decurrent, reddish ochre. **Stem** hollow, colour as cap but with a white base. **Latex** mild at first then slowly extremely hot to taste. **Spores** cream, ovate, 8–9 × 6–7 µm. *Not edible.* **Occurring** in birch or pine woods, summer to autumn, common.

*Lactarius rufus*

Prefers non-chalky soil

Spores 8–9 × 6–7 µm

*Lactarius torminosus*

Shaggy margin

Felty cap with concentric salmon-pink zones

Likes damp places

### Lactarius torminosus

**Key characters** cap pinkish, shaggy and zoned; milk acrid. **Description: Cap** 4–12 cm, convex then expanded, depressed; margin at first strongly inrolled, and extremely woolly-shaggy; pale pinkish to yellowish flesh-colour with faint zones. **Gills** adnate-decurrent, thin, crowded, paler than cap. **Latex** white, copious, extremely hot to taste. **Stem** rather short, pale flesh-pink. **Spores** cream, ovate, 7–9 X 6–8 µm. *Inedible.* **Notes:** in damp birch woods, autumn, frequent. **Notes:** The equally common *L. pubescens*, also found under birch, has a paler, almost white unzoned cap and smaller spores.

Spores 7–9 × 6–8 µm

### Lactarius deterrimus

*Lactarius deterrimus*

Gills are paler than cap

Slightly acrid orange milk turns purple on exposure

**Key characters** orange with concentric zones, staining green; copious carrot-red milk turning deep green; flesh orange then red, finally green. **Description: Cap** 4–10 cm, convex then expanded and slightly depressed, viscid when moist then dry, orange-brick to bright orange with concentric zones, staining greenish with age or bruising. **Gills** adnate-decurrent, crowded, orange-ochre. **Latex** orange-red, reddening and soon green. **Stem** rather short, solid, colour as cap, usually smooth. **Spores** cream, 7–9 X 6–7 µm. *Edible but not particularly*

Spores 7–9 × 6–7 µm

*good.* **Occurring** in spruce woods, summer to late autumn, common and widespread. This species was for many years confused in Britain with *L. deliciosus*, which differs in growing with pines, its pleasant taste, and unchanging carrot-coloured milk. Its stem surface is usually pitted.

## Lactarius tabidus

**Key characters** pale brown wrinkled cap with tiny umbo; milk turns yellow on handkerchief. **Description: Cap** 3–5 cm, convex then expanded and usually with a minute umbo; surface dry, slightly roughened and puckered-wrinkled at centre; pale brick-red to tan, paler when dry. **Gills** adnate-decurrent, slightly distant, colour as cap. **Latex** white, turning yellow in about one minute on a handkerchief (not on the gills), taste mild. **Stem** rather soft, slender, tapered above, colour as cap. **Spores** cream, ovate, 8–10 X 5–7 µm. *Edible but not recommended.* **Occurring** in mixed woods, summer to autumn, very common. **Notes:** the similar *L. subdulcis* differs in its slightly pinker cap usually without wrinkles, and white unpleasant tasting milk not turning yellow; it grows with beech.

Acrid white milk turns yellow

*Lactarius tabidus*

Spores 8–10 × 5–7 µm

## Lactarius vietus

**Key characters** cap grey-lilac; milk turns deep grey. **Description: Cap** 4–10 cm, convex then expanded and shallowly depressed; smooth, slightly viscid when moist; pale greyish-brown with a flush of lilac. **Gills** adnate-decurrent, thin, crowded, white to pale ochre. **Latex** white, turning grey on the gills in about 20 minutes; taste hot. **Stem** rather soft, slightly paler than cap. **Spores** pale cream, ovate, 8–9 X 6–7 µm. *Not edible.* **Occurring** in damp deciduous woods especially birch, autumn, frequent. **Notes:** *L. uvidus* in wet woods, is a pale pinkish buff, has flesh when cut turning violet-lilac and white latex, mild and slowly turning violet.

*Lactarius vietus*

White milk dries grey

Spores 8–9 × 6–7 µm

In large numbers on damp ground

### *Lactarius piperatus*

**Key characters** cap white, soon funnel-shaped; gills extremely crowded; milk hot. **Description: Cap** 5–15 cm, convex, soon expanded and funnel-shaped; white to pale cream, smooth, cracking with age; margin inrolled at first. **Gills** adnate-decurrent, extremely crowded, thin, repeatedly forking, cream to yellowish. **Latex** white, copious, very hot and peppery. **Stem** firm, solid, stout, tapering downwards, colour as cap. **Spores** white, ovate, 6–9 X 5–7 μm. *Inedible.* **Occurring** in deciduous woods, summer and autumn, common. **Notes:** the similar and larger (to 25 cm) *L. vellereus* also has a depressed cap, but has a woolly-tomentose surface, especially at the strongly inrolled margin, gills rather widely spaced, and a short stout stem.

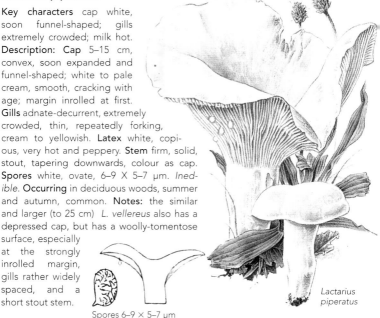

Spores 6–9 × 5–7 μm

*Lactarius piperatus*

---

*Lactarius turpis*

### *Lactarius turpis*

**Key characters** ugly, dark cap, olive-brown to black; gills yellowish; latex hot, unpleasant; specific chemical test. **Description: Cap** 5–15 cm, convex then soon expanded and depressed, margin often rather irregular, inrolled; viscid when moist, colour very dull, greenish brown to almost sepia or black, more yellowish at margin. **Gills** adnate-decurrent, crowded, dull straw-yellow, spotted red-

Spores 7–8 × 6–7 μm

dish brown. **Latex** white, copious, very hot and unpleasant. **Stem** rather short, viscid, surface often pitted and spotted, deep olive. **Spores** cream, ovate, 7–8 X 6–7 µm. **Chemical test:** ammonia on any part = deep violet. *Inedible.* **Occurring** in deciduous woods on damp, boggy soil, summer to autumn, common.

### Lactarius volemus

**Key characters** rich tawny-orange to reddish-orange cap (often cracking) and stem; smell of herring; white milk stains brown. **Description:** Cap 5–10 cm, convex then expanded and slightly depressed; surface dry, matt-velvety, often minutely cracking concentrically, bright orange, tawny. **Gills** adnate-decurrent, rather crowded, cream. **Latex** white, copious, turning slightly brownish, mild, odour of herrings. **Stem** often tall; stout, firm, slightly hollow, smooth, orange, reddish orange. **Spores** white, globose, 8–10 µm. *Edible and good.* **Occurring** in deciduous woods, autumn, uncommon.

*Lactarius volemus*

Spores 8–10 µm

### Lactarius glyciosmus

**Key characters** cap pale greyish lilac with umbo; smell of dried coconut. **Description: Cap** 3–6 cm, convex then expanded with obtuse umbo; pale greyish lilac, dry. **Gills** adnate-decurrent, thin, yellowish flesh-colour. **Latex** white, mild at first then slightly hot. **Odour** strong of confectioner's dried coconut. **Stem** soft, slightly longer than cap diameter, colour as cap only paler. **Spores** deep cream, ovate, 7–8 X 6–7 µm. *Edible and quite good.* **Occurring** in deciduous woods, especially birch, autumn, frequent. **Notes:** also with a coconut odour, but under conifers, is *L. mammosus*, cap darker, brownish, with acute umbo; rather rare.

*Lactarius glyciosmus*

Strong smell of coconut oil

Spores 7–8 × 6–7 µm

185

## BOLETACEAE

The Boletes are found throughout the world in both temperate and tropical climes and without doubt can claim some of the most luridly coloured, delicious and often huge fruitbodies in the entire range of fungi. There are species whose caps reach 60 cm in diameter with gross stems to match, while others are only a few centimetres across. Almost all share the characteristics of a soft, fleshy body, and spores produced in a tubular fertile layer instead of on gills. These tubes are densely packed under the cap, their exits (the only part visible without breaking or cutting the cap) being referred to as the pores. Colour changes within the flesh are extremely common within this family and are valuable guides to identification. Almost all species are considered edible, with only a few exceptions which are either just bitter or mildly upsetting. One species, the Cep or Porcini (*Boletus edulis*) is one of the most famous edible fungi in the world.

Genera included within the family and described here are: *Boletus*, *Leccinum*, *Suillus*, *Aureoboletus*, *Strobilomyces*, *Gyroporus*, *Porphyrellus* and *Tylopilus*. Many of these were formerly included in the genus *Boletus* but are now believed to be genera in their own right. Also included within the wider order Boletales are some toadstools which, despite having gills, not pores, are believed to be closer to the rest of the boletes than to other gilled fungi; these are the Gomphidiaceae and the Paxillaceae.

## BOLETUS

### Boletus aereus

*Boletus aereus*

**Key characters** cap very dark sepia; stem rich brown, with paler network. **Description: Cap** distinctly rough, granulate-matt, tending to crack into minute scales; colour deep intense sepia-brown, almost black, often with discoloured, paler patches. **Pores** cream then pale yellowish. **Stem** strongly coloured, rich reddish brown with paler brown network. **Spores** 13–15 X 4–5.5 μm. *Edible and delicious.* **Occurring** in deciduous woods, summer and early autumn, uncommon, mainly southern distribution. **Notes:** a beautiful and distinctive species, *B. aestivalis* has a similar cap texture, but colours pale, ochre-brown to cinnamon; stem buff with dense white net.

Spores 13–15 × 4–5.5 μm

## *Boletus edulis* (Cep, Penny Bun)

**Key characters** cap rich brown, robust; stem cream with white network; flesh firm, white, almost unchanging. **Description: Cap** 5–18 cm, convex then expanded, smooth, slightly greasy in wet weather; thick-fleshed and firm; rich toasted brown, chestnut or bay; margin paler, white at edge. **Tubes** white then yellowish. **Pores** white then cream, finally lemon-yellow in some forms. **Stem** robust, often very fat (tall and straight in the subspecies *trisporus*, with three-spored basidia); paler than cap, almost white, with a white network, especially at apex. **Spores** olive-brown, subfusiform, 14–17 X 4–6 µm. *Edible and perhaps the most delicious of all fungi.* **Occurring** in deciduous or conifer woods, summer and autumn, common. **Notes:** the related *B. pinophilus* occurs only under conifers; cap and stem are wine-red with vinaceous tints; flesh also turning vinaceous.

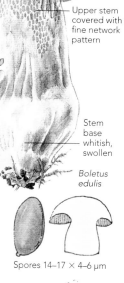

Cap sticky when moist

Upper stem covered with fine network pattern

Stem base whitish, swollen

*Boletus edulis*

## *Boletus calopus*

**Key characters** cap greyish clay; pores yellow; stem pale to deep red with fine white network overall; flesh bitter. **Description: Cap** 5–15 cm, convex, thick-fleshed, margin inrolled when young; smooth, dry, pale greyish-clay or almost white, darker with age. **Tubes** and pores pale yellow, bluish when cut. **Stem** stout, often swollen, firm and solid; apex yellow, bright red below with a fine white network in upper half. **Flesh** cream to lemon-yellow, blue when cut. **Spores** olive-brown, subfusiform, 12–16 X 4–6 µm. *Not edible, very bitter.* **Occurring** In deciduous and conifer woods, autumn, uncommon. **Notes:** the related *B. radicans* (= *B. albidus*) differs in the paler whitish-grey cap, often very large size (>20 cm); stout pale yellow stem, with only very faint white network; taste also bitter.

Spores 14–17 × 4–6 µm

*Boletus calopus*

Lemon-yellow pores bruise blue

Red stem with network ornamentation

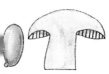

Spores 12–16 × 4–6 µm

187

*Boletus satanas*

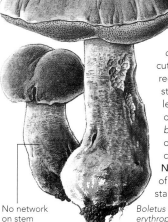

Solitary, on chalky soil

### Boletus satanas (Devil's Bolete, Satan's Bolete) ☻

**Key characters** large cap pale, white then greyish; red network on the bulbous stem; flesh very pale yellow then bluish. **Description: Cap** 10–30 cm, thick-fleshed, pale greyish white to greenish grey; smooth, minutely velvety especially when young. **Tubes** yellowish green, blue on cutting; pores small, round, blood-red to orange with age, yellow at the extreme margin, green-blue upon bruising. **Stem** very stout, swollen, orange to yellow at apex flushing red to purplish in lower half, with raised red network over most of stem. **Flesh** pale yellow becoming pale bluish on cutting, smelling foul of old garlic with age. **Spores** olive-brown, subfusiform, 11–14 X 4–6 µm. *Reputedly very poisonous but probably just upsetting and emetic.* **Occurring** in deciduous woods especially on chalky soils, midsummer and early autumn, uncommon to locally common. **Notes:** the related *B. legalliae* (= *B. satanoides*) differs by a reddish-purple flush that appears in the cap, a less swollen stem and flesh blueing strongly.

Spores 11–14 × 4–6 µm

Cap dark brown with olive or reddish tints

### Boletus erythropus (= B. luridiformis)

**Key characters** cap deep brown; pores deep red; deep red speckled; yellow flesh instantly deep blue if cut. **Description: Cap** 5–10 cm, convex then expanded, dry, smooth to slightly tomentose; dark brown to olive-brown, yellower at margin (yellowish in the var. *discolor*). **Tubes** lemon-yellow, bluish green on cutting. **Pores** dark red, sometimes almost maroon red, paler, more orange when expanded. **Stem** stout, smooth, bright red, without network, under lens visible as red stippling on yellow. **Spores** olive-brown, subfusiform, 12–15 X 4–6 µm. *Edible but not recommended.* **Occurring** in deciduous and conifer woods, summer and autumn, common everywhere. **Notes:** the commonest of the red-pored, bluestaining boletes.

No network on stem

*Boletus erythropus*

Spores 12–15 × 4–6 µm

## *Boletus luridus*

**Key characters** apricot-brick cap, red-flushed stem with prominent red network; flesh blueing; pores orange. **Description: Cap** 5–15 cm, convex then flattened, minutely tomentose then smooth; very variable from dark apricot to olivaceous and brown, usually retaining pinkish tones at margin and rather rust-coloured at centre; bruising blue-black. **Tubes** yellow-green, blue on cutting. **Pores** orange-red to pale orange bruising deep blue; usually yellow at margin. **Flesh** yellowish in cap and upper stem, brighter yellow below, often purplish red in base; turning blue; usually with red line of flesh above tube-layer. **Spores** olive-brown, subfusiform, 11–15 X 4–7 µm. *Apparently edible when cooked, but best avoided.* **Occurring** in deciduous woods especially on chalky soils, summer to autumn, occasional. **Notes:** The similar but rarer *B. queletii* has a rich orange to reddish brown cap, orange-apricot pores and stem yellowish above, deep purple-red below as is the flesh; there is no network.

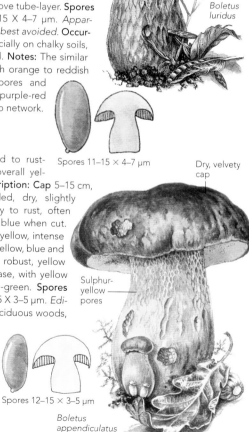

Yellowish-olive cap

Flesh yellow, turns deep blue when broken

*Boletus luridus*

Spores 11–15 × 4–7 µm

## *Boletus appendiculatus*

**Key characters** cap brick-red to rust-brown; bright yellow pores; overall yellowish network on stem. **Description: Cap** 5–15 cm, convex then slightly expanded, dry, slightly roughened; rich brick-red, bay to rust, often cracking. **Tubes** lemon-yellow, blue when cut. **Pores** bright lemon to golden yellow, intense blue when bruised. **Flesh** pale yellow, blue and patchily pink on cutting. **Stem** robust, yellow above becoming reddish at base, with yellow network overall, bruising blue-green. **Spores** olive-brown, subfusiform, 12–15 X 3–5 µm. *Edible and good.* **Occurring** in deciduous woods, late summer, early autumn, uncommon, mainly southern. *B. fechtneri*, closely related, has a very pale greyish-buff cap bruising coffee-brown, stem yellow with a reddish zone. The rare *B. regius* is very similar but has a rich carmine-red cap.

Dry, velvety cap

Sulphur-yellow pores

Spores 12–15 × 3–5 µm

*Boletus appendiculatus*

*Boletus badius*

### Boletus badius

**Key characters** bay-coloured cap and stem; pores pale yellowish, pale blue on bruising and cutting. **Description:** Cap 4–15 cm, convex, at first, minutely tomentose then smooth and often slightly viscid when wet; deep bay-brown to rather pale ochrebrown in some forms. **Tubes and pores** cream to pale yellow, turning grey to bluish green. **Stem** equal to swollen, solid, ochre to pale chestnut, smooth. **Flesh** pale, white to yellowish, turning bluish on cutting. **Spores** olive-brown, subfusiform, 13–15 X 4–6 µm. *Edible and quite good.* **Occurring** in deciduous and coniferous woods, summer to autumn, very common.

No network on stem

Spores 13–15 × 4–6 µm

### Xerocomus porosporus

**Key characters** cap dull sepia; cracking; spores with a distinct pore. **Description:** Cap 4–8 cm, convex then flattened, tomentose, soon cracking to expose whitish flesh beneath; olive-brown, soon dull, dirty sepia. **Tubes** yellow-olive.

*Xerocomus porosporus*

Pores angular, large, lemon-yellow then olivaceous, finally dull brownish. **Flesh** pale lemon-yellow in cap and upper stem, reddish brown below, turning bluish when cut. **Stem** fairly slender, tall; apex yellowish, then a narrow band of red, dull greyish sepia below; no network but some longitudinal ridges. **Spores** olive-brown, subfusiform, truncate at one end (and with a distinct pore), 13–15 X 4–6 µm. *Edible but not recommended.* **Occurring** in mixed woods, autumn, frequent and widespread.

Spores 13–15 × 4–6 µm

## *Xerocomus subtomentosus*

**Key characters** woolly cap, yellow-green to reddish brown; flesh pale yellowish, pinkish in base. **Description: Cap** 5–12 cm, convex then expanded, tomentose, hazel-brown to olivaceous-buff; with a woolly tomentum often bright yellowish-green. **Pores** and tubes lemon to chrome-yellow bruising only slightly blue if at all. **Stem** rather slender, buff to reddish brown or olive, often with slight ridges at apex. **Flesh** pale yellowish, pale pink in stem base, date-brown below cuticle. **Spores** olive-brown, subfusiform, 10–13 X 3–5 μm. *Edible and quite good.* **Occurring** in mixed woods, summer and autumn, common. **Notes:** the extremely similar *X. ferrugineus* often has strong brown ribs almost as a net on stem apex, and flesh white throughout.

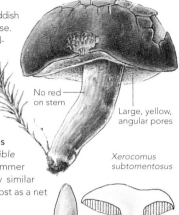

No red on stem

Large, yellow, angular pores

*Xerocomus subtomentosus*

Spores 10–13 × 3–5 μm

## *Xerocomus chrysenteron*

**Key characters** brown cap cracking to expose reddish flesh. **Description: Cap** 4–12 cm, convex then flattened, subtomentose then smooth; hazel to olivaceous brown or buff, cracking to expose red-stained fissures. **Tubes** lemon-yellow then greenish. **Pores** large and angular, lemon-yellow then greenish, sometimes bruising blue. **Flesh** cream-yellow to lemon, browner in stem base, slightly blue when cut. **Stem** rather slender, smooth, yellowish to buff with dense reddish floccose granules overall, but variable. **Spores** olive-brown, subfusiform, 12–15 X 3–5 μm. *Edible and quite good.* **Occurring** most commonly in coniferous woods but occasionally broadleaf also, autumn, frequent. **Notes:** Earlier in the season occurs *X. cisalpinus*, also red-cracking, but with stem bright yellow above, reddish below and intense blue staining, mainly southern under broadleaf trees. *X. engelii* grows in summer, is medium brown without red cracks, and has carrot-orange flesh in extreme base of stem, very common along roadsides, wood- and paths, etc.

Red cracks on cap surface

Carmine-red colour on stem

*Xerocomus chrysenteron*

Spores 12–15 × 3–5 μm

191

### Xerocomus pruinatus

**Key characters** cap dark, reddish bay to black-brown with white "bloom" when young; chrome-yellow stem and flesh. **Description: Cap** 3–6 cm, convex, deep plum-brown, reddish-bay to almost black, margin often red, surface with a whitish bloom when fresh. **Tubes**, pores lemon-yellow, bruising bluish. **Flesh** bright yellow throughout bruising bluish. **Stem** rather swollen, smooth, bright yellow, slightly reddish at base, noticeable yellow mycelium matting together the leaf litter. **Spores** olive-brown, subfusiform, 11–14 X 4–6 μm. *Edible and quite good.* **Occurring** in beech and oak woods, late autumn, occasional to common.

*Xerocomus pruinatus*

Spores 11–14
X 4–6 μm

### Xerocomus rubellus (= Boletus versicolor)

*Xerocomus rubellus*

**Key characters** carmine-red to purplish cap and stem; all parts bruise blue, under oaks. **Description: Cap** 3–8 cm, convex then expanded; subtomentose, bright scarlet to carmine-red, sometimes cracking, soon fades when old to reddish brown or olive. **Pores** and tubes lemon-yellow then greenish. **Flesh** dull buff-yellow, carrot-orange in extreme base in stem. **Stem** rather slender, tapered at base, blood-red to carmine or purplish, yellow at apex, bruising blue. **Spores** olive-brown, subfusiform, 11–14 X 4–6 μm. *Edible but not very good.* **Occurring** in grass verges near oaks, summer to autumn, frequent.

Spores 11–14
X 4–6 μm

## *Pseudoboletus parasiticus*

**Key characters** unique in growing only on common earthball (*Scleroderma citrinum*). **Description: Cap** 2–5 cm, subglobose to convex, hardly expanding; rich ochre-yellow to olivaceous brown; surface velvety, sometimes cracking. **Tubes** and pores bright lemon-yellow, pores often stained reddish. **Stem** rather stout, short, tapered at base, which attaches to the bottom of the earthball, colour as cap.
**Spores** olive-brown, fusiform, 11–21 X 3–5 µm. *Edible but not recommended.* **Occurring** always on the common earthball (*Scleroderma citrinum*), summer to autumn, uncommon but widespread.

Spores 11–21 × 3–5 µm

*Pseudoboletus parasiticus*

## *Chalciporus piperatus*

**Key characters** cinnamon-coloured cap and stem; rust-coloured pores; bright yellow stem base and flesh; peppery taste. **Description: Cap** 3–10 cm, convex then expanding, smooth to slightly greasy-viscid when moist; ochre-brown to bright cinnamon. **Tubes and pores** cinnamon to rust, pores large and angular. **Stem** rather slender, colour as cap except base, which is bright golden yellow, as is flesh in base. **Flesh** in rest of stem and cap pale buff-ochre to reddish. **Spores** olive-brown with cinnamon tints, subfusiform, 8–11 X 3–4 µm. *Not poisonous but usually considered inedible because of very peppery taste.* **Occurring** usually under birches, sometimes conifers, often in association with the Fly Agaric (*Amanita muscaria*), autumn, common.

*Chalciporus piperatus*

Spores 8–11 × 3–4 µm

### Leccinum scabrum

**Key characters** cap nut-brown, rather soft; stem brown floccose; flesh white, almost unchanging in colour. **Description: Cap** 5–15 cm, convex then expanding, smooth, moist and sticky in wet weather, otherwise dry; pale hazel-brown to buff. **Tubes and pores** very pale, almost white, then clay-buff to ochre with age, bruising cinnamon. **Stem** rather long, white to buff covered with small, woolly, brown to blackish scales (scabrosities). **Flesh** very soft especially in cap, white and unchangeable to very slightly pale pinkish buff. **Spores** tobacco-brown, subfusiform, 14–20 X 5–6 µm. *Edible and quite good.* **Occurring** under birches, summer and autumn, common everywhere. **Notes:** this species has now been split into several closely related species among which are *L. roseofracta*, stouter and darker brown with very dark, blackish stem scabrosities and flesh strongly pink or reddish when cut, and *L. variicolor* with greyish-black, marbled cap and greyish scabrosities, flesh bright pink in cap and upper stem, bright blue-green below.

Rough, scaly stem

*Leccinum scabrum*

Spores 14–20 × 5–6 µm

### Leccinum quercinum

*Leccinum quercinum*

**Key characters** cap deep fox-red to chestnut; stem scales reddish brown; under oaks and poplar. **Description: Cap** 5–20cm, rounded to flattened, dry and slightly roughened, bright fox-red to red-brown with overhanging margin. **Tubes and pores** cream-buff. **Stem** stout, fleshy, cream with dark reddish-brown squamules overall, flesh white then soon reddish lilac and finally smoky grey-black. **Spores** brown, fusiform, 13–18 X 4–5 µm. *Edible and good.* **Occurring** under oaks and rarely poplars, late summer and autumn, frequent in southern England. **Notes:** *L. aurantiacum*, also found under poplars has an orange cap but white stem and white floccules only slowly browning.

Spores 13–18 × 4–5 µm

## Leccinum versipelle

**Key characters** cap often tawny-orange; pores dark when young; stem with blackish scales. **Description: Cap** 6–20 cm, convex then expanding, with narrow pendent fringe of cap cuticle at margin; surface dry, downy to smooth with slightly flattened-scaly centre; bright yellow-orange to orange-buff or tawny. **Tubes** white to buff, **pores** small, very dark greyish to black when young then soon paler, buff. **Stem** rather stout to massive, white to buff, densely speckled with darker brown to black woolly squamules; often bruising greenish at base when handled. **Flesh** white, then pinkish, finally violaceous grey to black when cut. **Spores** tobacco-brown, subfusiform, 12–16 X 4–5 µm. *Edible and highly regarded by many.* **Occurring** always under birch, summer and autumn, common and widespread.

*Leccinum versipelle*

White flesh blackens on exposure

Tall stem with blackish scales on a white background

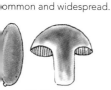

Spores 12–16 × 4–5 µm

## Leccinum holopus

**Key characters** white cap, pores, stem and stem squamules; cap greenish buff with age; in sphagnum bogs under birch. **Description: Cap** 4–12 cm, convex then expanding, downy when young, smooth and viscid with age; pure white then pale buff with greenish tints. **Pores** white to buff. **Stem** rather slender, white with white squamules. **Flesh** white, unchanging. **Spores** tobacco-brown, subfusiform, 15–18 X 5–6 µm. *Edible and quite good.* **Occurring** especially in northern regions, more rarely in southern districts, autumn, rare to occasional.

*Leccinum holopus*

Spores 15–18 × 5–6 µm

195

### *Leccinum crocipodium*

**Key characters** cap bright yellow, then ochre-brown cracking; yellow pores and scaly stem; all parts blacken when cut or bruised. **Description:** Cap 4–10 cm, convex then expanded, smooth and slightly downy when young; bright lemon-yellow to yellow-orange when fresh, soon dulling to ochre-brown, cracking all over like mosaic with age to show white flesh. **Tubes and pores** lemon-yellow. **Stem** rather stout, pale yellow with squamules of same colour. Flesh yellow soon blackening when cut. **Spores** ochre-brown, subfusiform, 12–17 × 4–7 μm. *Edible and good.* **Occurring** in warm southern oak woods, early summer to autumn, uncommon.

*Leccinum crocipodium*

Spores 12–17 × 4–7 μm

### *Suillus grevillei* (= *Suillus elegans*)

*Suillus grevillei*

**Key characters** only under larch; cap yellow to brick-colour; yellow stem with ring; pores lemon-yellow. **Description:** Cap 4–10 cm, convex then expanded, very viscid when moist, smooth and polished when dry; bright yellow-orange, darker with age and distinctly dark brick-colour in the variety *badius*. **Tubes** rather decurrent, pale yellow. **Pores** quite small, angular, lemon-yellow, bruising rust-colour. **Stem** rather slender to medium, with a distinct fleshy ring; pale yellow above, more ochre below with reddish stains. **Flesh** yellowish becoming slightly blue in stem base. **Spores** ochre, subfusiform, 8–11 × 3–4 μm. *Edible but may upset some people; slimy cap cuticle is usually discarded.* **Occurring** under larches, late summer to autumn, common.

No granules on stem

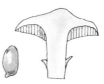

Spores 8–11 × 3–4 μm

### *Suillus luteus* (Slippery Jack)

**Key characters** under pines; cap deep purplish brown to chestnut; stem has a ring, with violet flush below. **Description: Cap** 5–10 cm, convex then expanded and slightly umbonate, smooth and very viscid-glutinous, shiny when dry; deep purplish brown to chocolate-brown or chestnut. **Tubes** pale yellow to straw-colour. **Pores** straw-yellow to yellow-olive. **Stem** medium pale straw with large white or violaceous fleshy ring at apex, flushed violaceous below ring, apex with darker glandular dots. **Flesh** yellowish. **Spores** ochre, subfusiform, 7–10 X 3–4 μm. *Edible but causes mild upsets in some people.* **Occurring** below pines, autumn, common and widespread everywhere.

*Suillus luteus*

Stem covered in brownish granules

Large, spreading ring

Spores 7–10 × 3–4 μm

### *Suillus viscidus (= Suillus aeruginascens)*

**Key characters** pallid buff-olive to greyish colours; whitish ring; under larch. **Description: Cap** 4–10 cm, convex then expanded, rather wrinkled and irregular, very viscid when moist; pale olive-buff to cream or straw, often blotched with greyish or brownish spots. **Tubes and pores** pale olive-buff to straw with grey-green flush. **Stem** rather short, slender, colour as cap but with greyish flush at apex; white or greyish ring above. **Spores** tobacco brown, subfusiform, 10–12 X 4–5 μm. *Edible but not recommended.* **Occurring** under larch, autumn, rare to uncommon.

Slimy surface

Sticky ring erodes with age, leaving brown zone

*Suillus viscidus*

Spores 10–12 × 4–5 μm

Spores 8–10 × 3–4 μm

## Suillus bovinus

**Key characters** cap orange-buff with white margin; no ring, pores are subdivided. **Description:** Cap 4–10 cm, convex then expanded, smooth and viscid, pale buff to clay with a pinkish-ochre tint. **Tubes** rather decurrent, dull olive-grey. **Pores** rather large and angular, "compound" (i.e. there are pores within pores), dull yellowish olive to buff or ochre. **Stem** rather short, tapered, colour as cap. **Spores** olive-brown, subfusiform, 8–10 X 3–4 μm. *Edible but soft and gelatinous.* **Occurring** with pines, summer to autumn, common.

Slimy or
sticky-shiny

*Suillus
bovinus*

Large, greenish-
yellow pores

## Suillus variegatus

**Key characters** tawny-ochre colours and small felty scales on cap; no ring; cap only slightly moist. **Description:** Cap 4–10 cm, convex then slightly expanded, rather thick-fleshed, slightly moist but usually subtomentose especially when young; tawny ochre to sienna or rust with small, slightly darker, felty scales. **Tubes and pores** yellowish, distinctly flushed olive at first, finally cinnamon, bruising greenish. **Stem** rather short, stout, often swollen, colour as cap but paler; base often with a matted, rooting mycelial mass spreading outwards. Flesh pale yellowish often flushing pale blue when cut. **Spores** tobacco-brown, subfusiform, 9–11 X 3–4 μm. *Edible and quite good.* **Occurring** under conifers, especially pines, and on poor sandy soils, autumn, occasional to frequent.

*Suillus
variegatus*

Stem is
ringless

Spores 9–11 × 3–4 μm

# Suillus granulatus

**Key characters** cap reddish-brown to golden ochre, smooth and viscid; stem (without ring) and pores exude milky droplets in damp weather. **Description: Cap** 3–8 cm, convex then expanded; reddish fawn to rust, finally often golden ochre, smooth and viscid when wet. **Tubes and pores** pale lemon-yellow. **Stem** rather slender, pale yellowish with pinkish or coral base; apex with white or yellowish floccose granules, which also exude droplets. **Spores** ochre, subfusiform, 8–10 X 2–4 µm. *Edible and quite good.* **Occurring** with pines, autumn, common.

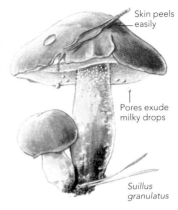

Skin peels easily

Pores exude milky drops

*Suillus granulatus*

Spores 8–10 × 2–4 µm

# Aureoboletus
## (= Boletus cramesinus) gentilis

**Key characters** cap sticky, clay-pink, tubes and pores vivid golden yellow. **Description: Cap** 2–5 cm, convex, smooth and viscid-tacky, often wrinkled; pale pinkish clay to coral or strawberry-pink, with darker radial streaks. **Tubes and pores** bright golden yellow, unchanging. **Stem** rather slender, tapered downwards, rooting, pale yellow with reddish lower half. **Spores** ochre, subfusiform, 11–15 X 4–6 µm. *Edible.* **Occurring** in broadleaf woods, often on clay soils, summer to autumn, rare to uncommon.

*Aureoboletus gentilis*

Spores 11–15 × 4–6 µm

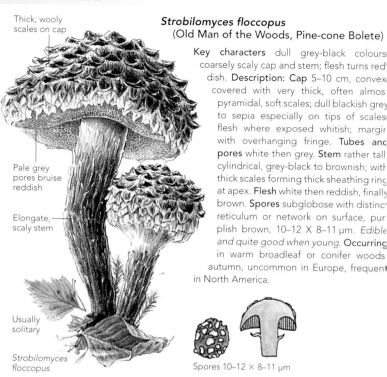

Thick, wooly
scales on cap

Pale grey
pores bruise
reddish

Elongate,
scaly stem

Usually
solitary

*Strobilomyces
floccopus*

## *Strobilomyces floccopus*
### (Old Man of the Woods, Pine-cone Bolete)

**Key characters** dull grey-black colours; coarsely scaly cap and stem; flesh turns reddish. **Description: Cap** 5–10 cm, convex, covered with very thick, often almost pyramidal, soft scales; dull blackish grey to sepia especially on tips of scales; flesh where exposed whitish; margin with overhanging fringe. **Tubes and pores** white then grey. **Stem** rather tall, cylindrical, grey-black to brownish; with thick scales forming thick sheathing ring at apex. **Flesh** white then reddish, finally brown. **Spores** subglobose with distinct reticulum or network on surface, purplish brown, 10–12 X 8–11 μm. *Edible and quite good when young.* **Occurring** in warm broadleaf or conifer woods, autumn, uncommon in Europe, frequent in North America.

Spores 10–12 × 8–11 μm

## *Gyroporus castaneus*

**Key characters** cap and stem velvety-granular, dry; stem hollow; flesh rather hard, brittle, spore print pale yellow. **Description: Cap** 4–10 cm, convex then expanded and flattened, minutely velvety then smooth-granular; rich tawny brown to cinnamon or chestnut. **Tubes and pores** cream to straw-colour, not changing colour when bruised. **Stem** rather short, stout, minutely velvety, hollow and chambered, colour as cap. **Spores** elliptic, 8–11 X 4–6 μm. *Edible and delicious.* **Occurring** usually with oaks, summer to autumn, uncommon to locally common, mainly southern in distribution.

Tough
stem

*Gyroporus
castaneus*

Spores 8–11 × 4–6 μm

## Gyroporus cyanescens

**Key characters** whitish cap and stem with rough, hard texture; stem hollow; flesh turns deep blue. **Description: Cap** 4–15 cm, convex then expanded, dirty whitish to cream, pale straw or buff; texture rough, velvety-scaly, fibrillose, margin shaggy. **Tubes and pores** white then yellowish to greenish yellow. **Stem** rather stout, hollow and chambered; colour as cap, fibrillose-tomentose, especially below, rather smooth above; surface often cracking to form ring zones. **Flesh** firm, white, turning immediately deep blue-green to indigo on cutting. **Spores** pale straw-yellow, elliptic, 9–11 X 4–6 µm. *Edible and good.* **Occurring** on acid soils below birch or spruce, northern in distribution, autumn, uncommon.

Gyroporus
cyanescens

Spores 9–11 × 4–6 µm

## Porphyrellus pseudoscaber
## (= Boletus porphyrosporus)

**Key characters** sooty-brown, grey, to blackish colours overall; spore print purple-brown. **Description: Cap** 5–15 cm, convex then expanded, velvety then smooth. **Tubes and pores** pale greyish to pinkish buff, more olive-buff with age, bruising blue-green. **Stem** quite long, equal or tapered upwards; colour as cap with paler, olive-flushed base; slightly velvety, then smooth. **Flesh** whitish to buff, when cut pinkish grey then grey-olive; rather dark blue-green above tubes and at stem apex. **Spores** subfusiform, 12–16 X 5–7 µm. *Apparently edible, but quality doubtful; best avoided.* **Occurring** in mixed woodlands, mainly deciduous, autumn, widespread but rather rare. Note that cut flesh on white paper stains it green.

Porphyrellus
pseudoscaber

Spores 12–16 × 5–7 µm

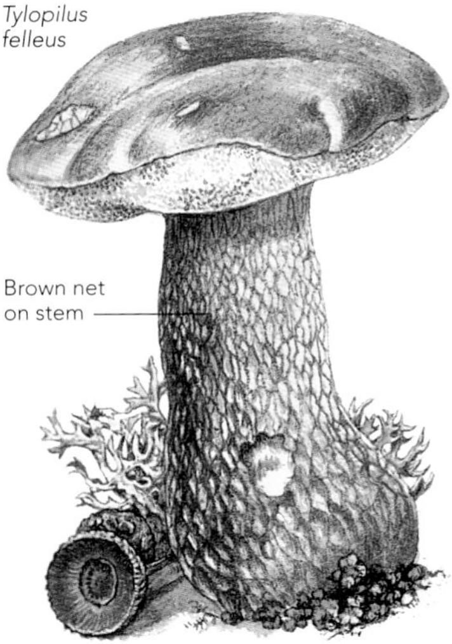


### *Tylopilus (= Boletus) felleus*

**Key characters** cap ochre-brown; paler stem with raised network; pores pink when mature, bitter flesh. **Description: Cap** 5–15 cm, convex then expanding, subtomentose then smooth; tawny ochre to reddish brown, occasionally very pale buff. **Tubes and pores** white, soon salmon-pink. **Stem** rather stout, paler, more ochre-yellow or buff than cap; darker, brown network over most of length. **Flesh** white to pinkish, more or less unchanging. **Spores** clay-pink, subfusiform, 11–15 X 4–5 μm. *Not edible; extremely bitter to taste.* **Occurring** in mixed deciduous woods, autumn, frequent. **Notes:** Sometimes mistaken for the Cep (*Boletus edulis*), but differing in the distinctly pinkish pores and bitter flesh even when cooked.

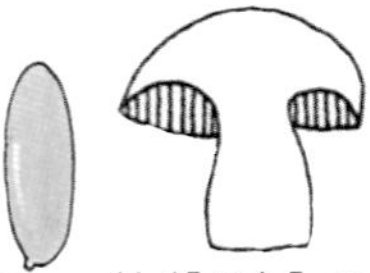

Spores 11–15 × 4–5 μm

# *PAXILLACEAE*

## *PAXILLUS*

### *Paxillus involutus* (Brown Roll-rim)

**Key characters** cap ochre-brown, margin inrolled, woolly, gills and flesh yellowish and bruise dark reddish brown. **Description: Cap** 5–15 cm, at first convex, rather umbonate with very inrolled, woolly-shaggy margin; soon expanding, depressed, margin inrolled until fully expanded; subtomentose but often viscid after rain; rich reddish ochre to tawny brown, when young clearly olivaceous at margin. **Gills** yellow ochre, decurrent, crowded, soft and often branched. **Stem** short, tapered downwards, colour as cap. **Flesh** pale ochre-buff, darkening when cut. **Spores** ochre-brown, elliptic, 8–10 X 5–6 μm. *Poisonous; formerly considered edible and indeed usually is after cooking, but it has been proved to have caused*

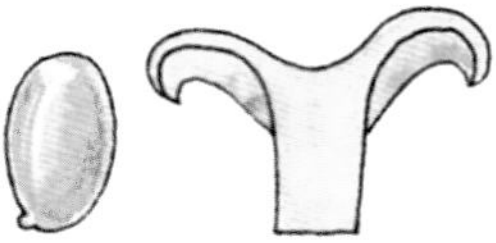

Spores 8–10 × 5–6 μm

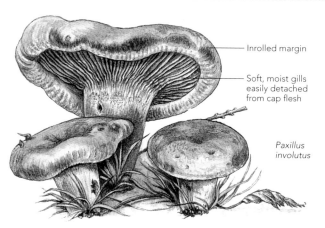

Inrolled margin

Soft, moist gills easily detached from cap flesh

*Paxillus involutus*

*severe poisonings, perhaps through a cumulative toxin.* **Occurring** in mixed woodlands, especially under birch and oak, autumn, common everywhere.

## *Tapinella (= Paxillus) atrotomentosus*

**Key characters** very large brown cap; short, stout, velvet-black stem; on conifer stumps and base of trees. **Description: Cap** 10–30 cm, rounded then soon broad and expanded with inrolled margin, rich reddish brown, chestnut, with velvety-matt surface. **Gills** decurrent, crowded, butter-yellow, ochre, soft, easily separated from cap flesh. **Stem** very stout, black and densely velvety, offset to one side of cap. **Spores** ochre-brown, ovate, 4–7 X 3–5 μm. *Not edible.* **Occurring** on stumps of conifers, summer to autumn, frequent.

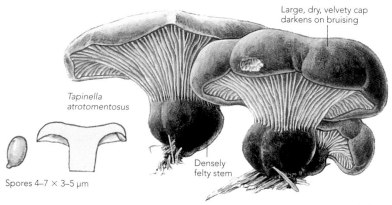

Large, dry, velvety cap darkens on bruising

*Tapinella atrotomentosus*

Densely felty stem

Spores 4–7 × 3–5 μm

203

Cap is sticky
but not slimy

Cobweb-like
ring zone

*Chroogomphus
rutilus*

Spores 15–22 × 5–7 µm

## GOMPHIDIACEAE

### Chroogomphus (= Gomphidius) rutilus

**Key characters** top-shaped cap with acute umbo and overall red-brown tints; yellow stem base.
**Description:** Cap 4–15 cm, convex then expanded with more or less acute umbo at centre; smooth and often sticky when wet, shiny when dry; brick-red to reddish brown or reddish olive. **Gills** deeply decurrent, rather thick, widely spaced, branched at base, olive-green then soon darkening to blackish brown, edge paler. **Stem** rather tall, cylindrical, flushed vinaceous (greyish wine-red) at apex, yellowish to ochre below and bright yellow at base; with slight ring zone at apex, surface rather floccose-viscid. **Flesh** reddish salmon in cap, yellower in stem and bright yellow at base. **Chemical test:** Flesh + ammonia = violet. **Spores** sepia brown to blackish, subfusiform, 15–22 X 5–7 µm. *Edible and quite good.* **Occurring** under conifers, summer to autumn, frequent and widespread.

Slimy, grey-brown
cap

Thick,
forking
gills

*Gomphidius
glutinosus*

### Gomphidius glutinosus

**Key characters** cap pale greyish violet to brownish, with black or brown spots; stem also blackens; bright yellow base.
**Description:** Cap 5–12 cm, convex then expanded with broad umbo then becoming rather depressed; smooth and viscid, pale, whitish to purplish grey or brown and often spotted and mottled

Spores 17–20 × 5–6 µm

black, brown or deep purple-brown. **Gills** deeply decurrent, whitish then grey, brownish black when mature. **Stem** medium to long, tapered slightly upwards, covered with glutinous veil which is at first attached to the cap but tears to leave thick, black (with spores deposited) ring at apex, often disappearing; lower stem flushed yellow, fading to whitish above and spotted grey-brown to purple-black as on cap. **Chemical test:** Flesh + ammonia = vinaceous then brick-red. **Spores** deep blackish brown, subfusiform, 17–20 X 5–6 µm. *Edible but not recommended*; rather slimy. **Occurring** under conifers, especially spruce, autumn, widespread but uncommon.

## Gomphidius roseus

**Key characters** pink-red cap, decurrent grey gills, pinkish sticky stem. **Description: Cap** 2–6 cm, convex then slightly expanded with low, broad umbo, rather wavy and irregular margin, surface very viscid-glutinous; coral-pink to purplish pink then brick-red with age. **Gills** deeply decurrent, thick, white then grey, finally deep olive-brown. Stem rather short, stoutish, whitish to pink with wine-red tints; viscid below then dry, with white viscid veil leaving a ring zone at apex. **Spores** brownish black, subfusiform, 15–18 X 5–6 µm. *Edible but not recommended*. **Occurring** with pines, sometimes in troops, autumn, occasional. **Notes:** this attractive little species often grows in association with *Suillus bovinus*.

Gomphidius
roseus

Gills white
then grey

Flesh white,
unchanging

Spores 15–18 × 5–6 µm

# BRACKETS, TOOTHED FUNGI, CHANTERELLES AND ALLIES

The Bracket fungi and their relatives (often conveniently grouped in the Order Aphyllophorales but now known to be a rather artificial assemblage of often unrelated Orders, Families and genera) form a very diverse group varying greatly in shape and size. All tend to be rather tough and fleshy, sometimes even hard and woody. The Bracket fungi are familiar, but there are stranger forms such as the coral fungi and the spiny hydnums. The group provides a number of edible species, including the Chanterelle (*Cantharellus cibarius*), eaten by the thousand in Europe. Many, especially brackets, can be serious pests and cause serious losses of timber.

## *HERICIALES*

### *HERICIACEAE*

#### *Hericium coralloides (= H. ramosum)*

**Key characters** branched white fruitbodies with long pendent spines in bunches at tips. **Description:** Fruitbody varies from 15–40 cm across, and the individual branches have pendent clusters of thin pendant spines up to 2–3 cm long at the ends, also scattered along the branches. **Spores** more or less globular, 6–8 μm. *Edible and good after scalding.* **Occurring** in deciduous woods, usually on standing trees, especially beech and oak, autumn, rare to occasional mainly in the south. **Notes:** these spectacular fungi are one of the most beautiful sights of the autumn although unfortunately rare and should not be collected for food (they are, however, available for cultivating as kits from specialist fungi growers).

*Hericium coralloides*

Spores 6–8 μm

### Hericium erinaceus

**Key characters** rather rounded fruitbody with dense branches with long 6–10 cm spines. **Description: Fruitbody** much more globular in shape than the previous species, with the pendent spines very long, 5–8 cm clustered at ends of the branches (branches usually hidden). **Spores** white, globose, 6–7 μm. *Edible and good after scalding* (but see notes on previous species). **Occurring** on deciduous trees, especially beech, autumn, rare and mainly southern.

*Hericium erinaceus*

Spores 6–7 μm

## *LENTINELLACEAE*

### Lentinellus cochleatus

**Key characters** cap irregularly lobed, funnel-shaped, pale, ochre to date-brown; toothed gills; often with aniseed smell. **Description: Cap** 3–8 cm, smooth, pale yellow-brown, tawny, irregularly shaped, trumpet- or funnel-shaped. **Gills** decurrent, margins toothed; paler than cap with pink-buff tints. **Stem** tapered below, fusing into large clumps, colour as cap. **Flesh** rather tough, often with fragrance of aniseed. **Spores** white, subglobose, minutely spiny, 5 X 4 μm. *Edible and quite good.* **Occurring** on deciduous wood stumps, autumn, uncommon.

Smells of aniseed

*Lentinellus cochleatus*

Spores 5 × 4 μm

207

## AURISCALPIACEAE

### Auriscalpium vulgare (Earpick Fungus)

*Auriscalpium vulgare*

**Key characters** on pine cones; lateral fuzzy stem; spines below tiny rounded cap **Description: Cap** 0.5–1.5 cm, semicircular or kidney-shaped with lateral stem; upper surface minutely hairy, deep brown. **Underside** with short, pendent spines, brown with greyish flush. **Stem** slender, very hairy, colour as cap. **Spores** white, spherical, minutely spiny, 4–5 µm. *Not edible.* **Occurring** on pine cones, autumn, frequent but difficult to spot as it is extremely well camouflaged. **Notes:** named after the tiny silver ear-spoons used to clean ears in earlier centuries.

Spores 4–5 µm

## THELEPHORALES

## THELEPHORACEAE

### Sarcodon imbricatum

*Sarcodon imbricatum*

**Key characters** thick scaly brown caps with short greyish spines; under conifers. **Description: Cap** 5–20 cm, convex then slightly depressed, funnel-shaped at centre when expanded; dull grey-brown to blackish brown with large, thick, overlapping scales especially at centre. Undersurface with short, decurrent pegs or spines, densely packed, brittle, greyish. Stem short, stout, pale brown. Flesh thick, greyish, rather bitter with age. Spores ochre, globular, minutely spiny, 5–7 µm. *Edible when scalded but not recommended.* **Occurring** in pine woods on sandy soils. Autumn. Occasional.

Spores 5–7 µm

# STEREALES

## STEREACEAE

### Stereum hirsutum

**Key characters** greyish-yellow brackets; upper surface hairy-woolly, with faint zones. **Description: Fruitbody** a thin, tough, semicircular or elongate bracket 3–8 cm across; yellow-ochre to tawny with slight darker zones and the upper surface distinctly finely hairy with a greyish flush. **Undersurface** smooth, rather bright yellow when fresh then fading to buff, not bruising another colour. **Spores**, white, oblong, 5–7 X 2–4 µm. *Inedible*. **Occurring** on deciduous wood, usually fallen logs, branches and twigs, perennial, very common. **Notes:** *S. sanguinolentum* is a greyish-buff species forming rather more resupinate (flattened on the wood surface) fruitbodies which only turns up at the edge to form a bracket; it grows on conifer timber, and bruises blood-red.

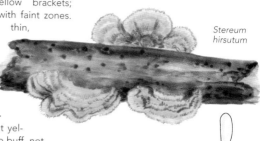

*Stereum hirsutum*

Spores 5–7 × 2–4 µm

### Chondrostereum (= Stereum) purpureum (Silver-leaf Disease)

**Key characters** small bright purplish brackets; greyish on top. **Description: Fruitbody** forms thin, narrow wrinkled brackets 3–8 cm across; upper surface slightly hairy-woolly, greyish purple. **Undersurface** (hymenium) bright purplish lilac; **Spores** white, slightly sausage-shaped, 5–9 X 3–4 µm. *Inedible*. **Occurring** on various deciduous timber (beeches, poplars and also on fruit trees such as plums) where it causes silver-leaf disease, autumn, common.

*Chondrostereum purpureum*

Spores 5–9 × 3–4 µm

# MERULIACEAE

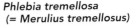

*Phlebia tremellosa*

### Phlebia tremellosa
### (= Merulius tremellosus)

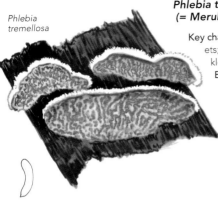

**Key characters** soft rubbery-gelatinous brackets; furry upper surface, pinkish wrinkled-poroid lower surface. **Description: Brackets** with upper surface densely woolly-hairy, whitish, lower surface with a series of remarkably wrinkled and convoluted shallow pores, pinkish or orange-buff. **Spores** white, sausage-shaped, 4–5 X 1 µm. *Inedible.* **Occurring** on fallen and decaying logs of deciduous trees, late autumn and winter, common and widespread.

Spores 4–5
X 1 µm

### Phlebia radiata

**Key characters** flat, spreading, radiately wrinkled; bright pinkish orange against pale bark in early winter. **Description: Fruitbody** a spreading sheet or disc of gelatinous tissue, bright pinkish orange, rather wrinkled, with radiating veins or ridges of tissue, only the edges are free and at all raised. **Spores** white, sausage-shaped, 4–7 X 1–3 µm. *Inedible.* **Occurring** on bark of deciduous trees especially birches, alders, late autumn and winter, common.

*Phlebia radiata*

Spores 4–7 X 1–3 µm

# HYMENOCHAETALES
# HYMENOCHAETACEAE

### Inonotus hispidus

**Key characters** large, rust-brown, fleshy bracket, very shaggy on top. **Description: Brackets** very thick, fleshy 15–20 cm (6–8 in) across; the upper surface is rich rust- to reddish brown very densely hairy, darkening to almost black with age. **Pores** are yellowish at first then reddish, often "weeping" droplets. **Flesh** deep reddish brown. **Spores** yellowish brown, subglobose, 8–9 X 7–8 μm. *Inedible; tough.* **Occurring** on the trunks of various deciduous trees, especially ash, summer to autumn, frequent. **Notes:** a rather striking species, easily recognized, often found fallen to the ground when old and black.

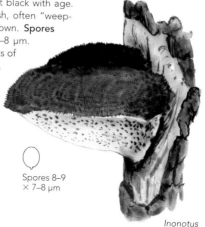

Spores 8–9
X 7–8 μm

*Inonotus
hispidus*

# GANODERMATALES

## GANODERMATACEAE

*Ganoderma
australe*

### Ganoderma australe (= G. adspersum)
(Artist's Fungus)

**Key characters** large thick brown brackets; margin and pores white; rust-coloured spores. **Description: Brackets** large, extremely hard fruitbodies 5–40 cm across composed of many layers, one added each year. **Upper surface** smooth, rather irregular, lumpy, rich red-brown with thick white margin. **Flesh** thick, deep red-brown with strong odour. **Pores** white to pale brownish cream, bruising red-brown. **Spores** rust brown, ovate with truncate end, complex channelled spore-wall, 10–11 X 6–7 μm; they stain the tree below red-brown. *Inedible; far too hard to eat.* **Occurring** on trunks of deciduous trees, especially beech, perennial, abundant, one of the commonest species on beech. **Notes:** called for many years *G. applanatum*, but the true *G. applanatum* is a thinner species with pale cinnamon-coloured flesh. The common name refers to the practice of scratching pictures on the pore-surface.

Spores 10–11 X 6–7 μm

211

### *Ganoderma lucidum* (Lacquered Bracket)

**Key characters** bracket with hard, very shiny ("lacquered", reddish surface; lateral stem. **Description:** Bracket semicircular to kidney-shaped 10–20 cm, glossy, like lacquer; reddish chestnut to purplish red, margin paler, white or yellow. **Pores** cream, minute. **Stem** short to quite long, polished surface just like the cap. **Spores** brown, ovate, with complex chanelled wall, 11–14 × 6–8 μm. *Not edible.* **Occurring** on deciduous trees and logs (causes white rot), always low down, summer to autumn, occasional but widespread in the south. **Notes:** a beautiful and unmistakable species it is an annual forming a new fruitbody each year. On Yew trees (*Taxus*) grows a rare look-alike *G. carnosum*.

*Ganoderma lucidum*

Spores 11–14 × 6–8 μm

## PORIALES

## *CORIOLACEAE*

### *Piptoporus betulinus* (Birch Polypore)

*Piptoporus betulinus*

**Key characters** thick kidney-shaped, pale brown to whitish, spongy brackets; only on birch. **Description:** Bracket 10–20 cm across, kidney-shaped with short or no stem, upper surface leathery, pale brownish to white or greyish silver, cracking when very old. **Pores** (one layer only) pure white, minute when young, soft. **Flesh** white, sponge-like with many uses by man (styptic, blotter, tinder etc.). **Spores** white, sausage-shaped, 5–6 × 1–2 μm. *Inedible.* **Occurring** only on birch, all year, abundant everywhere.

Spores 5–6 × 1–2 μm

## *Fomes fomentarius* (Tinder Fungus, Hoof Fungus)

**Key characters** thick hoof-like bracket; dull yellow-brown to greyish with paler pores. **Description:** Brackets 15–30 cm, thick and hoof-shaped, margin blunt; margin pale buff. **Flesh** pale brown. **Pores** pale cinnamon with white "bloom". **Spores** white, elongate, 15–18 X 5–6 μm. *Inedible.* **Occurring** on beech in Europe and southern England, but usually on birch in Scotland, causes a white rot, perennial, frequent.

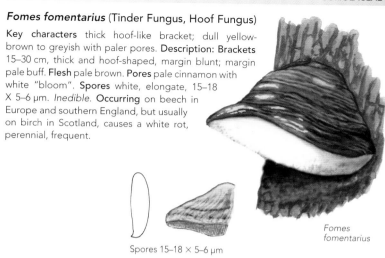

*Fomes fomentarius*

Spores 15–18 × 5–6 μm

## *Laetiporus (= Polyporus) sulphureus* (Sulphur Polypore)

**Key characters** soft-fleshed brackets, bright yellow to pinkish orange overall. **Description:** Brackets large often overlapping, irregular but more or less semicircular, 10–40 cm across. **Flesh** soft and fragrant. **Spores** white, pip-shaped, 5–7 X 4–5 μm. *Edible and good; best when young (although should not be eaten if found on exotic trees or conifers when it can cause stomach upsets).* **Occurring** on oaks, chestnuts, and other deciduous trees, occasionally conifers, autumn, common.

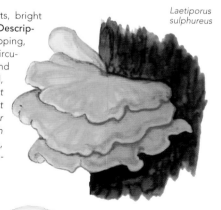

*Laetiporus sulphureus*

Spores 5–7 × 4–5 μm

### Phaeolus schweinitzii

**Key characters** at base of conifers; shaggy brown round bracket with bright yellow edge. **Description: Bracket** 10–30 cm across, rounded and irregular, very shaggy-furry. Reddish-brown with bright yellow margin. **Pores** dull greenish-yellow, angular, decurrent on to a thick, brown basal stalk. **Spores** greenish yellow, elliptic, 8 X 4 μm. *Not edible.* **Occurring** at the base of conifers on the tree roots or buttresses, autumn, common. **Notes:** this fungus causes serious heart rot within conifers.

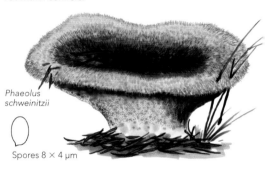

Phaeolus
schweinitzii

Spores 8 × 4 μm

### Trametes gibbosa

Trametes
gibbosa

**Key characters** thick white brackets, sometimes completely circular; often green with algae. **Description: Bracket** thick, irregular to completely circular when growing on top of a stump, 5–12 cm across, very tough, fleshy, upper surface rough and tomentose, knobbly; white to cream, often with green algae embedded in the surface. **Pores** white, elongated (3–4 times as long as wide). **Spores** white, elongated, 4–6 X 2–3 μm. *Not edible.* **Occurring** on stumps of deciduous trees, especially beech, late autumn, common.

Spores 4–6 × 2–3 μm

## *Lenzites betulinus* (= *Trametes betulinus*)

**Key characters** pores remarkably thin and elongate, like hardened gills. **Description: Bracket** 5–10 cm across, quite thick, fleshy, upper surface pale brown, slightly tomentose-hairy, zoned. **Pores** usually very elongate, forming thin plate-like or gill-like structures, often branching, but can also be strictly poroid. **Spores** white, elongate, 4–6 X 2–3 µm. *Not edible.* **Occurring** on stumps of deciduous trees especially beech and birch, autumn, common.

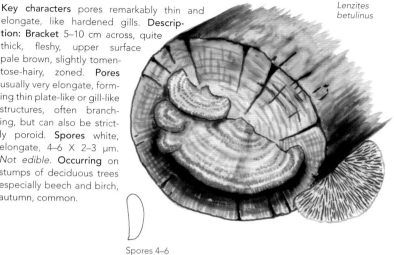

*Lenzites betulinus*

Spores 4–6
X 2–3 µm

## *Daedaleopsis confragosa* (Blushing Bracket)

**Key characters** very evenly formed semi-circular brackets with buff-brown or reddish-brown zones; pores white, bruising red. **Description: Bracket** perfectly shaped rounded 3–8 cm across, of medium thickness, with thin margin, tough and fleshy; upper surface distinctly zoned, pale brownish buff to reddish brown or tan-grey; margin paler. **Pores** quite large, irregular, rather elongate, white, bruising immediately pinkish red. **Spores** white, elongate, slightly sausage-shaped, 10–11 X 2–3 µm. *Not edible.* **Occurring** on deciduous trees and saplings, especially willow, autumn, common.

*Daedaleopsis confragosa*

Spores 10–11 × 2–3 µm

### Bjerkandera adusta

**Key characters** overlapping greyish brackets, edges soon blackish; pores deep grey to black, minute. **Description** Brackets forming masses of rather thin overlapping brackets 4–8 cm across, very similar in appearance to *Trametes versicolor* but differing in the less evenly zoned cap of a dark greyish-brown tint, darker at the edge when old but white at first. **Spores** white, ovate, 4–6 X 24 µm. *Not edible.* **Occurring** on stumps and logs of deciduous trees, all year round, very common everywhere.

*Bjerkandera adusta*

Spores 4–6
X 24 µm

### Meripilus (= Polyporus) giganteus

**Key characters** very large ochre brackets at base of deciduous trees; pores bruise black in 10 minutes. **Description** Brackets irregularly shaped 20–50 cm across united to form a clump often 200 cm across! Brackets rather thin and quite fleshy, surface leathery, ochre-brown, paler at margin. **Pores** minute, soft, pale cream bruising blackish. **Stem** sometimes present although indistinct and merged with cap. **Spores** white, pip-shaped, 5–6 X 4–5 µm. *Edible but not recommended.* **Occurring** most commonly at base of beech trees but on other hosts also, summer to autumn, common.

*Meripilus giganteus*

Spores 5–6 X 4–5 µm

## Grifola frondosa

**Key characters** mass of small brackets from one base; greyish above, white pores. **Description: Brackets** form dozens of small overlapping shelves clumped to 20–40 cm high and across, base large, fleshy; individual brackets 4–6 cm, thin, fleshy, spoon-shaped, greyish brown on top, white below. **Spores** white, elliptic, 5–7 X 3–5 μm. *Edible especially the tips; regarded as delicious by many.* **Occurring** at base of deciduous trees especially oaks, summer to early autumn, uncommon to rare.

Grifola
frondosa

Spores 5–7 × 3–5 μm

## Daedalea quercina

**Key characters** greyish-buff colours; pores maze-like; usually on oak stumps. **Description: Bracket** 5–15 cm across, rounded, hoof-like, rather thick-fleshed with hard, corky texture; pale greyish brown, slightly zoned and furrowed. **Flesh** pale brown. **Pores** long and irregular, pale greyish brown. **Spores** white, pip-shaped, 5–7 X 2–3 μm. *Not edible.* **Occurring** most commonly on oaks, usually on hard, barely decayed wood, all year, common.

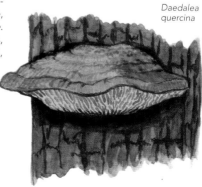

Daedalea
quercina

Spores 5–7 × 2–3 μm

### Trametes (= Coriolus) versicolor

**Key characters** thin brackets with many-coloured zones; margin white. **Description: Brackets** forming semicircular caps which are thin and tough, with clearly defined, silky-velvet, concentric zones of colour, a mixture of browns, yellow-browns, greys, purple, greens and black, but always with the extreme margin paler, white or cream. **Pores** cream, small. **Spores** white, elongate, 6–8 X 2–3 μm. *Not edible.* **Occurring** on a wide range of fallen broadleaf timber, all year, abundant everywhere. **Notes:** perhaps our commonest of the smaller brackets.

*Trametes versicolor*

Spores 6–8 × 2–3 μm

## POLYPORACEAE

### Polyporus squamosus (Dryad's Saddle)

**Key characters** cap-like bracket, large with darker scales; stem short, black, off-centre. **Description: Bracket** when young a flattened, top-shaped knob, rather like an upturned hoof, soon expanding into a large, almost circular to kidney-shaped bracket 15–35 cm across; pale yellowish brown, with darker radiating scales flattened onto surface. **Pores** large, angular, decurrent, pale cream. **Stem** short, thick, hard, white above but deep blackish brown below. **Flesh** with strong but not unpleasant odour **Spores** white, elongate 10–15 X 4–5 μm. *Edible when young and finely shredded; but hardly to be recommended.* **Occurring** on stumps, trunks and logs of deciduous timber, causes white rot on living trees, summer and early autumn, common.

*Polyporus squamosus*

Spores 10–15 × 4–5 μm

## *Polyporus brumalis* (Winter Polypore)

**Key characters** small round greyish-brown cap; whitish central stem. **Description: Bracket** forming a round cap 3–8 cm across, rather thin and flattened, smooth, greyish yellow to pale brown. **Pores** on undersurface white and decurrent, small. **Stem** thin, tapered at base, whitish and smooth, without a blackish crust at base as in the next species. **Spores** white, elongate, 5–8 X 1–3 µm. *Edible but not recommended.* **Occurring** on fallen deciduous branches and twigs, late autumn, through winter to spring, frequent. **Notes:** one of a small number of brackets to form a cap and stem.

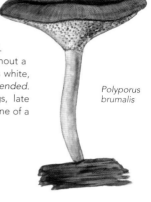

*Polyporus brumalis*

Spores 5–8 × 1–3 µm

## *Polyporus durus* (= *P. badius*, = *P. picipes*)

**Key characters** glossy brown funnel-shaped cap; black central stem. **Description: Bracket** round and funnel-shaped, very smooth, glossy and polished, tawny brown to chestnut. **Pores** small, whitish, decurrent. **Stem** narrow, tapered at base, covered with a blackish crust. **Spores** white, elliptic, 7–8 X 4 µm. *Not edible.* **Occurring** on stumps and fallen wood of deciduous trees, throughout the year, occasional. **Notes:** the similar *P. leptocephalus* is distinguished by its matt, slightly striate cap set off-centre on the thick, black stem.

*Polyporus durus*

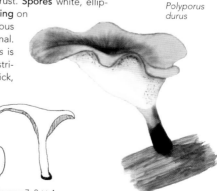

Spores 7–8 × 4 µm

219

# FISTULINALES

## FISTULINACEAE

### Fistulina hepatica (Beefsteak, Ox-tongue)

*Fistulina hepatica*

**Key characters** soft, flesh-like, reddish bracket; looks like large tongue. **Description: Bracket** resembles a large fleshy, soft tongue, to 30 cm across, upper surface soft and spongy, often gelatinous when wet; colour of raw flesh or liver. **Flesh** red, "bleeds" a reddish juice. **Pores** pale reddish cream to yellowish, easily separated one from another. **Spores** pinkish brown, globose, 4–6 X 3–4 μm. *Edible and liked by many (taste rather acidulous, sweet), disliked by others.* **Occurring** on oaks, chestnut and rarely beech, summer and early autumn, common. **Notes:** causes a brown heart-rot of oak.

Spores 4–6 × 3–4 μm

# CANTHARELLALES

## HYDNACEAE

### Hydnum repandum (Wood Hedgehog)

**Key characters** cap pinkish buff with densely packed spines underneath; stem white, often to one side. **Description: Cap** 3–15 cm, convex then expanded, thick and fleshy, inrolled at margin, smooth; pinkish-yellow to orange-ochre. **Underside** with short, pendent spines or pegs, densely packed, pinkish buff. **Stem** rather short, stout, tapered at base, white; often eccentric, giving an uneven, lop-sided appearance. **Flesh** thick, white, with a pleasant smell, and a distinctly spicy and slightly bitter taste. **Spores** white, elliptic, 7–8 X 6–7 μm. *Edible and good, especially when young; best after scalding.* **Occurring** in mixed broadleaf woods, autumn, occasional. **Notes:** the closely related *H. rufescens* grows under pines and differs in its smaller, deeper reddish brown cap and central stem.

*Hydnum repandum*

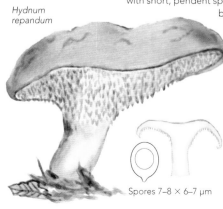

Spores 7–8 × 6–7 μm

# CANTHARELLACEAE

## Cantharellus infundibuliformis
## (= C. tubaeformis)

**Key characters** cap brown, funnel-shaped; "gills" greyish; yellow-orange stem. **Description: Cap** dark brown, "gills" greyish yellow, stem deep yellow to orange (fruitbody entirely yellow-orange in variety *lutescens*). **Spores** cream, elliptic, 9–11 X 6–9 µm. *Edible and delicious.* **Occurring** often in large numbers in deciduous woods in damp, mossy areas, autumn, occasional to common. **Notes:** more slender than the Chanterelle, with a longer stem.

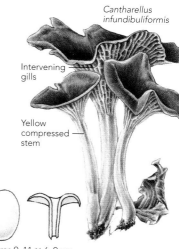

*Cantharellus infundibuliformis*

Intervening gills

Yellow compressed stem

Spores 9–11 × 6–9 µm

## Cantharellus cibarius
## (Chanterelle)

**Key characters** egg-yellow to orange-apricot colours; wrinkled folds instead of gills. **Description: Cap** 3–10 cm, bright egg-yellow, orange to apricot, top-shaped then rather funnel-shaped, margin inrolled, then wavy and irregular; smooth, fleshy. **Undersurface** bears a series of irregular, blunt gill-like wrinkles and folds, decurrent, paler than cap, often slightly pinkish. **Stem** short, colour as cap, tapered at base. **Flesh** thick, whitish, fragrance of apricots when fresh. **Spores** pale cream, elliptic, 8–10 X 5–6 µm. *Delicious; one of the best edible fungi.* **Occurring** in mixed woods, often in small troops in moss and leaf litter, autumn, frequent to common although seems to be declining in recent years. Compare with False Chanterelle.

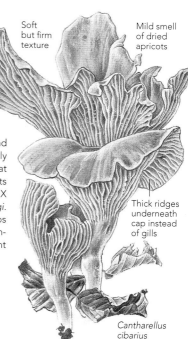

Soft but firm texture

Mild smell of dried apricots

Thick ridges underneath cap instead of gills

*Cantharellus cibarius*

Spores 8–10 × 5–6 µm

*Craterellus cornucopioides*

— Surface lacks gills

# CRATERELLACEAE

## Craterellus cornucopioides
### (Horn of Plenty, Black Trumpet)

**Key characters** funnel-shaped blackish cap and paler stem; no gills or folds on underside. **Description: Cap** 3–8 cm, funnel-shaped with the margin thin, wavy and irregular; surface minutely roughened-scaly; deep brown to black when moist, paler greyish brown when dry. **Underside** quite smooth to slightly wrinkled, running smoothly into the stem, pale grey to bluish grey. **Stem** short, tapered, and quite hollow right down the centre; colour paler than cap. **Spores** cream, elliptic, 10–11 X 6–7 µm. *Edible and good; dries well for grinding as seasoning.* **Occurring** in deciduous woods in troops below beeches, autumn, occasional to frequent.

Spores 10–11 X 6–7 µm

# CLAVARIADELPHACEAE

## Clavariadelphus pistillaris

*Clavariadelphus pistillaris*

**Key characters** large, swollen clubs, ochre-brown to peach-yellow and rather wrinkled. **Description: Club** or pestle-shaped fruit-bodies reaching heights of 10–25 cm; the wrinkled surface is yellow-ochre, peach-yellow to orange, then reddish-brown. **Flesh** whitish, slightly bitter. **Spores** pale yellow, ovate, 11–16 X 6–9 µm. *Edible but not recommended.* **Occurring** in beech woods in leaf-litter, autumn, rare to uncommon. **Notes:** this is the largest of the simple club fungi and along with other club fungi it is believed to be closely related to the Chanterelles. Related species include *C. truncatus*, with club also large but flattened on top, more wrinkled, and *Macrotyphula fistulosus*, with very slender, tall clubs, rather pointed; both rather uncommon.

Spores 11–16 X 6–9 µm

# CLAVARIACEAE

## Clavulinopsis fusiformis

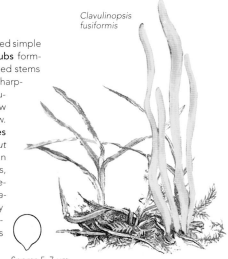

*Clavulinopsis fusiformis*

**Key characters** pointed, spindle-shaped simple clubs, bright yellow. **Description: Clubs** forming tufts of simple, slender, unbranched stems 5–12 cm high, spindle-shaped and sharp-pointed, often flattened and irregularly grooved; joined at the base below the soil surface; bright golden yellow. **Flesh** whitish, with bitter taste. **Spores** white, globose, 5–7 μm. *Edibible; but not of culinary interest.* **Occurring** in open grass in meadows, heathlands, etc,. autumn, quite common and widespread. **Notes:** the rather similar *Clavulinopsis helvola* is distinguished by its blunter shape, deeper, orange-yellow coloration and rounded spores with large spines.

Spores 5–7 μm

## Clavulina coralloides (= C. cristata)

**Key characters** many-branched, sharp-pointed clubs, white often with darker greyish tips. **Description: Clubs** 3–7 cm high, branching repeatedly and usually arising from a central thickened stem but ending in fine, pointed branchlets. **Spores** white, subglobose, 9–10 X 7–8 μm. *Edibility uncertain; best avoided.* **Occurring** in mixed woodlands especially by damp paths and often abundant on streamsides, summer to autumn, common. **Notes:** a closely related species, *C. cinerea*, is uniformly grey with blunter, more irregular tips to the branches.

*Clavulina coralloides*

Spores 9–10 × 7–8 μm

## *SPARASSIDACEAE*

### *Sparassis crispa* (Cauliflower Fungus)

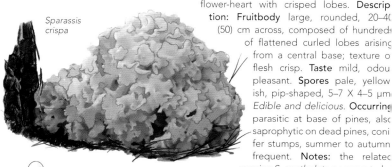

*Sparassis crispa*

**Key characters** like a large, pale ochre-brown to tan cauliflower-heart with crisped lobes. **Description:** Fruitbody large, rounded, 20–40 (50) cm across, composed of hundreds of flattened curled lobes arising from a central base; texture of flesh crisp. **Taste** mild, odour pleasant. **Spores** pale, yellowish, pip-shaped, 5–7 X 4–5 µm. *Edible and delicious.* **Occurring** parasitic at base of pines, also saprophytic on dead pines, conifer stumps, summer to autumn, frequent. **Notes:** the related species *S. spathulata* appears to be confined to oaks and has less-branched lobes, longer and more ribbon-like. Both edible and recommended, especially young; may be difficult to clean.

Spores 5–7
X 4–5 µm

# *GOMPHALES*

## *GOMPHACEAE*

### *Ramaria abietina* (= *R. ochraceovirens*)

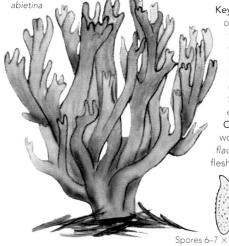

*Ramaria abietina*

**Key characters** branched; deep yellow-ochre colour, bruising green; in conifer woods. **Description:** Fruitbody with a short, thick stem branching into tufts, 3–8 cm across, deep yellow-ochre, ochre-brown, bruising darker green, tips bluntly pointed. **Spores** pale brownish, elongate-elliptic, 6–7 X 3–4 µm. *Not edible.* **Occurring** on needle litter in conifer woods, autumn, common. **Notes:** *R. flaccida* is tougher, has more elastic flesh, not bruising green.

Spores 6–7 X 3–4 µm

### Ramaria botrytis

**Key characters** robust, many-branched; pale tan to ochre with pinkish-red tips. **Description:** Fruitbody with thick stem branching into a coral-like head 5–20 cm across; base whitish, branches tan-ochre with pinkish tips. **Flesh** firm, brittle, white, mild to taste. **Spores** pale ochre, elongate-elliptic, striate, 12–18 X 4–6 μm. *Not edible; can cause upsets.* **Occurring** in leaf litter, usually in beech woods, autumn, rare in Britain, commoner in mainland Europe. **Notes:** the similar *R. formosa* has a bitter taste, more orange coloration and branch tips yellow.

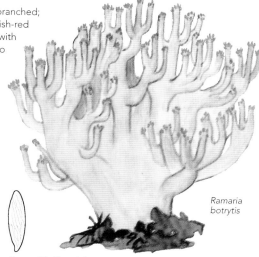

Ramaria botrytis

Spores 12–18 × 4–6 μm

## AURICULARIALES (JELLY FUNGI)

Although often referred to as jelly fungi the Auriculariales differ from the Tremellales below by their basidia not having transverse cross-walls. The texture is also rather more rubbery.

### AURICULARIACEAE

#### Auricularia auricula-judae (Jew's Ear, Judas' Ear)

*Auricularia auricula-judae*

**Key characters** soft, reddish brown "ear" on branches, especially on elder. **Description: Fruitbody** very like a soft, floppy, velvety-brown ear or cup 3–8 cm across, the outside being velvety, the inner surface smooth and wrinkled; rubbery, greyish brown to wine-red. **Flesh** dries bone-hard, but on remoistening resumes its original texture. **Spores** white, elongate, curved, 16–18 X 6–8 μm. *Edible and considered a delicacy* especially in the Far East, where similar species are cultivated, all year, common. **Notes:** the common name refers to the legend that Judas hanged himself on an elder, the "ear" being his returned spirit.

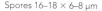

Spores 16–18 × 6–8 μm

# TREMELLALES (JELLY FUNGI)

All the members of this order have a soft, gelatinou. rubbery or jelly-like consistency and (microscopically) th basidia always divided internally by longitudinal cross-wa or septa.

## TREMELLACEAE

### Tremella mesenterica

*Tremella mesenterica*

**Key characters** yellow, gelatinous and wrinkled; on decid. ous wood. **Description: Fruitbody** a gelatinous, slimy irregu lar "blob" 3–10 cm across, bright yellow-orange, very irregu lar and convoluted. Dries bone-hard and turns deep orang **Spores** white, ovate, 7–8 X 5–6 μm. *Inedible.* **Occurrin** parasitic on the mycelium of a fungus called *Penio phora*, on fallen branches and stumps of decid. ous trees, especially holly and hazel, late autum through winter and spring, common.

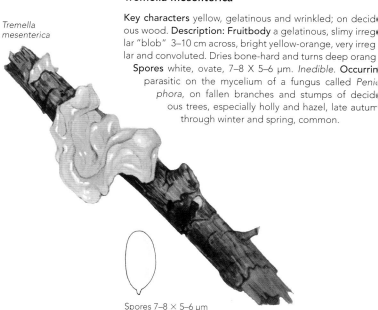

Spores 7–8 × 5–6 μm

## EXIDIACEAE

### Pseudohydnum gelatinosum
(Jelly Tongue)

**Key characters** pearly grey-white, gelatinous "tongue' small rubbery spines below. **Description: Fruitbody** form a very soft, gelatinous tongue-shaped body 2–6 cm across on a short stem, with the underside covered with short so pegs or spines; almost translucent, pearly grey. **Upper sur** **face** slightly hairy. **Spores** white, ovate, 5–7 X 5 μm. *Edibl*

*Pseudohydnum gelatinosum*

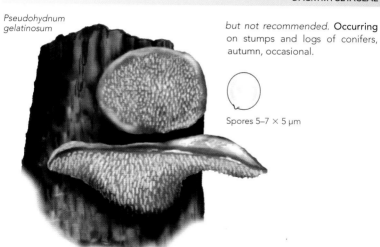

but not recommended. **Occurring** on stumps and logs of conifers, autumn, occasional.

Spores 5–7 × 5 μm

## DACRYMYCETALES

## DACRYMYCETACEAE

### Calocera viscosa

**Key characters** yellow-orange, branched, rubbery, like antlers; on conifer stumps. **Description:** Fruitbody forms slightly sticky, yellow-orange "antlers" shaped like stag's horns, 3–10 cm in height, rooting in the stump. **Spores** yellow, ovate, 8–12 × 3–5 μm. *Inedible.* **Occurring** on conifer logs and stumps, autumn, common. **Notes:** the related *C. cornea* grows on deciduous timber and is a simple, unbranched, pointed club, 1–4 cm high.

*Calocera viscosa*

Spores 8–12 × 3–5 μm

227

## PUFFBALLS, STINKHORNS AND ALLIES

Traditionally placed in one Order called the Gasteromycetes (Stomach fungi) they are actually a group of unrelated Orders and genera that happen to have adopted similar spore-dispersal mechanisms. They may be divided into the Phallales (stinkhorns), Nidulariales (bird's nest fungi), Lycoperdales (puffballs and earthstars), Sclerodermatales (earthballs) and Hymenogastrales (false truffles). Despite the remarkable diversity of form, all produce their spores within an outer sterile covering (peridium) and do not discharge them as in ordinary Basidiomycetes. Instead they usually rely on some external agency to spread the spores, such as insects or mammals, or the physical effects of wind and rain.

### *PHALLALES*

### *PHALLACEAE* **(STINKHORNS)**

### *Phallus impudicus* (Common Stinkhorn)

**Key characters** unmistakable phallic shape and repulsive odour; begins as an "egg". **Description: Fruitbody** begins as a smooth, egg-like body 5–8 cm high, buried in the soil, then slowly expanding and protruding above soil level. The "egg" is connected to very long, tough, white mycelial cords, which can often be traced several metres. The outer skin (peridium) splits to reveal a thick jelly-like layer; very rapidly (in a matter of hours) a white spongy stalk surmounted by a globose green head pushes upwards through the jelly, to a final height of 10–20 cm. Spore-mass greenish black, soon liquefies to produce an obnoxious and extremely penetrating smell which attracts flies to aid in spore-dispersal. **Spores** 3–5 X 2 µm. *Edible when young, in the unexpanded egg-stage; but usually avoided.* **Occurring** in woodlands, parks and often gardens, usually near deciduous or coniferous stumps, summer and autumn, common. **Notes:** this is one of the few fungi possible to hunt by smell! The similar *P. hadriani*, in coastal sand dunes, is rather rare and has pinkish eggs.

*Phallus impudicus*

Spores 3–5 × 2 µm

## *Mutinus caninus* (Dog Stinkhorn)

**Key characters** cap sharply pointed, not separable; stem rather small, slender, flushed orange. **Description:** Fruitbody smaller, 5–10 cm than the Common Stinkhorn above and without the repulsive odour. The slender stem is often flushed orange and has a pointed orange apex covered with a greenish-black sticky spore-mass. **Spores** 4–5 X 1–3 μm. *Inedible.* **Occurring** usually in beech woods close to logs and stumps, summer and autumn, frequent.

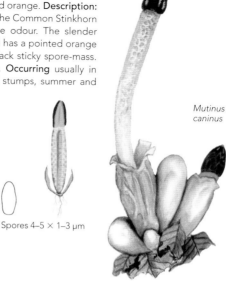

*Mutinus caninus*

Spores 4–5 × 1–3 μm

## *Clathrus ruber* (Cage Fungus)

**Key characters** reddish cage-like body bursting from "egg"; unpleasant foetid odour. **Description:** Fruitbody beginning as an "egg", like the Stinkhorn but soon bursting to release a spongy, latticed, structure 6–12 cm across. **Outer surface** bright scarlet or pink, inside smeared with sticky, foul-smelling olive-brown slime, the spore mass. **Spores** cylindric 5–6 x 2 μm, soon attracts flies which eat and disperse the spores. *Not considered edible.* **Occurring** mainly southern in distribution, frequent in continental Europe rather rare in England, cemeteries, hedgerows and gardens, summer and autumn.

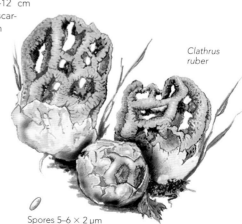

*Clathrus ruber*

Spores 5–6 × 2 μm

229

## *NIDULARIALES*

## *NIDULARIACEAE* (BIRD'S NEST FUNGI)

### *Cyathus striatus* (Bird's Nest Fungus)

*Cyathus striatus*

**Key characters** tiny, elongate shaggy brown cups containing many small "eggs"; inner edge of cap greyish, strongly striate. **Description: Cups** small (1 cm) cone-shaped, shaggy brown externally; greyish fluted inner wall, composed of three thin layers, on which sit 10 or more small egg-like bodies (peridioles) which contain the spores 14–18 X 9–12 µm. When struck by a raindrop the peridioles, which are attached by very thin coiled cords to the inner wall, are splashed out to a distance of several feet. The cord which disengages from the wall helps the spore mass to adhere to surrounding objects (grass etc.). *Inedible.* **Occurring** on ground or rotten twigs etc. in mixed woods, autumn, uncommon. **Notes:** the similar *Cyathus olla* differs in its non-striate, more trumpet-shaped, flaring cones.

Spores 14–18
X 9–12 µm

### *Crucibulum vulgare* (Bird's Nest Fungus)

**Key characters** tiny cups with "eggs"; smooth inner surface. **Description: Cups** small 0.5–1 cm with yellowish brown, slightly shaggy external surface and smooth, pale yellow, internal peridial layer on which sit 10–12 white "eggs" (peridioles) containing the spores elliptic, 7–10 X 3–5 µm (see *Cyathus striatus*, above, for spore-dispersal mechanism). *Inedible.* **Occurring** on deciduous or coniferous twigs, clustered, often on garden mulch, summer to autumn, common. **Notes:** another related fungus, *Sphaerobolus stellatus*, is even smaller (0.25–0.5 cm), with star-shaped cups. The inner wall everts to flip the single egg several feet away.

*Crucibulum vulgare*

Spores 7–10
X 3–5 µm

# TULOSTOMATALES

## TULOSTOMATACEAE
### (STALKED PUFFBALLS)

### Tulostoma brumale

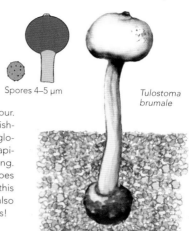

Spores 4–5 µm

Tulostoma
brumale

**Key characters** puffball with long slender stem often buried below sand. **Description: Puffball** 1–3 cm across, pale clay in colour. **Stem** 5–7 cm long, whitish with small, reddish-brown, shaggy scales. **Spores** pinkish, globose, warty, 4–5 µm; released through an apical pore by wind action and raindrops striking. *Not edible.* **Occurring** in warm, sandy slopes and dunes, autumn, uncommon. **Notes:** this small and easily overlooked fungus has also been recorded from cracks in old brick walls!

# LYCOPERDALES (PUFFBALLS)

## LYCOPERDACEAE

### Bovista nigrescens

**Key characters** small, whitish puffball without stem, turning deep purple-brown; often detached from ground. **Description: Puffball** small to medium-sized rounded, 3–8 cm across, without any basal stalk and with the outer skin (peridium) starting whitish at first, then soon darkening with age. The spores are released through an apical opening. The outer peridium layer often peels in irregular patches to expose the very thin, papery inner layer. The whole fungus often becomes detached and rolls around scattering the dark purplish-brown spores. **Spores** globose, smooth, 5–6 µm with long stalk. *Edible when young and still firm.* **Occurring** on soil in fields and pastures, summer to autumn, common.

Bovista
nigrescens

Spores 5–6 µm

### Handkea utriformis (= Calvatia utriformis)

**Key characters** medium-sized to large; pear-shaped, with hexagonal markings. **Description: Puffball** rather large, about 6–15 cm across, slightly pear-shaped with a sterile base. **Peridium** or outer skin is whitish, soon cracking into roughly hexagonal markings; with age turns dirty greyish brown and gradually flakes away to leave only the base. **Spores** olive-brown and smooth, spherical, 4–5 µm (not warty as in the following species). *Edible when young and firm.* **Occurring** in unimproved fields and pastures especially on sandy or neutral soils, summer to autumn, occasional to frequent.

*Handkea utriformis*

Spores 4–5 µm

### Handkea excipuliformis (= Calvatia excipuliformis)

*Handkea excipuliformis*

**Key characters** very large, tall, pestle-shaped, with fine granular warts. **Description: Puffball** reaching a height of up to 20 cm, greatly resembling a chemist's pestle, with a rounded head surmounting a tall sterile stem. **Peridium** is white and finely granular-warty; the warts soon falling off, leaving smooth skin which eventually flakes away at the apex. **Spores** olive-brown, warty, globose, 4–5 µm. *Edible when young and firm.* **Occurring** in woodlands, heaths and occasionally fields, summer to autumn, common. **Notes:** an often very large species and taller than other puffballs, but very variable.

Spores 4–5 µm

## Calvatia gigantea (= Langermannia gigantea) (Giant Puffball)

**Key characters** unmistakable, often huge; round, smooth and white. **Description: Puffball** one of the largest fungi of any kind in the world, it has reached diameters of up to 100 cm, although the usual size is around 20–50 cm. It forms an irregularly rounded fruitbody, often slightly flattened, with a thick, smooth white skin. **Spore mass** at first pure white then yellowish 3.5–5 µm, globose. *Edible and delicious when young; and widely sought after.* **Occurring** in fields, pastures and gardens especially by hedges and banks, often reappearing for many years in the same locality.

Spores 3.5–5 µm globose

*Calvatia gigantea*

## Lycoperdon pyriforme (Stump Puffball)

**Key characters** always on wood, with basal white "roots", often in very large numbers. **Description: Puffball** small, pear-shaped, 2–7 cm high, pale cream-colour to brownish with very fine pointed granules which easily brush off to leave a smooth skin. **Stem** has white mycelial cords at base penetrating the wood. **Spores** white then greenish yellow, almost spherical and very finely warty, 4 µm. *Edible when young.* **Occurring** in large clusters, always on old stumps, logs or buried wood, summer to autumn, often abundant. **Notes:** an easily recognized species and the only European puffball regularly on wood.

*Lycoperdon pyriforme*

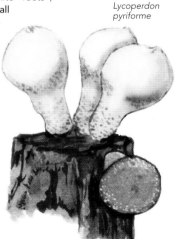

Spores 4 µm

233

### *Lycoperdon echinatum* (Spiny Puffball, Hedgehog)

**Key characters** brown extremely spiny fruit-body; usually ir beech woods. **Description: Puffball** pear-shaped to round ed, 4–6 cm, dark brown and covered with very long (3–6 mm brown spines connecting at the tips in small groups. **Spine** easily break off to leave small rounded scars on the skin **Spore**s deep purple-brown; round, warty 5–6 µm. *Not edible.* **Occurring** in lea litter in deciduous woodlands especially beech, autumn, uncom mon. **Notes:** this species is very frequently confused with the common *L. foetidum*, anothe dull brown species, in woods and pastures and with much shorte unconnected spines and slightl smaller spores, 3–4.5 µm. *Lycoperdor molle* (= *umbrinum*) is also similar bu occurs mainly in conifer woods and heaths, with a more distinct basa stem and shorter spines.

*Lycoperdon echinatum*

Spores 5–6 µm

## *GEASTRACEAE* (EARTHSTARS)

### *Geastrum triplex* (Common Earthstar)

**Key characters** fat, globose, tulip-bulb-like, splitting into 5–? arms; central puffball with basal collar. **Description: Earth star** when closed forms a rather robust tough brown bod like a tulip bulb, which proceeds to split. The outer peridia layer peels back to form five to seven thick, pointed arm: often cracking across their inner surface, while the inne peridial layer forms a rounded hollow ball containing the spores. There is an apical pore from which the spores are puffed i struck by a raindrop or dragged out by wind blowing across the aperture. The open fungus i:

*Geastrum triplex*

Spores 4–5 µm
globose

about 8–12 cm across the "star". At the base of the puff-ball-like structure is often a surrounding basal cup or collar. **Spores** 4–5 µm, globose. *Inedible.* **Occurring** in leaf litter of mixed woods, also in sand dunes and gardens, autumn, frequent. There are about 16 species of Earthstar in Britain.

*Geastrum fornicatum*

## *Geastrum fornicatum*

**Key characters** large 4-armed star with arms bent back and attached to tissue embedded in soil. **Description: Earthstar** which splits to form four abruptly turned-down arms, greyish brown, 5–10 cm tall, attached at the tips to a flattened mycelial layer buried in the soil. Central puffball-like chamber raised on a short stem, also dark brown. **Spores** finely warty, 3–4 µm. *Not edible.* **Occurring** on soil in woodland or in hedgerows, with mixed trees, autumn, rare.

Spores 3–4 µm

## *Geastrum striatum* (= *G. bryantii*)

**Key characters** small dark brown body splitting into 3–7 arms; central whitish chamber on stalk. **Description: Earthstar** much smaller than the other earthstars mentioned here, reaching only 2–5 cm across the "star". Develops as in the other species, the outer layer splitting to form three to seven dark brown, rather thin arms, but the central chamber is whitish and raised on a narrow stalk with an apical collar. **Spores** deep brown, warty, 5–6 µm. *Not edible.* **Occurring** in deciduous woods, parks, gardens and dunes, on mixed soils, autumn, uncommon to frequent.

*Geastrum striatum*

Spores 5–6 µm

# *SCLERODERMATALES*

## *SCLERODERMATACEAE* (EARTHBALLS)

### *Scleroderma verrucosum* 🕱

*Scleroderma verrucosum*

**Key characters** skin thin and finely warty-scaly, pale brown, rooting stem base; spores olive-brown. **Description:** Earthball with a rather smooth, rounded ball and with a quite distinct stem-like rooting base which binds together a mass of soil. **Skin** (peridium) is pale brownish with fine wart-like scales. **Spores** olive-brown, 10–14 µm, with fine spines and ridges. *Not edible; has caused poisoning.* **Occurring** in mixed woods, especially on sandy soils, summer to autumn, frequent.

Spores 10–14 µm

### *Scleroderma citrinum (= S. aurantium)* 🕱 (Common Earthball)

*Scleroderma citrinum*

**Key characters** skin thick, scaly, yellowish; central spore mass purple-black. **Description:** Earthball an irregular rounded fruitbody, 4–8 cm across, with a thick, scaly, cracking outer skin, pale yellowish to tawny orange. The solid interior spore mass is white then soon purplish black with a strong, rather unpleasant odour of rubber. **Spores** rounded, 8–13 µm, with a fine reticulate network on the surface. *Not edible; case of poisoning recorded.* **Occurring** in mixed woodlands on acid soils, often near tree roots, summer and autumn, abundant.

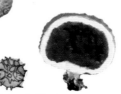

Spores 8–13 µm

The cup fungi (Discomycetes) are part of the Ascomycetes, an enormous worldwide group of several thousand species. Most are microscopic, many are important pests, and all produce their spores within a sac – the ascus (see Introduction). Few ascomycetes are "larger fungi" and most of these are cup fungi. In many ways cup fungi parallel the structures found in the gill fungi, with both toadstool-like and tuberous forms, but the majority produce the typical cup shape.

## PEZIZALES

This numerous, often colourful order includes the truly cup-shaped genera and the more complex sponge-like morels and saddle-shaped helvellas. All are rather soft, brittle and fragile, with the spores produced on an exposed layer.

### MORCHELLACEAE

#### Morchella elata (= M. conica) (Black Morel)

**Key characters** cap conical, with honeycomb-like pits and ridges aligned vertically. **Description: Cap** 4–8 cm, more or less conical, dark grey-brown to black often with the ridges paler, aligned more or less vertically. **Stem** short, stout, tapered, brittle and hollow: whitish with a scurfy texture. **Spores** yellowish, elliptic, 20–24 X 12–14 µm. *Edible and delicious.* **Occurring** in fields, pastures and hedgerows, especially on calcareous soils, also on woodchip mulch in gardens, in spring, frequent.

*Morchella elata*

Spores 20–24 X 12–14 µm

### Morchella esculenta (Common Morel)

**Key characters** cap rounded, yellow-brown to reddish; pits and ridges irregular. **Description: Cap** often large, 5–15 cm high; rounded, sponge-like, pale yellow-ochre to orange-ochre or pale brown. **Stem** white, hollow, often irregular, scurfy. **Spores** elliptic, 17–23 X 11–14 µm. *Edible; one of the most delicious of all edible fungi.* **Occurring** in fields, woods and hedgerows often near dying elms or apple trees, especially on calcareous soils, in spring, locally common.

*Morchella esculenta*

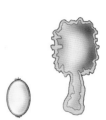

Spores 17–23 × 11–14 µm

*Morchella semilibera*

### Morchella semilibera (= Mitrophora semilibera)

**Key characters** cap short, conical; cap base free from the stem at its lower margin. **Description: Cap** conical with longitudinal pits and cross-ridges, pale to dark brown, lower margin hangs free of stem. **Stem** tall, 4–10 cm high, stocky to slender, white and scurfy. **Spores** elliptic, 21–30 X 12–18 µm. *Edible.* **Occurring** in woods and hedgerows, especially on chalky soils, in spring, uncommon to frequent and widespread.

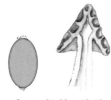

Spores 21–30 × 12–18 µm

## *Verpa conica* (Thimble Fungus)

**Key characters** thimble-shaped cap; stem with transverse lines of reddish-brown granular scales. **Description:** Cap 2–4 cm, smooth to slightly wrinkled, pale ochre-brown, only attached at the centre, margin entirely free. **Stem** more or less cylindrical, whitish, with transverse lines of reddish-brown granular scales. **Spores** elliptic, 20–24 X 12–14 μm. *Edible.* **Occurring** in woods, gardens and heaths, especially sandy or chalky soils, in spring, rare to occasional.

*Verpa conica*

Spores 20–24 × 12–14 μm

# *DISCINACEAE*

## *Gyromitra esculenta* (False Morel) ☠

**Key characters** cap brain-like, smooth and shiny, dark brown. **Description:** **Cap** dark brown, irregular, convoluted, very smooth, 4–12cm across. **Stem** rather short, stout, whitish. **Spores** elliptic, 17–23 X 9–12 μm. *Poisonous; the specific name G. esculenta is a misnomer; the False Morel is edible only when cooked correctly and is deadly under certain conditions.* **Occurring** in conifer woods, on sandy soils, sometimes in dune slacks; mainly northern, spring. Uncommon.

*Gyromitra esculenta*

Spores 17–23 × 9–12 μm

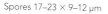

239

## HELVELLACEAE

### Helvella lacunosa

**Key characters** blackish-grey cap, irregularly lobed, folded back over fluted grey stem. **Description: Cap** saddle-shaped, irregular, folded and twisted, dark grey to black, paler below, 4–6 cm high. **Stem** tall, 2–10 cm, greyish, to almost black, longitudinally ribbed, fluted with sharp edges. **Spores** elliptic, 18–20 X 10–13 μm. *Edibility uncertain; not recommended.* **Occurring** in mixed woods, occasionally on decaying wood, along pathsides, autumn, frequent.

*Helvella lacunosa*

Spores 18–20 × 10–13 μm

### Helvella crispa

**Key characters** cap more or less saddle-shaped, white to fawn; stem tall, fluted, white. **Description: Cap** saddle-shaped, folded down, pale tan to white, 3–6 cm across. **Stem** 5–10 (15) cm high, white, with irregular longitudinal furrows with sharp ribs, often with cross connections. **Spores** elliptic, 17–20 x 10–13 μm. *Edible but best avoided.* **Occurring** in woods along pathsides in soil or grass, also in gardens, autumn, common.

*Helvella crispa*

Spores 17–20 × 10–13 μm

### Helvella elastica

**Key characters** small saddle-shaped, greyish cap, on slender smooth stem. **Description: Cap** rounded to saddle-shaped, bi-lobed,1–4cm across, pale brownish. **Stem** 5–8 cm, rather slender, smooth and white. **Spores** elliptic, 18–22 X 9–12 µm. *Edible but best avoided.* **Occurring** in mixed woods, especially by pathsides, summer to autumn, frequent.

*Helvella elastica*

Spores 18–22 × 9–12 µm

### Helvella (= Cyathipodia) macropus

**Key characters** small greyish cup on thin furry stem. **Description: Cup** 2–3 cm across, edge and lower surface distinctly hairy, colour grey-brown overall. **Stem** 2.5–4 cm, very slender, grey, woolly-furry. **Spores** elongate, 20–30 X 10–12 µm. *Edibility uncertain; best avoided.* **Occurring** in mixed woods, especially below nettle beds, sometimes by rotting wood, summer to autumn, occasional.

*Helvella macropus*

Spores 20–30 × 10–12 µm

241

## *PEZIZACEAE*

### *Peziza cerea*

**Key characters** pale yellow, ochre, flattened cups; often [...] wet plaster, mortar etc. **Description: Cup**, flattened 3–7 c[...] across, inside pale yellow to saffron, smooth, outer surfa[...] paler, whitish, pubescent. Sometimes with a small stem-li[...] base. **Spores** elliptic, smooth, 15–17 X 9–10 µm. *Inedib[...]* **Occurring** on wet plaster, mortar in cellars, garages, unc[...] sinks, etc., sometimes on straw or limy soil, all year, frequen[...]

*Peziza cerea*

Spores 15–17 × 9–10 µm

### *Peziza vesiculosa*

**Key characters** inrolled cups with notched, blistered ma[...] gins; on old straw, manure, rich soil. **Description: Cup** irreg[...] lar, rather inrolled, 2–5 cm across, with notched or blistere[...] margin, inner surface smooth, then puckered; pale straw-ye[...] low-ochre. Outer surface paler, granular-scurfy. **Spores** elli[...] tic, smooth, 20–23 X 9–12 µm. *Inedible.* **Occurring** on o[...] straw, compost, manured soil, etc., autum[...] and spring, common.

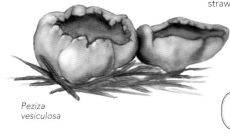

*Peziza vesiculosa*

Spores 20–23 × 9–12 µm

# PYRONEMATACEAE

## Aleuria aurantia (Orange Peel Fungus)

**Key characters** bright orange flattened cups; paler scurfy outer surface. **Description: Cup** flattened irregular 1–7 cm across, inside bright orange, smooth. Outer surface paler, whitish, scurfy-granular. **Spores** elliptic, 18–22 X 9–11 μm, with reticulate surface. *Edible*. **Occurring** in deciduous woods, gardens and fields especially on bare gravelly soils and pathsides, and in plantations, summer to autumn, common.

*Aleuria
aurantia*

Spores 18–22 × 9–11 μm

## Tarzetta (= Geopyxis) catinus

**Key characters** pale clay-brown cup on a short stem; outer surface woolly. **Description: Cup** 2–4 cm across, with distinct basal stem; entirely pale clay-brown, inner surface smooth, outer surface woolly-hairy. **Spores** elliptic, smooth, 20–24 X 10–12 μm. *Not of culinary interest*. **Occurring** on soil in deciduous woods, especially by pathsides, autumn, frequent.

*Tarzetta
catinus*

Spores 20–24 × 10–12 μm

### *Otidea onotica* (Hare's Ear, Rabbit's Ear)

*Otidea onotica*

**Key characters** often large rabbit's ear shape, pinkish-yellow. **Description: Cup** large, lop-sided 3–10 cm high, split down one side, with short, hairy basal stem; margin slightly inrolled, beautiful pinkish yellow to orange. Inner surface smooth. Outer surface paler, slightly granular. **Spores** elliptic, smooth, 10–14 X 5–7 µm. *Not of culinary interest.* **Occurring** on soil and leaf-litter in deciduous woods, summer to autumn, uncommon to occasional. **Notes:** a number of other, browner species are known but are poorly differentiated and requiring specialist literature to identify.

Spores 10–14
X 5–7 µm

### *Scutellinia scutellata* (Eyelash Fungus)

**Key characters** bright red tiny cups with fringe of black hairs. **Description: Cup** small (0.5 cm), flattened with age; bright scarlet with fringe of very fine black "lashes" or hairs. **Spores** elliptic, finely and regularly roughened, 18–22 X 10–13 µm. *Inedible.* **Occurring** on wet branches, twigs, soil, by streams, etc., most of the year, common. This is one of many closely related species.

*Scutellinia scutellata*

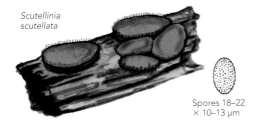

Spores 18–22
X 10–13 µm

# SARCOSCYPHACEAE

## Sarcoscypha austriaca (Scarlet Cup, Elf Cup)

**Key characters** bright scarlet cups with short stems; outer surface white, hairy. **Description:** Cup rounded, very regularly shaped, 2–5 cm across. Inner surface bright scarlet, smooth. Outer surface whitish and tomentose-hairy, with very short stem. **Spores** fusiform, smooth, 26–34 X 11–13 µm. *Inedible.* **Occurring** on twigs and branches, late winter and spring, locally distributed and common in places.

*Sarcoscypha austriaca*

Spores 26–34 X 11–13 µm

# TUBERACEAE (TRUFFLES)

All Tuberales (truffles) are underground, rounded, tuberous structures with the hymenium folded and convoluted within the fruitbody. The truffles are highly valued edible fungi.

## Tuber rufum (Red Truffle)

**Key characters** brick-red, small, and rounded truffle. **Description:** Truffle small, 1–2 cm, slightly warty, exterior smooth to scurfy, usually cinnamon-brown, brick-red, interior white to grey then pale reddish brown, with slightly darker veins. **Spores** ovate, 40–46 X 25–30 µm, spiny (spines are 3–4 µm), not reticulate. *Edible and good.* **Occurring** below soil level in oak woods, autumn, common.

*Tuber rufum*

Spores 40–46 X 25–30 µm

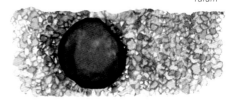

## Tuber aestivum (Summer Truffle)

**Key characters** blackish brown, warty and rounded; interior with veins. **Description: Truffle** 3–8 cm, covered by angular warts, blackish brown, interior pale greyish lilac, marbled with darker veins. **Taste** pleasant, nutty. **Spores** ovate, 35–40 X 20–30 μm, surface reticulate. *Edible and good; but not as highly valued as the commercial or Perigord truffle,* T. melanospermum, *a European but not British species.* **Occurring** below soil level in oak woods, especially on calcareous soil, autumn, rare.

*Tuber aestivum*

Spores 35–40
X 20–30 μm

# LEOTIALES
# (INCLUDING EARTH-TONGUES)

A few of this very large and varied order are "larger fungi". They are usually soft, often jelly-like in texture, or firm but not woody; some are cup-like.

## LEOTIACEAE

### Chlorociboria (= Chlorosplenium) aeruginascens (Green Wood-cup)

**Key characters** small jade-green cups; stains oak wood green. **Cups** tiny, 0.25–0.5 cm across, flattened, stalked, vivid blue-green. **Spores** fusiform 5–7 X 1–2 μm. *Not of culinary interest.* On twigs and branches of deciduous woods especially oak, most of the year, occasional to frequent. **Notes:** usually all one sees is the green-stained timber, the cups are quite rare. Provides the "Green-oak" of traditional Tunbridge ware.

*Chlorociboria aeruginascens*

Spores 5–7
X 1–2 μm

## Ascocoryne sarcoides

**Key characters** purple gelatinous mass, more rarely disc-shaped. **Description: Asexual** state at first an irregular, convoluted, gelatinous mass 1–5 cm across, bright reddish-purple. **Sexual** state a thick, gelatinous disc 0.5–1 cm across, with short stem, bright purple. **Spores** oblong, 10–18 X 3–5 µm, septate. *Not of culinary interest.* **Occurring** on deciduous logs and stumps, autumn, common.

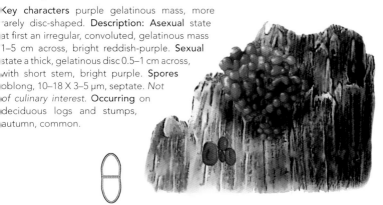

Spores 10–18
× 3–5 µm

*Ascocoryne sarcoides*

## Bulgaria inquinans (Rubber Buttons)

**Key characters** black, rubbery, flattened "buttons". **Description: Fruitbody** thick, flattened, rounded stud-like, 1–4 cm across (globose, margin inrolled, when young). The flat disc is smooth, shiny, black; outer surface roughened, brown. **Spores** ovate, smooth, 10–14 X 5–7 µm. *Not edible.* **Occurring** in clusters on deciduous wood, especially oak and beech, autumn, common.

*Bulgaria inquinans*

Spores 10–14 × 5–7 µm

247

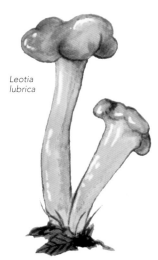

*Leotia lubrica*

### *Leotia lubrica* (Jelly babies)

**Key characters** head olive-green, slimy; stem soft, slimy, yellowish. **Description: Club** 2–5 cm tall, cap small, button-shaped; soft and gelatinous, slimy; margin inrolling; olive-green to yellowish. **Stem** cylindrical, soft, gelatinous, slimy; yellowish, dotted green occasionally. **Spores** elongate-fusiform, 20–25 X 5–6 μm, septate. *Not of culinary interest.* **Occurring** in deciduous woodlands on damp soil and leaf-litter, autumn, frequent.

Spores 20–25 × 5–6 μm

## GEOGLOSSACEAE (EARTH TONGUES)

*Trichoglossum hirsutum*

### *Trichoglossum (= Geoglossum) hirsutum*

**Key characters** blackish club-shaped head; with slender very velvety stem. **Description: Club** 4–8 cm, tongue-shaped on slender stem, head flattened or grooved, black. **Stem** coloured as cap, densely velvety-hairy. **Spores** very long, 110–150 X 6–8 μm, multi-septate. *Not of culinary interest.* **Occurring** in grasslands, pastures, etc., on acid soils, autumn, frequent.

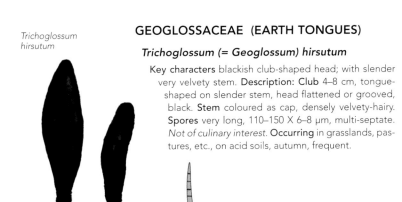

Spores 110–150 × 6–8 μm

## Microglossum viride

**Key characters** club-shaped with olive green colours. **Description: Club-shaped** or tongue-shaped fruit-bodies 4–8 cm high on a slender stalk, club usually flattened or grooved, dark olive-green. **Stem** coloured as cap, with granular surface. **Spores** elongate, 15–20 X 5–6 μm, 4–5-septate. *Not of culinary interest.* **Occurring** in deciduous woods on bare soil or leaf-litter, tufted, autumn, uncommon.

*Microglossum viride*

Spores 15–20 × 5–6 μm

## Mitrula paludosa

**Key characters** in pond margins on fallen leaves; yellow clubs on slender white stem. **Description: Cap** 0.5–1 cm high, soft, smooth, yellow, distinct from but clasping the stem. **Stem** 2–4 cm high, very slender, cylindrical, white or yellowish, smooth. **Spores** elliptic-elongate, 12–15 X 3–4 μm, 1-septate. *Not of culinary interest.* **Occurring** in clusters in the water margins, spring to early summer, frequent.

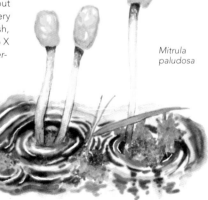

*Mitrula paludosa*

Spores 12–15 × 3–4 μm

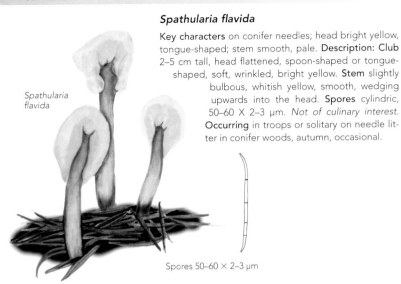

### Spathularia flavida

*Spathularia flavida*

**Key characters** on conifer needles; head bright yellow, tongue-shaped; stem smooth, pale. **Description:** Club 2–5 cm tall, head flattened, spoon-shaped or tongue-shaped, soft, wrinkled, bright yellow. **Stem** slightly bulbous, whitish yellow, smooth, wedging upwards into the head. **Spores** cylindric, 50–60 X 2–3 μm. *Not of culinary interest.* **Occurring** in troops or solitary on needle litter in conifer woods, autumn, occasional.

Spores 50–60 × 2–3 μm

# FLASK FUNGI

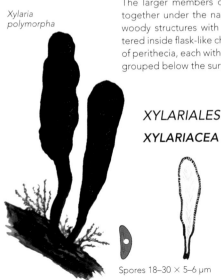

*Xylaria polymorpha*

The larger members of the Flask fungi (formerly grouped together under the name Pyrenomycetes) are mostly hard, woody structures with the asci containing the spores clustered inside flask-like chambers called perithecia. Thousands of perithecia, each with an aperture to release the spores, are grouped below the surface of the woody tissue.

## XYLARIALES

## XYLARIACEA

### Xylaria polymorpha
(Dead Man's Fingers)

**Key characters** irregular, black, finger-like clubs. **Description:** Clubs 3–8 cm high, swollen and irregular, tapered at base, roughened where the spore-chambers protrude, black. **Flesh** white, brittle, dotted with the perithecia. **Spores** fusiform, 18–30 X

Spores 18–30 × 5–6 μm

5–8 µm. *Inedible.* **Occurring** clustered on stumps of deciduous trees, especially beech, all year, common. **Notes:** the more slender *X. longipes* will bend rather than snap if the stem is bent.

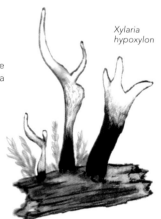

Xylaria
hypoxylon

## *Xylaria hypoxylon* (Candle-Wick Fungus)

**Key characters** simple or branching, looks like a snuffed-out candle-wick. **Description. Club** a simple pointed body 1–5 cm high, soon branching, antler-like; with black base and white powdery upper half when young, finally completely black, rough. Sometimes unbranched forms are found. **Spores** bean-shaped, 10–14 X 4–6 µm. *Inedible.* **Occurring** on deciduous stumps, logs and twigs, all year, common.

Spores 10–14 × 4–6 µm

## *Daldinia concentrica*
## (King Alfred's Cakes, Cramp Balls)

**Key characters** black, very hard, woody, rounded; shows concentric circles when cut. **Description: Fruitbody** deep chocolate-brown to black, pushing up through the bark, smooth matt to shiny. **Flesh** white with fine concentric zones of white and grey-black. **Spores** black (often dusting the surrounding wood), elongate, 11–17 X 6–8 µm. *Inedible.* **Occurring** on dead or dying deciduous trees, especially birch and often abundant on trees scorched by fire, most of year, common. The first common name refers to the blackened, burnt-looking appearance; the second to a widespread folk belief that the fungus cures night-cramp in the legs if placed at the bottom of the bed.

Spores 11–17 × 6–8 µm

Daldinia
concentrica

# INDEX